Electrical power equipment and meas
electrical applications

Second edition

Electrical power equipment and measurements: with heavy current electrical applications

Second edition

Alan Symonds

Formerly Lecturer in Electrical Engineering, Grimsby College of Technology

McGraw-Hill Book Company (UK) Limited

London · New York · St Louis · San Francisco · Auckland · Bogotá
Guatemala · Hamburg · Johannesburg · Lisbon · Madrid · Mexico
Montreal · New Delhi · Panama · Paris · San Juan · São Paulo
Singapore · Sydney · Tokyo · Toronto

Published by

McGRAW-HILL Book Company (UK) Limited
MAIDENHEAD · BERKSHIRE · ENGLAND

British Library Cataloguing in Publication Data
Symonds, Alan
   Electrical power equipment and measurements.—2nd ed.
   1. Electric apparatus and appliances
   I. Title
   621.31'042   TK452   80-40505

   ISBN 0-07-084625-1

2345   MoC   8543

Contents

Preface to the first edition

The primary purpose of this book is to provide Electrical Technician students with a textbook covering Electrical Power Equipment. The book is intended to cover two years' work, but in order to preserve subject continuity no attempt has been made to divide either the book or the individual chapters into two distinct parts.

Much of the subject matter is descriptive and illustrated by drawings, circuit diagrams, and phasor diagrams. In general, the theory and mathematics have been limited to that necessary to give an understanding of the principles, characteristics, and practical uses of particular pieces of equipment. From this point of view the practical technician in industry, whose days of studying may be behind him, may find the book helpful.

SI units have been used, although some units, for example the horsepower, have not been completely omitted since old machines will still carry the old rating on their nameplates.

Although based upon a particular syllabus, much of the book will be found useful for Electrical Installation students and students taking Electrical Craft Study courses.

The author wishes to thank the City and Guilds of London Institute for permission to use their Electrical Technician Course syllabus as a basis for the contents of this book and for the inclusion of questions from past examination papers; the East Midland Education Union for permission to use questions from past examination papers; the Institution of Electrical Engineers for permission to use information contained in their *Regulations for the Electrical Equipment of Buildings*; and Her Majesty's Stationery Office for permission to use material quoted in the 1969/70 Annual Report of the Central Electricity Generating Board.

Questions from past examination papers are printed in an Appendix. The order in which the questions appear corresponds with the sequence of chapters. The source of the questions is indicated but where numerical answers are given these are the author's, and the relevant examination body is in no way responsible for their accuracy.

In writing this book, the author has been helped by the reading of scripts and the constructive comments of several of his colleagues and wishes to thank Mr S. Busby, Mr D. V. Miles, Mr F. G. Vivian, and Mr R. Wilson for their help, and also Mr J. Cleveland and Mrs E. Cleveland for typing the scripts.

Alan Symonds

Preface to the second edition

Since the first edition was published in 1971 considerable changes have taken place in the structure of technical education courses. Many colleges are now offering courses based upon syllabuses issued by the Technical Education Council. In revising this book much material has been added to enable the book to give a complete coverage of the TEC Level III Syllabus Unit U76/362. The title of this unit, 'Heavy Current Electrical Applications', is used as a sub-title for this present edition.

Inevitably, some of the original material has had to be condensed to give space for the new and some material has been rearranged. This new edition will now appeal to students taking a number of TEC courses, but particularly Unit U76/362, and also to technicians, installation and craft students who have previously used the book.

Basically the chapters follow the same general order as in the first edition although some chapter headings have been changed and new chapters introduced, particularly on three-phase rectification and control systems.

Many colleges today introduce basic electronic theory at an early stage and in most cases students will be familiar with this work before reaching Level III. For this reason much of this basic work has now been omitted from the new edition.

Questions in the Appendix have now been placed under chapter headings.

The author wishes to thank those colleagues who have helped with this second edition by reading the scripts and making constructive comments. In particular he wishes to mention Mr S. Busby, Mr R. Wilson, Mr C. S. J. Evens, and Mr R. Taylor.

Alan Symonds

1. Consumer's supply

1.1 From the grid to the consumer

Since the initial 132 kV network was completed in 1936 the Grid has been extended until it now covers virtually the whole of Great Britain. The *Grid System* consists of an extensive interconnected transmission network supplying the whole country and is controlled by the Central Electricity Authority. When the supply industry was nationalized in 1948 generation also became part of the system. The Grid network is now supplied from a small number of very large and highly efficient power stations strategically placed where fuel (usually coal) and water are easily available. The basic networks are still 132 kV but increasing demands and the necessity to supply bulk power over long distances has brought about the introduction of the Super Grid. This consists of transmission lines with voltages of 275 kV and 400 kV forming the main 'arteries' of the supply system.

Figure 1.1 is typical of the Grid supply system from the generating plant to the consumer. Most consumers receive supplies from the medium-voltage (415/240 V) distribution system, but it will be seen from the diagram that supplies to some large industrial consumers may be given at 11 kV or even 33 kV.

The advantages of the Grid system can be summarized as follows:

1. The whole country is linked by a common e.h.v. network.

2. Best use is made of large, highly efficient generating stations built upon the most advantageous sites.

3. Load flow is under a centralized control, enabling generating plant to be operated at its highest efficiency.

4. Small and inefficient stations are eliminated.

5. Standby plant and spares are kept to a minimum.

6. Supply frequency and voltage can be standardized.

7. Loss of supply due to breakdown is minimized.

8. Electricity is more readily available to isolated communities.

1

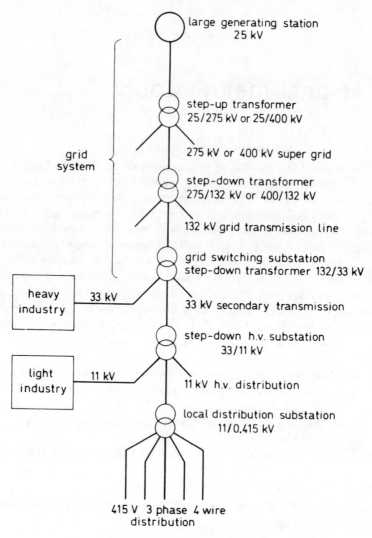

Fig. 1.1 Typical supply system

1.2 The local distribution system

The main substation feeding a particular area is usually placed as close to the load centre as possible. This substation will be supplied from the Grid transmission line, probably by means of a 33 kV secondary transmission line or underground cable. From the main substation there will be high-voltage distribution cables radiating outwards to feed the local distribution substations. This will probably be at 11 kV. The local substations will also be interconnected by means of further 11 kV cables, so that a ring system of feeders is formed. By employing this ring system, it is possible to isolate any one of the cables without interrupting the supply to any substation. In the case of a fault, this may be done automatically by the use of suitable protective equipment at the substations. Transformers at each substation feed into a network of low-voltage distributors which radiate from the substation and to which the consumers' supplies are connected. These low-voltage cables may also be interconnected by means of link pillars or underground boxes, the use of which enables faulty cables to be isolated, feeds to be changed, and even a substation to be taken out of commission for maintenance work to be carried out, usually with no interuption to the consumer's supplies.

Figure 1.2 shows a typical arrangement for such a distribution system.

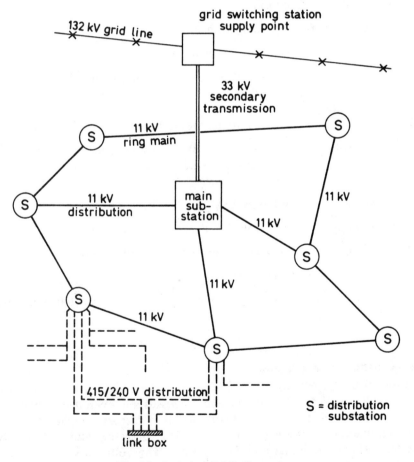

Fig. 1.2 Layout of distribution system

1.3 Operating voltages

On long transmission lines, the losses can be high. By raising the operating voltage, thereby reducing the current for a given power being delivered, the losses can be reduced and the efficiency of transmission increased. For any given line there is also a definite voltage which will give the minimum cost. This is the 'economic voltage' for the line. To find this voltage, a number of factors have to be taken into account, including local conditions, but a rough guide is 1000 V per mile of line. However, in order to standardize in the manufacture of equipment, certain standard voltages are used. These are:

400 kV and 275 kV for the Super Grid;

132 kV for the original Grid;

66 kV and 33 kV for secondary transmission;

11 kV, 6.6 kV, and 3.3 kV for h.v. distribution.

The standard distribution voltages for consumer's supplies are 415 V three-phase 50 Hz a.c. for power, and 240 V single-phase 50 Hz a.c. for lighting and heating supplies.

The voltages of consumer's circuits are normally classified as follows:

Extra-low voltage   Not exceeding 50 V between conductors, and not exceeding 30 V a.c. or 50 V d.c. between any conductor and earth.

Low voltage   Between 50 V and 250 V.

Medium voltage   Over 250 V and not exceeding 650 V.

High voltage   Over 650 V and not exceeding 3000 V.

Extra-high voltage   Over 3000 V.

The above voltages are either between conductors or between one conductor and earth.

1.4 Consumer's supplies

Nowadays, the supply to the consumer is almost always a.c. However, there is still a need for d.c. for specific processes and even if the supply is a.c. there may still be a d.c. network within a factory supplied through either rectifiers or a motor–generator set. The following outline of supply systems includes both a.c. and d.c. supplies. The voltages shown are for standard supplies.

The main form of lighting is by means of the filament lamp. As it is uneconomical to manufacture such lamps much above a 250 V rating, this gives a limit to supply voltages for lighting circuits. Since such supplies are required in domestic premises there is also the safety aspect to be considered. Thus, the standard voltage for supplies to lighting circuits is limited to 250 V or less.

For power purposes, a higher voltage leads to greater efficiency. It will be seen below that by developing the three-wire and three-phase systems a higher voltage can be provided for power circuits while the lower voltage for lighting circuits is still maintained.

D.C. Two-wire System. This is the simplest system, consisting of two conductors known as the positive and negative leads (Fig. 1.3a). The voltage is limited to under 250 V for both lighting and power loads. Higher voltages may be used for power supplies only, as for traction where 1000 V or more may be used.

D.C. Three-wire System. By adding a third conductor, called the *middle wire or neutral*, the voltage of the system can be doubled for the supply of

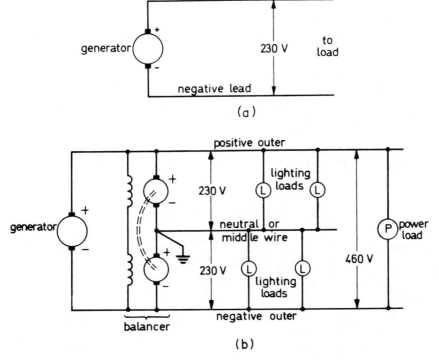

Fig. 1.3   D.C. systems: (a) two-wire system, (b) three-wire system

power loads. The full voltage will exist between the two *outers*, with half the voltage for lighting circuits between one of the outers and the middle wire. One problem with this system is that any out-of-balance between the positive and negative lighting loads will cause a rise in voltage on the lightly loaded side, with a corresponding reduction of voltage on the heavily loaded side. To overcome this, a *balancer*, consisting of two similar shunt machines coupled together, is connected into the circuit, as shown in Fig. 1.3b. The machine connected in the lightly loaded side operates as a motor to drive the other machine as a generator, thereby transferring power from one side to the other and thus reducing the out-of-balance and equalizing the voltages.

A.C. Single-phase Two-wire System (Fig. 1.4a). This is similar to the d.c. two-wire system, except that in this case the supply is normally from the secondary of a transformer at the distribution substation. One side of the secondary is always earthed, and the conductor connected to this side is

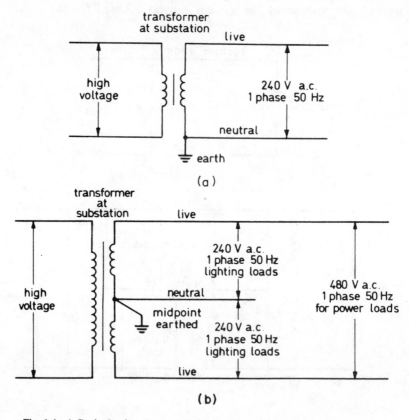

Fig. 1.4   A.C. single-phase systems: (a) two-wire system, (b) three-wire system

6

the *neutral*. The conductor connected to the other end of the secondary winding is called the *live* conductor.

A.C. Single-phase Three-wire System. Supply is from the secondary of a distribution transformer, but with double the voltage of the two-wire case. The transformer is centre-tapped and is earthed at this point. The third

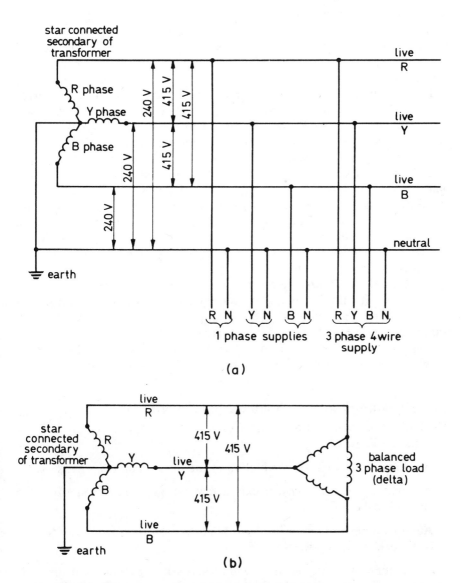

Fig. 1.5 Three-phase systems: (a) four-wire system, (b) three-wire system

conductor is connected to the centre tapping, and this becomes the *neutral*. The two outer conductors are live conductors (Fig. 1.4b). Power circuits are connected to the two live conductors and lighting loads to one of the live conductors and the neutral. This type of supply is quite common in rural areas where power is required for farming purposes and the high-voltage system is single-phase.

A.C. Three-phase Four-wire System. This is the system used for general distribution purposes wherever three-phase supplies are available. Essentially, this consists of three single-phase circuits with a common earthed conductor called the *neutral*. The transformer windings are connected in *star* formation, the star point being earthed and also connected to the neutral conductor. Since there is a phase difference between the voltages of each phase, the total voltage across two phases will be 1.73 times the phase voltage. The conductors connected to the outer terminals of each phase are known as *live* conductors. To distinguish one phase from another it is usual to give the phases a colour coding—red, yellow (or white), and blue. The cores of cables are marked or numbered accordingly. Three-phase power supplies are connected to the three live or line conductors, and lighting and single-phase supplies are connected to one of the lines and the neutral. By connecting the single-phase supplies to each phase in rotation, a fair balance of load over the three phases is usually obtained. Figure 1.5(a) shows the system from the distribution transformer, with connections made for both single-phase and three-phase supplies.

A.C. Three-phase Three-wire System. This system is not usual for general supplies, but it may be found for certain circuits within a factory. If a three-phase power load is balanced on all phases, as is often the case with a three-phase motor, then there will be no current in the neutral and it can be omitted. In such a case, a three-wire system can be used. Single-phase supplies, however, cannot normally be taken from this system (Fig. 1.5b).

1.5 Equipment at the consumer's supply point

There are three essential features of every supply point as required by the regulations. These are:

1. A means of isolating all conductors of the installation from the supply.

2. Automatic protection against excess current by fuses or some form of circuit breaker.

3. Automatic protection against earth-leakage currents by fuses or an earth-leakage circuit breaker.

This equipment must be in a readily accessible position and must be capable of being operated without causing danger. Isolation can be achieved by a linked switch which opens or closes all conductors simultaneously. With three-phase circuits the switch can be in the line conductors only with a solid link in the neutral, provided the neutral link cannot be removed before opening the switch.

Fuses may be used for excess-current protection, but these must be placed only in the live conductors. Fuses are not permitted in the neutral conductor. Circuit breakers may be used instead of fuses, in which case the circuit breaker may also be used as the means of isolation. However, where large circuit breakers are used a further means of isolation is generally provided to enable maintenance work to be carried out on the circuit breaker itself.

For small consumers, the excess-current fuses are often sufficient to give earth-leakage protection also, but where the earth-loop impedance is high an earth-leakage circuit breaker must be installed. In any case, coarse excess-current fuses of 100 A or more cannot always be relied upon to clear an earth fault successfully and an earth-leakage circuit breaker should be installed. Where circuit breakers are used as the main means of control, they are usually fitted with both excess-current and earth-leakage protection.

At the incoming supply point the supply authority have a means of isolating the consumer's circuits from the supply by the installation of fuses or a circuit breaker. The metering equipment is also connected at this point. The meters may be connected direct, but for supplies of about 50 kV A and over it is usual to supply the meter from a current transformer.

The general sequence of equipment for a small single-phase supply is shown in Fig. 1.6. An earth-leakage circuit breaker is shown, but this can be omitted if the circuit fuse is adequate to give earth-leakage protection.

The above small consumer will be supplied direct from the three-phase, four-wire distributor in the adjacent street. Larger consumers with loads of up to 300–500 kV A may require a supply direct from a local substation, as shown in Fig. 1.7. In this case, no other consumer will be connected to the supply cable, even when it is laid for some distance along a public street.

A consumer with a load of up to 1000 kV A will probably receive supply from a separate substation situated on his own land or in part of his factory premises. This substation will supply only the one consumer. Figure 1.8 shows this arrangement. Fuses are shown for the protection of the consumer's circuits, but these may be replaced by circuit breakers in many cases,

The type of supply offered to a consumer depends somewhat upon the nature of the consumer's load and the type of process being carried out. In all the cases above a *single supply* has been given. This is adequate for many consumers, where the process is such that a shutdown for several

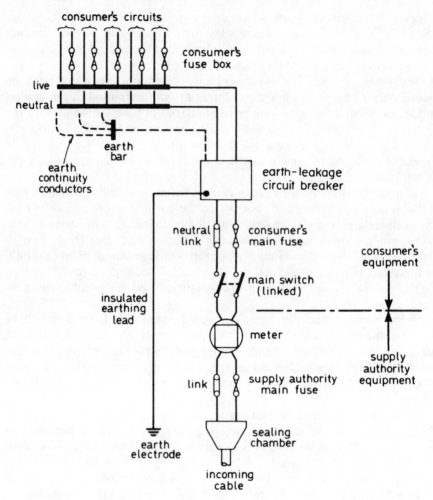

Fig. 1.6 Equipment at the supply point for a small single-phase supply

hours due to a fault can be tolerated and will not have a very serious effect. This is the risk that has to be taken with a single supply, but the supply system today is generally so reliable that shutdowns are rare and the risk involved by taking a single supply is quite small.

If the process is such that a lengthy shutdown would have serious consequences to either machines or production then an *alternative supply* can be given, as shown in Fig. 1.9. In this case, the consumer's substation is connected into a high-voltage ring system, or a system where an alternative feed is possible. The consumer will normally receive the supply

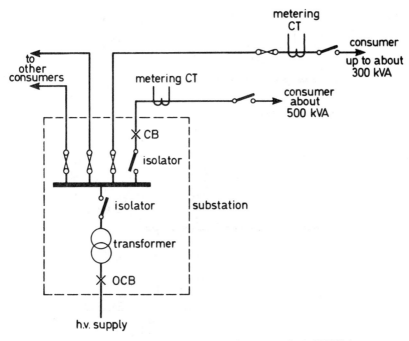

Fig. 1.7 Supplies to consumers with loads up to about 500 kV A

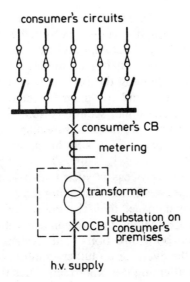

Fig. 1.8 Supply to consumer with a load up to 1000 kV A

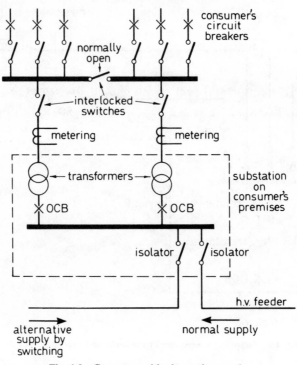

Fig. 1.9   Consumer with alternative supply

from only one feeder. In the event of a fault on this feeder, the supply authority can give an alternative supply by suitable switching in their h.v. system. The time the supply is actually off is limited to the time taken for switching, and may be only a matter of minutes. The alternative feeder may not be capable of providing the full factory load, but at least it will keep the essentials running until the main feeder repairs are carried out. The diagram shows the consumer's circuits split into two sections with interlocked switching. This provides a safeguard against either of the transformers being fed from the l.v. side in the event of the h.v. circuit breaker being opened.

Where a manufacturing process is such that it is essential to keep the machines running continuously and that a stoppage, even for a short time, would cause extensive damage, then the consumer will be given a *firm supply*. The h.v. network feeding the consumer's substation will be a ring system being fed from both directions. The system will have automatic protection, so that in the event of a fault the faulty section will be isolated automatically without affecting the other feed. Thus the consumer's supply will be maintained even when a fault occurs. The substation equipment is

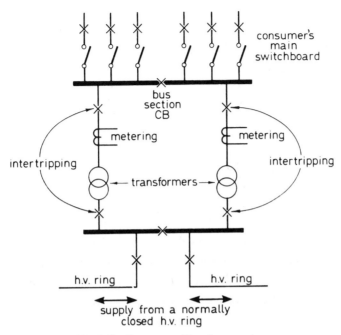

Fig. 1.10 Consumer with a firm supply

also duplicated to give security of supply, and to allow maintenance to be carried out on part of the equipment without interrupting the supply. The general arrangement for a firm supply is shown in Fig. 1.10.

Consumers with loads of 1000 kV A and over usually receive a high-voltage supply, the consumer providing his own substation and transformer and the associated switchgear. The supply authority circuits will terminate in a high-voltage circuit breaker and the metering equipment will be connected at this point. The h.v. supply can be given as a single, alternative, or firm supply in a similar way to the medium voltage supplies, depending upon the importance of the consumer's processes.

1.6 Factory layout

The layout of factory circuits will depend upon the size of the installation. For a very small installation, the consumer's distribution board from which the final power, heating, and lighting circuits are fed will be supplied direct from the equipment at the supply intake. An arrangement similar to that shown in Fig. 1.6, but for three-phase working, would be suitable.

Even small industrial consumers, however, usually require a supply that justifies the installation of a small busbar system situated in a special

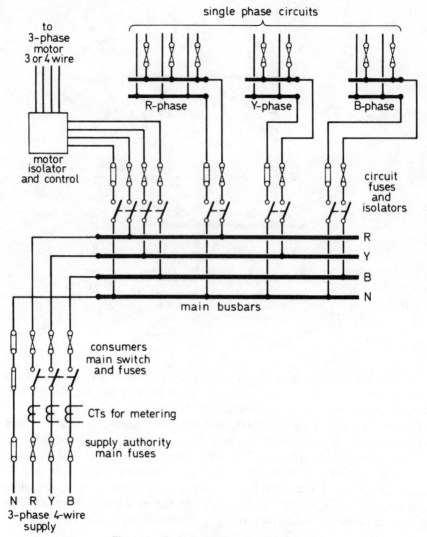

Fig. 1.11   Typical supply for a small factory

switchroom. The supply intake and metering equipment will be placed in this room. The busbars will be fed through an isolator and the consumer's main fuses, or through a circuit breaker. A typical layout is shown in Fig. 1.11.

A larger factory may have its supplies connected to a ring main system, as shown in Fig. 1.12.

14

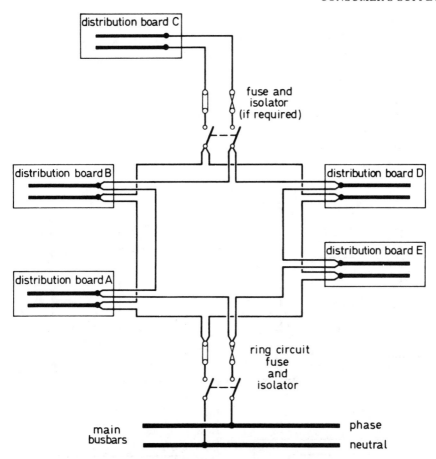

Fig. 1.12 Factory ring main system (normally three-phase and neutral—one phase and neutral only shown for simplicity)

The ring will be a three-phase and neutral system, but for simplicity only one phase and the neutral are shown in the diagram. Each distribution board will supply different sections of the factory, and the fact that they are on a ring main system gives greater security. Fuses and/or isolators can be used to protect or isolate any of the boards, as shown for board C in the diagram. For heavy loads, circuit breakers can be used instead of fuses.

Figure 1.13 is a single-line diagram of a section of a typical three-phase, four-wire factory distribution system. Oil circuit breakers control the output from the main factory substation. These feed into main distribution boards in each section of the factory. Large motors will be supplied direct

15

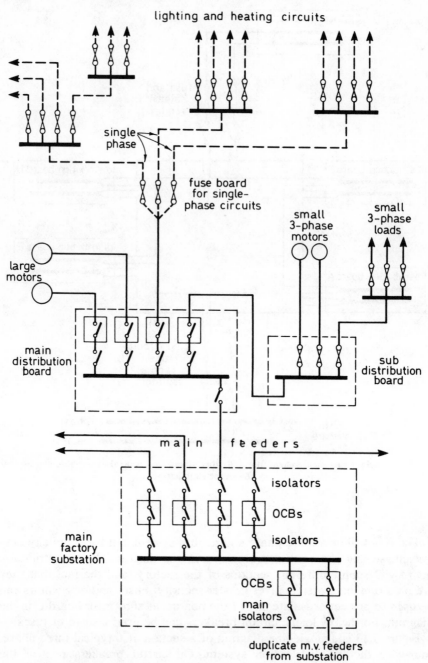

Fig. 1.13 Typical factory three-phase, four-wire m.v. distribution—single-line diagram

from this main board through circuit breakers or the motor control equipment. Other sub-distribution boards are supplied from the main board, and from these are fed the circuits for small power, lighting, and heating loads. Although not shown in the diagram, the various main distribution boards in different sections of the factory may be connected on a ring main system.

2. Switchgear and protection

2.1 Control and protection of circuits

Switchgear provides a means of opening and closing a circuit, thereby controlling the flow of current in the circuit. It may also incorporate some form of protection against overloads, faults, earth leakage and undervoltage. Sustained overloads may bring about excessive heating, resulting in a burnout of the circuit and possibly causing a fire in adjacent equipment. A fault may be in the form of a short circuit or breakdown of insulation, giving rise to excessive currents and possibly dangerous flashovers. Earth leakage may be a fault to earth, causing excessive currents and overheating, or it may be due to deterioration of the insulation to earth, giving rise to small currents which may not be excessive compared with the normal circuit current but which may none the less be dangerous; it may be especially dangerous to life, since associated metalwork can become alive. With electrical machines undervoltage can also be a drawback, as it may cause motors to stall or lose speed, or to stop completely in the extreme case of no-voltage, that is, the loss of supply. A dangerous condition would exist if a motor were to start without warning when the supply was restored.

Circuits must be protected from these adverse conditions and various forms of protection are provided in many types of switchgear, depending upon its position and importance in a circuit. Switchgear can be divided into four general groups. These are (1) switches, (2) isolators, (3) contactors, and (4) circuit breakers.

1. Switch. The word *switch* is often applied in general terms to all classes of switchgear, but the correct definition of a switch is 'non-automatic mechanical device capable of opening or closing a circuit under normal load conditions'. Switches are hand-operated and have a quick make-and-break action to enable loads to be switched in or out without undue arcing. For light and medium work, switches are usually air-break, but oil-immersed switches may be used for heavy current operation.

2. Isolator. This is the simplest type of switchgear and, as the name implies, it is used merely as a means of isolating a circuit. An isolator may be in the form of a simple knife switch, but with no provision for quick make-and-break, or it may be a solid link which can be withdrawn when

18

isolation is required. Isolators are usually air-break but they can be oil-immersed.

The isolator is always used in conjunction with some other form of switchgear which is required for making or breaking the load in the circuit, and the isolator is only operated after the load has been removed. Thus an isolator must *never* be operated in a loaded circuit. An isolator is usually installed to enable work to be carried out in safety on other types of switchgear.

3. Contactor. A contactor is a device for opening or closing a circuit under load conditions by pushbutton control. The operation is usually electromagnetic, but it may be electropneumatic. The contactor is ideal for remote and automatic control and is made use of in many appliances and, in particular, in many types of motor starters. It may be either air-break or oil-immersed.

The contactor is usually closed by energizing an electromagnet which pulls a set of moving contacts on to fixed contacts. A set of auxiliary contacts keeps the electromagnet coil energized while the main contacts are closed. An 'open' or 'stop' pushbutton is used to open this circuit, thus causing the main contacts to open by means of a spring or gravity. The auxiliary contacts open at the same time, so that the contactor cannot reclose automatically. This action gives the contactor an inherent no-volt release characteristic which is ideal when used in a starter circuit.

There is a 'latched type' of contactor which is closed by an operating coil but without auxiliary contacts, so that it is held in the closed position by a mechanical latch. To open this type of contactor a second coil is required to trip the latch mechanism, or a mechanical trip is employed.

The principle of contactor control is shown in the diagrams of Fig. 2.1. With the two-wire control (Fig. 2.1a), a switch is required in the operating coil circuit and this must remain closed to keep the contactor closed. This is not generally a convenient method, as supply failure will cause the contacts to open, but when supply is restored the contacts will immediately close again if the operating switch has not been opened. In some cases this could be a source of danger.

The three-wire control (Fig. 2.1b) uses 'on' and 'off' pushbuttons. The 'on' pushbutton energizes the operating coil and closes the contactor. This closes the auxiliary contacts which short out the 'on' pushbutton so that it can be released, and the contactor will remain closed. Operating the 'off' pushbutton opens the operating coil circuit, causing the contactor to open. This also opens the auxiliary contacts so that the contactor cannot be reclosed without operating the 'on' pushbutton. Failure of supply or a serious reduction in voltage causes the contactor to open without the danger of reclosing as supply is restored.

A no-volt or undervoltage release can be incorporated in a hand-operated

19

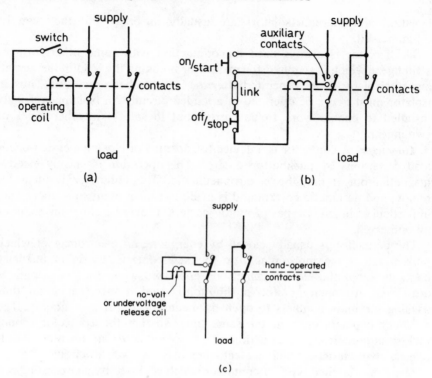

Fig. 2.1 Contactor control: (a) two-wire control, (b) three-wire (pushbutton) control, (c) hand-operated contactor with undervoltage release

switch or contactor as shown in Fig. 2.1(c). The switch is closed by hand. This closes the auxiliary contacts, which energizes the holding-in coil and keeps the switch closed. The switch can be opened by hand or a 'stop' pushbutton could be included in the coil circuit. The switch will open automatically if the coil becomes de-energized owing to undervoltage or supply failure.

Figure 2.2(a) shows the circuit modified for remote pushbutton control. A link is usually provided in the contactor for this purpose. This is removed and three wires are extended to the remote control position, as shown. Any number of remote control positions can be connected, if we remember that all the 'on' or 'start' pushbuttons are connected in parallel, and all the 'off' or 'stop' pushbuttons are in series.

Another useful circuit is shown in Fig. 2.2(b), in which several 'emergency stop' pushes are connected in series. This could be useful in a workshop where several small machines or processes are supplied by one contactor. 'Emergency' pushes at each machine, or at strategically placed

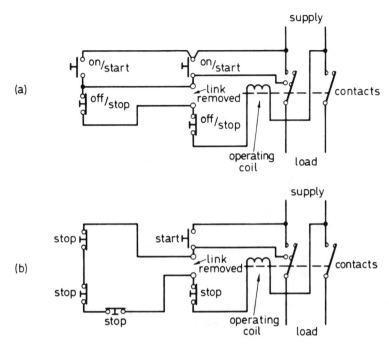

Fig. 2.2 **Remote control of contactor: (a) remote on/off control, (b) emergency 'stop' push-buttons**

points, allow the supply to be cut off quickly without having to go to the contactor.

4. Circuit Breaker. This is a mechanical device for opening or closing a circuit safely under all, including abnormal, conditions. Some circuit breakers can be operated manually but for high-voltage and heavy-current circuits they are generally spring- or electromagnetically assisted, or remote-controlled.

Overload trips, generally with some form of time lag, are fitted so that the circuit breaker will trip in the event of a serious overload or a fault. Most breakers are also fitted with earth-leakage protection. Electromagnetic trips are generally employed. These may be directly connected in the circuit with an oil dashpot type of time lag, or they may be operated by a relay of the induction type where a more precise time lag is required and where it is necessary to have discrimination (i.e., the ability to isolate a faulty circuit by the operation of the nearest protective equipment, leaving other circuits and their protection healthy).

In a circuit breaker provision must be made to extinguish any arc forming between contacts as they open and also to ensure that the arc does not reform. This is particularly important when heavy currents are passing

21

at high voltages, especially under fault conditions. The arc formed as the contacts open produces heat which may ionize the insulating medium. This tends to maintain the arc and causes it to re-strike at a comparitively low voltage. Thus the essential features of the circuit breaker are to extinguish the arc quickly by increasing the length of its path, and to dispel the ionized gases by replacing them with a cool insulating medium. There are several ways of achieving this, depending upon the type of circuit breaker which is employed, and largely determined by the voltage of the circuit and the current the breaker may be called upon to interrupt.

For low-voltage circuits and for small breaking capacities, where insulation is not a critical requirement, an *air-break circuit breaker* may be used. A magnetic blowout is common for air-break circuit breakers. This consists of an electromagnet carrying the load current and placed on each side of the contacts. Any arc produced will be in a strong magnetic field, which causes the arc to be extended to such a length that it cannot be maintained and it is extinguished. Heat is produced and the ionized gases are dispelled by convection.

The arcing time of the air-break circuit breaker can be relatively long, resulting in considerable burning of the contacts, which may have to be replaced more often than with other types of breakers. Obviously, the air-break circuit breaker cannot be used where there is a flammable environment.

In the *oil circuit breaker* the contacts are immersed in an insulating oil and the contacts are opened in this oil. The insulating properties of the oil are better than air and the breaker can be used at high voltages and for high breaking capacities. When the breaker opens an arc is formed which produces gases and a little oil is carbonized. The pressure produced by these gases is utilized to extinguish the arc in an arrangement called an 'explosion pot'. This is a box-type structure round the fixed contacts and is constructed with a series of baffles and channels. When the contacts open the pressure set up by the gases forces oil through the channels and across the arc to extinguish it (Fig. 2.3). The arc is contained under the oil and does not affect the surrounding atmosphere. In some types of oil circuit breakers the oil is pumped mechanically across the opening contacts instead of relying upon the pressure set up by the gases.

Although oil circuit breakers can be placed in flameproof enclosures, the presence of oil can none the less be a fire hazard and the changing of oil during maintenance can be very messy. When the contacts open some oil is carbonized, which causes sludge to accumulate in the tank, so from time to time the oil has to be drained off and cleaned and the tank refilled. Other types of circuit breakers have been developed which overcome some of these disadvantages.

As the contacts open in an *air-blast circuit breaker* a jet of compressed

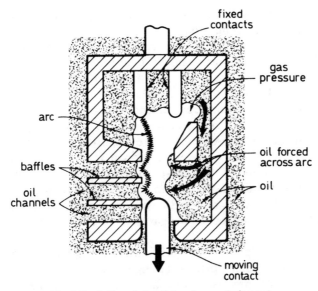

Fig. 2.3 Action of circuit breaker explosion pot

air is directed across the path of the arc as it is formed and quickly extinguishes it, as indicated in the simplified diagram of Fig. 2.4.

There are several designs of the air-blast circuit breaker. In some the contacts are spring assisted and in others the compressed air itself is used both to open and to close the contacts. The air is at a pressure of about

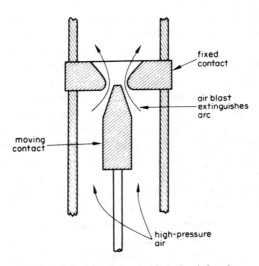

Fig. 2.4 Principle of the air-blast circuit breaker

17–21 bar (250–300 lbf/in^2) and as the blast moves across the contacts the arc is lengthened and extinguished quickly. This type of breaker requires a considerable amount of auxiliary equipment (compressors, compressed air reservoirs, etc.), so it is more complex than the oil circuit breaker and its initial cost greater. At voltages of 66 kV and over it has the advantage over the oil circuit breaker in its higher speed of operation, which is essential at these higher voltages and for large currents. Although its initial cost is high, the arcing time is shorter than that of the OCB, there are no oil changes required, maintenance is less, and the fire hazard is negligible.

Another type of circuit breaker developed for very high voltages and high breaking capacities is the *gas-blast circuit breaker*. The principle is similar to that of the air-blast type, and auxiliary equipment is required to keep the gas under pressure. As the gas is expensive, leakage must be avoided and during maintenance the gas must be pumped into storage tanks with the minimum of loss.

The gas used is sulphur hexafluoride which, under pressure, has better insulating properties than either insulating oil or compressed air. The gas is also inert and stable, non-flammable, and non-toxic. The gas at a pressure of about 3 bar (about 40–45 lbf/in^2) forms the insulating medium around the contacts. As the contacts are opened a jet of gas from a gas reservoir at a pressure of 15–16 bar (220–230 lbf/in^2) is directed across the contacts. The gas at this pressure would liquify if its temperature dropped below 10°C, so for outdoor switchgear heaters must be provided. The gas has a property that reduces ionization, causing the arc to be quenched quickly, and reduces the amount of contact burning. The duration of the arc is less than with a similar air-blast breaker.

A *vacuum circuit breaker* has been developed and is being used in high voltage distribution circuits. The contacts are placed in a sealed container in a vacuum and they are in the form of flat disks with their faces together. The moving contact is connected to the outside operating mechanism by means of metal bellows to maintain the vacuum. Since the contacts are in a vacuum, there are no particles to cause ionization when the arc is formed as the contacts part. However, some ionization occurs at the contact surface, owing to vaporized metal at this point, but the arc is extinguished at the first current zero after the contacts start opening. Thus the duration of the arcing time is very short, there is no oxidization of the contacts, contact burning is negligible, and since they are in a vacuum the contacts require no maintenance. Apart from a visual inspection from time to time the vacuum circuit breaker requires very little maintenance.

The operating mechanism of a circuit breaker is usually of a link or toggle type. Figure 2.5 shows a simplified form of one type of mechanism. For simplicity, the links are shown as straight rods. The links are hinged at the points F and H, but points F are fixed to the main structure, whereas

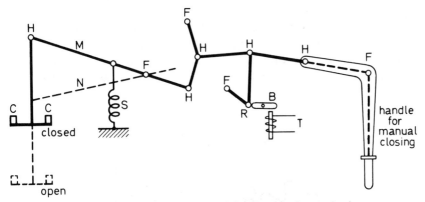

Fig. 2.5 Simplified diagram of circuit-breaker tripping mechanism.

C, main moving contacts;   M, closed position;
N, open position;   H, hinged points;
F, fixed hinged points;   R, hinged roller;
B, hinged bar or prop;   S, accelerating spring;
T, trip coil

points H are floating. A careful examination of the diagram will show that the hinged roller R is held fixed when bar B is in the horizontal position. The handle can then be lowered to the position shown in the diagram; the contacts are closed and held in this position. If bar B is dislodged by being struck by the tripping coil plunger then roller R is no longer fixed and the whole link system collapses. This causes spring S to pull the main arm from the closed position M to the open position N.

To enable inspection and maintenance to be carried out a means of isolating the circuit breaker from the busbars is required. In some cases the operating mechanism is on a truck which can be pulled clear of the busbar chamber either at ground level or by a rack and pinion arrangement. There are other cases where the circuit breaker has to be raised to make contact with the busbar chamber and lowered for inspection and maintenance. In all cases interlocks are fitted, so that the switch must be in the 'off' position before the circuit breaker can be pulled clear of the busbars. The connection to the busbars is by means of a plug and socket arrangement and as the circuit breaker is withdrawn a shield automatically covers the socket on the busbar chamber to ensure that contact cannot be made with the live busbars.

2.2 Circuit protection

Fuses. The fuse is the simplest form of circuit protection and consists of a fuse element suitably mounted and designed to melt safely, thus opening the circuit when an excess current flows. The fuse mount and carrier are so designed that the carrier can be safely withdrawn without danger of touching live parts and the fuse element is so enclosed that molten metal is safely contained and arcing effectively extinguished.

The simple wire fuse (Fig. 2.6) is connected between two terminals in a porcelain carrier and is usually threaded through an asbestos tube. The

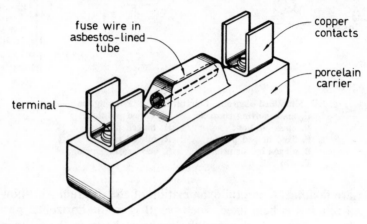

fuse wire in asbestos–lined tube

copper contacts

porcelain carrier

terminal

Fig. 2.6   Wire fuse

fusing current for this type of fuse may vary considerably. Circulating air can cool the wire, thereby increasing the fusing current. Air will also oxidize the wire in time, and this will cause a reduction of the fusing current. If discrimination is required, or accuracy in the value of the fusing current is necessary, then the wire fuse is most unreliable. The wires deteriorate and are subject to misuse, since it is easy for the wrong size of wire to be fitted. In circuits where the energy level is high, the wire fuse can be a source of danger, as it may not be adequate in extinguishing the arc.

Some of the disadvantages of the rewirable fuse are overcome if the wire is enclosed in a cartridge-type container. The cartridge may vary in length to match the fuse rating of the circuit to be protected so that the wrong size of fuse cannot be fitted. The fuse wire does not deteriorate and is more reliable in operation (Fig. 2.7).

For large currents and where the energy level is high, the high-breaking-capacity (h.b.c.) fuse is used. This is a cartridge-type fuse in which a silver fuse element is connected between two end-contacts of a ceramic tube filled with a special quartz powder. When the fuse blows there is a fusion of the silver vapour produced with the filling powder, so that globules of high-resistance material are formed in the path of the arc, causing it to be extinguished.

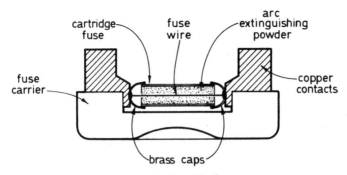

Fig. 2.7 Cartridge fuse

This type of fuse is very reliable in performance and can be used when discrimination is required. It does not deteriorate and has a high speed of operation (Fig. 2.8).

The characteristic of an h.b.c. fuse is compared with that of an induction relay in Fig. 2.13(b).

The disadvantage of all types of fuses, of course, is the fact that when they have operated they have to be replaced. The type of fuse chosen to protect a factory circuit will depend upon the type of load and the circuit conditions. It is important to realize the difference between the current rating of a fuse and its fusing current.

The *current rating* of a fuse is the current the fuse will carry continuously without blowing or deteriorating.

The *rated minimum fusing current* is the minimum current at which the fuse will blow in a specified time. This may vary between 1.25 and 2.5 times the current rating.

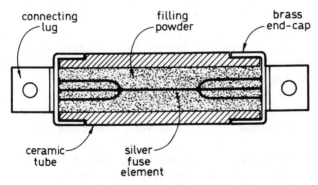

Fig. 2.8 High-breaking-capacity (h.b.c.) fuse

The relationship between the rated minimum fusing current and the current rating is called the *fusing factor*.

$$\text{Fusing factor} = \frac{\text{rated minimum fusing current}}{\text{current rating}}$$

There are four classes of fuses, depending upon their fusing factors. These are as follows:

Class P fuses   These having a fusing factor of 1.25 or less and provide protection for circuits that cannot withstand even small sustained overloads.

Class Q fuses   These fuses are for circuits that can withstand small overcurrents but give protection against higher values of overload. There are two types:
Class Q1—fusing factor between 1.25 and 1.5
Class Q2—fusing factor between 1.5 and 1.75

Class R fuses   These fuses have a fusing factor between 1.75 and 2.5 and will protect a circuit against relatively large overcurrents only. Their main use is as back-up protection where the normal protection is provided by some other device such as a circuit breaker or a motor overload trip.

A fuse provides *close protection* if its fusing factor is less than 1.5, that is fuses of classes P and Q1.

Coarse protection is provided by fuses with a fusing factor over 1.5, that is fuses of classes Q2 and R.

Overload Trips. Overload trips are used to open circuit breakers when a more precise form of protection and a higher degree of discrimination is required. Another advantage over the fuse is that they can be reset after each operation, whereas a fuse must be replaced which can be costly. This type of trip is also used in starters for the protection of motors and their circuits. One of the simplest is an electromagnetic trip, as shown in Fig. 2.9. The armature is attracted to the electromagnet when the current reaches a certain predetermined value. The force of the armature will trip the link mechanism of the circuit breaker, or it may operate as a relay and close the contacts of a separate tripping circuit. The armature is attracted against gravity or a spring. By adjusting the distance of the armature from the electromagnet, or the tension of the spring, the current at which the trip operates can be varied to suit the circuit conditions.

This simple trip is instantaneous in its operation but it can be given an inverse time lag by connecting a fuse in parallel with it. This means that the time taken for the fuse to blow depends inversely upon the severity of the

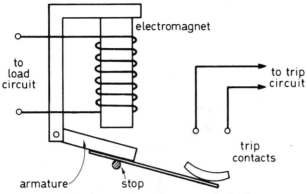

Fig. 2.9 Simple electromagnet overload trip

overload or fault. When the fuse blows the trip will then operate instantaneously (Fig. 2.10).

Figure 2.11 shows a type of electromagnetic trip or relay in which a plunger is attracted into a solenoid when a predetermined current is reached. The operating current can be adjusted by varying the position of the plunger with respect to the coil. Various types of time lags may be

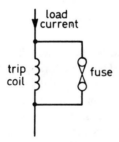

Fig. 2.10 Fuse to give an inverse time lag

fitted, the one shown being an oil dashpot type. When the plunger is attracted to the solenoid by excess current the oil in the dashpot must pass through a small by-pass hole in the piston before the plunger can travel far enough to make the tripping contacts, thus delaying operation. There is usually a means of varying the size of by-pass hole so that the time lag can be changed to suit the particular load conditions.

In some cases, and particularly for a.c. motor starters, the heating effect of a bimetal strip is used as the basis of the thermal overload trip. This consists of two strips of different metals welded or riveted together, each

29

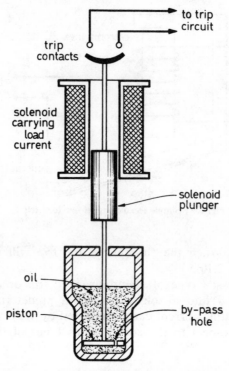

Fig. 2.11 Overload trip with oil dashpot time lag

having a different rate of expansion when heated. 'Invar' and brass or a nickel alloy are materials often used (Fig. 2.12a). The bimetal strip is wound with a coil of wire which carries the load current of the main circuit. This current heats the bimetal strip; the brass expands more than the 'Invar', which causes the strip to bend and operate the tripping mechanism. The amount of bending depends upon the heating, and there-fore upon the current producing the heat. If the distance between the bimetal strip and the tripping bar is adjusted, the current at which the trip operates can be determined. Heating effect is not instantaneous, as time is required for sufficient heat to be transferred to the bimetal strip to cause it to bend. Thus a time delay is inherent in this type of trip and oil dashpots are unnecessary.

The characteristic curve for a thermal overload trip is shown in Fig. 2.12(c). Although the time delay is useful when the overload is short-lived, as in the case of starting an induction motor, when serious faults occur like a short circuit, the heating of the thermal trip may be too slow. In such cases an instantaneous trip set to operate when the current is excessive is sometimes used in conjunction with the thermal unit.

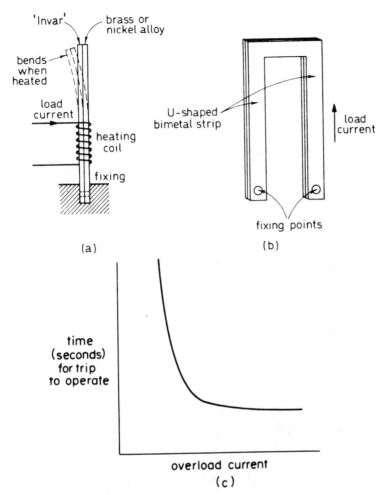

Fig. 2.12 Thermal overload trips: (a) bimetal strip heated by coil, (b) bimetal strip carries load current (c) characteristic

For larger currents, the coil may be dispensed with and the bimetal strip made in the form of a U (Fig. 2.12b). The load current is fed through the U-shaped strip, which causes it to bend by direct heating.

On extensive installations, and particularly where h.v. feeders controlled by circuit breakers are concerned, a high degree of discrimination may be necessary requiring greater precision than can be obtained from trips of the above types. In these cases, an induction type of relay can be used. Figure 2.13(a) is a simplified diagram of such a relay. This relay, however, can only be used in a.c. circuits.

The principle of operation is similar to that of the induction-type watt-

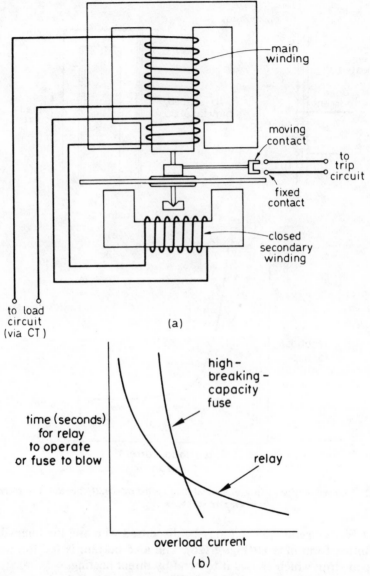

Fig. 2.13 Induction type overload relay: (a) relay (simplified), (b) inverse-time characteristics of relay and fuse

meter in which a metal disk is mounted on a spindle between two electromagnets. The alternating magnetic field produced by these electromagnets causes eddy currents to be formed in the disk. The upper three-limbed magnet carries the main windings on its centre limb. The air gap

32

of this magnet is very narrow, giving a highly inductive circuit. The lower magnet has a wide air gap and is energized from the secondary winding on the centre limb of the upper magnet. By this means the magnetic fluxes which produce the eddy currents in the disk are so displaced in phase that a motor effect is produced and the disk rotates.

The main coil is usually supplied by means of a current transformer in the circuit to be protected; full-load current in the main circuit corresponding to the relay full-load setting, which is usually 5 A. A spiral spring holds the disk against rotation when normal current is flowing. Excess current causes the disk to rotate. After a rotation of about 180°, a moving contact attached to the disk spindle shorts two fixed contacts and operates the tripping circuit. The main coil is normally tapped, so a range of operating currents is obtained. The greater the severity of the overload or fault the faster the disk will rotate, giving a shorter operating time. This gives the relay an inverse time characteristic as shown by the graph of Fig. 2.13(b). For any given fault current, the time of operation can be adjusted by moving the start position of the disk so that it has a smaller angle of rotation before tripping occurs.

In some circuits it is sometimes desirable for the relay to have a dual characteristic in which an inverse time characteristic applies only up to a certain value of overcurrent. Above this value, that is, for very large overcurrents and faults, the tripping is instantaneous.

2.3 Earth-leakage protection

Figure 2.14 shows a consumer's circuit consisting of an appliance being fed through the local distribution system from the supply authority substation. One point of the distribution transformer secondary is connected to earth. At the consumer's premises the live conductor is protected by a fuse. Suppose a fault occurs in the consumer's equipment causing the metal case to be connected to the live conductor.

In Fig. 2.14(a) the metal casing is unearthed. The fault will cause it to have a potential above earth the same as the live conductor, that is, full mains voltage V. A person standing on an earthed floor or touching an earthed part of the building structure will receive a severe and possibly fatal shock if he also touches the equipment casing. Thus unearthed metal associated with an electrical installation is a source of danger. All such metal must be earthed to comply with IEE Regulations and with the Factories Act.

Figure 2.14(b) shows the path of the fault current when the casing is earthed. The earth return path should be of low impedance so that the whole of the earth fault circuit, consisting of the transformer winding, the live conductor, earth-continuity conductor, earthing lead, and earth return,

33

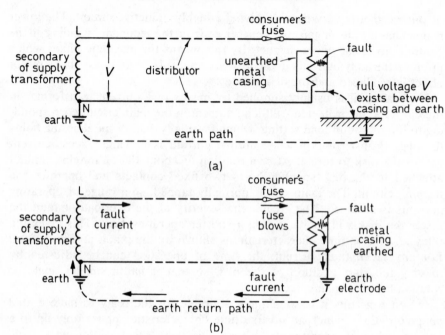

Fig. 2.14 Earth-leakage protection: (a) dangerous condition, (b) safe condition

has a low impedance. In most cases, the earth return path will be metallic, consisting of the metal sheath of the underground supply cable or a continuous earth wire on an overhead system. When there is no metallic path, the return is through the earth via earth plates or electrodes. If the total earth loop or earth fault circuit impedance is Z_e then the fault current will be $I_f = V/Z_e$. This current should be large enough to blow the consumer's fuse and protect the circuit. The IEE Regulations state that the impedance of the earth loop circuit must be low enough to create a fault current at least three times a *coarse* fuse rating, 2.4 times a *close* fuse rating, or, if circuit breakers are used, $1\frac{1}{2}$ times the circuit breaker setting.

In cases where there is no metallic earth return, the path through earth may have an impedance too high to create a fault current sufficient to blow the fuse. In such cases, and usually in cases where the fuse rating is 100 A or over, the circuit must be protected by an earth-leakage circuit breaker or trip. The operating coil of the trip is connected in the earth-continuity conductor circuit. Even a high-impedance earth fault will cause a small current to flow in the earth-continuity conductor and this will be sufficient to trip the circuit. These earth-leakage circuit breakers can be set to trip with currents as small as 30–40 mA. An earth fault causes metal casing and the associated earth-continuity conductor to have their potential raised above earth and produce the fault current. It is a requirement of the IEE Regulations that the earth-leakage circuit breaker shall protect the circuit so that no part of the earth-continuity conductor can have its voltage raised by a fault more than 40 V above earth.

Typical arrangements of voltage-operated earth-leakage circuit breakers are shown in Fig. 2.15. In (a), the trip coil opens the contacts when the

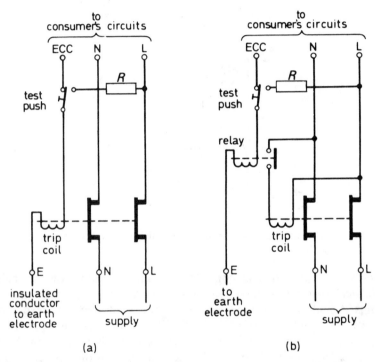

Fig. 2.15 Voltage-operated earth-leakage circuit breakers: (a) direct trip, (b) relay-operated trip

earth fault current flows. The current may have to be fairly large to give this direct tripping. A more sensitive circuit is shown at (b), where only a very small fault current is sufficient to operate the relay, which closes contacts so that the tripping coil is connected directly across the supply to give a more definite action. In both cases, a test push places an artificial earth fault on to the circuit through the high resistance R so that a check can be made of the operation of the circuit breaker. After tripping, the breaker has to be reclosed manually. To safeguard against the trip coil being by-passed, the lead between the earth-leakage circuit breaker and the earth electrode must be insulated.

Another form of earth-leakage circuit breaker is the current-operated

35

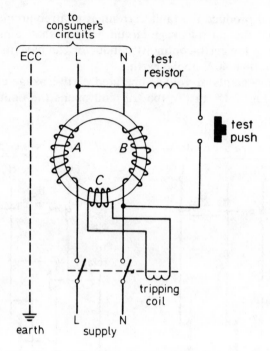

Fig. 2.16   Current-operated earth-leakage circuit breaker

type shown in Fig. 2.16. This consists of a current-balance or core-balance transformer which has three windings, *A*, *B*, and *C*, on a ring core. Windings *A* and *B* carry the line and neutral load currents, respectively, which will be equal in a healthy circuit. They are wound in opposition so that the total magnetic flux is zero and no current is induced in the third coil, *C*. If a fault occurs between line and earth, then the return current in the neutral will be less than the current in the live conductor. The balance between *A* and *B* will be upset and the resultant magnetic flux will induce a current in coil *C*. This is connected to the tripping coil of the earth-leakage circuit breaker, which it will open.

In three-phase circuits a combination of overload and earth-leakage relays supplied from current transformers is often used. However, a simple form of earth-leakage protection can be given in a star-connected circuit by placing a relay between the neutral point and earth. The relay may be operated by a current transformer as shown in the circuit of Fig. 2.17.

If an earth fault occurs in any phase, for example at point F, then the fault current will flow through the earth path to the neutral. The current in the current transformer will operate the relay, which will trip the circuit breaker.

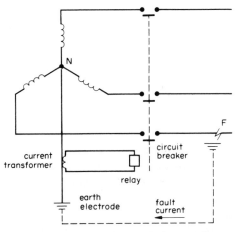

Fig. 2.17   Three-phase earth fault protection

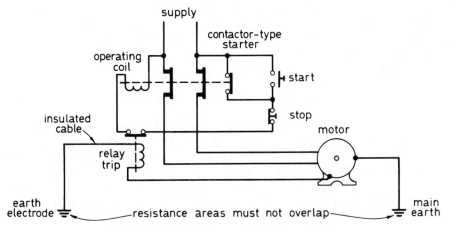

Fig. 2.18   Earth-leakage protection for a motor

The shutdown of a large installation can be avoided by protecting individual appliances against earth leakage. A motor, for example, can be protected by having an earth-leakage relay connected to open the operating coil circuit of a pushbutton contactor-type starter (Fig. 2.18). The tripping circuit is in parallel with the main earthing circuit as shown. It is essential that the resistance areas of the two electrodes do not overlap. (The resistance of earth from an electrode increases with distance from the electrode until a point is reached when the resistance becomes constant. This area round an electrode in which the earth resistance varies is called the *resistance area of the electrode* and it can be a few metres in good soils or up to 7 or 8 m or more in soils of poor conductivity.)

37

3. Economics—Tariffs

3.1 The basis of electricity tariffs

At one time, the cost of electricity to the consumer was based upon the *flat-rate tariff*, that is, there was a fixed cost of, say, six old pence per unit for all electricity used. This type of tariff is now largely obsolete, since it is economically unsound.

For general supplies, electricity cannot be stored. Generating plant must always be available to give a supply to a consumer on demand. The cost of this plant, spread over a number of years, must be recovered by making a minimum (constant) charge whether energy is used or not. When energy is used then fuel is consumed at the generating station. The cost of this fuel must be recovered by making a running charge proportional to the energy consumed. The total charge will be of the type

$$\text{Charge} = a + (b \times \text{energy consumed}) \tag{3.1}$$

This is called a *two-part tariff* and is the basis of most modern tariffs.

Charge a is determined by the size of the generating plant and the transmission system, i.e., upon the kW capacity of the plant (it will be seen later that kV A is used rather than kW). The size of plant is determined by the load connected by the consumers after applying a *diversity factor*. This factor takes into account the fact that it is most unlikely that all connected plant will be in use at any one time.

$$\text{Diversity factor for a consumer} = \frac{\text{total connected load}}{\text{max. load in use at any instant}} \tag{3.2}$$

When considering a supply system as a whole, it is unlikely that all consumers will have their maximum loads on at the same time, also the maximum load in, say, a domestic area is not likely to be at the same time as the maximum load in an industrial area or a commercial district. So for a supply system:

$$\text{Diversity factor} = \frac{\text{sum of max. demands of all consumers}}{\text{max. demand upon the generating plant}} \tag{3.3}$$

This factor is generally much greater than unity.

38

EXAMPLE

The maximum demands (m.d.s) of all consumers connected to a generating station total 300 000 kW. As these do not occur at the same time a diversity factor of 15 can be applied. What will be the maximum load or rating of the generator? If the capital charge of generating plant is £9 per kW, what will be the charge per kW of maximum demand to the consumer?

$$\text{Generator rating} = \frac{\text{sum of maximum demands}}{\text{diversity factor}} = \frac{300\,000}{15} = 20\,000 \text{ kW}$$

$$\text{Maximum demand charge} = \frac{\text{charge per kW of plant}}{\text{diversity factor}} = \frac{£9}{15} = £0.6 \text{ per kW}$$

The charges for transmission equipment, steam plant, etc., are made in the same way to arrive at the total maximum demand charge.

Charge a is applied to a tariff by *annualizing* the actual cost of plant. That is, after considering the possibility of plant becoming redundant, or obsolete, owing to modernization, reorganization, load increases, etc., the equipment is given an *economic life*. This may be 10, 15, or 20 or so years, and usually bears no relationship to the mechanical life of the machine. The capital cost of plant is spread over this economic life, giving an annual figure for depreciation to which interest must also be added. Thus, the capital cost of plant is annualized as interest and depreciation and this is applied to the tariffs as charge a. This annual charge is usually in the range of about 8% to 15% of the capital cost.

Charge a depends upon the cost of plant and is therefore related to the plant rating, which in turn depends upon the maximum demand of the consumers. Charge a is collected by making a charge upon a consumer based upon his maximum demand. That is, there will be a charge per kW (or kV A) of maximum demand.

It has been seen that a large diversity factor will lower the cost of the m.d. charge. Two other factors must also be considered:

1. Load Factor.

$$\text{Load factor} = \frac{\text{units used in a given time}}{\substack{\text{units if maximum load has been continuous} \\ \text{during the same time}}} \qquad (3.4)$$

The importance of load factor can be seen from the daily load charts of Fig. 3.1.

Chart (a) shows a loading with high peaks and also times of light load.

Area A = units used in 24 hours (kW h)
Area $A + B$ = units that would have been used in 24 hours
if maximum load had been continuous

39

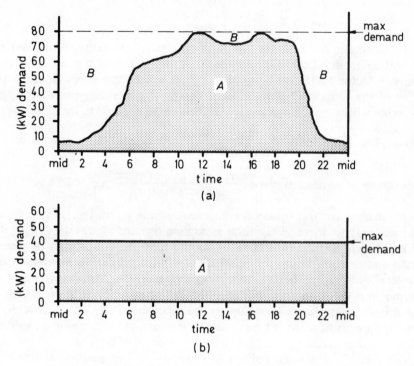

Fig. 3.1 Effect of load factor: (a) 50% load factor, (b) 100% load factor

$$\text{Load factor} = \frac{A}{A+B} = \text{(estimated)} \; \tfrac{1}{2} = 50\%$$

In chart (b), area A is exactly the same as before, that is, the number of units used in 24 hours remains constant, but the load has been spread evenly over the day to give the ideal load factor of 100%. Although the factory output has not been affected, the maximum demand has been reduced to half its previous value. A maximum demand charge of, say, £10 per kW, will give a considerable saving on the electricity account and at the same time relieve the supply authority's equipment, thus making a supply available to other consumers without the addition of more plant.

EXAMPLE

A consumer with a maximum demand of 500 kW consumes 4800 units of electricity per day. What is the load factor? If the load factor is improved to $66\tfrac{2}{3}\%$, what will be the saving on the m.d. charge if the tariff charge is £10 per kW of maximum demand? The energy used remains unaltered.

Number of units a day if m.d. is maintained = m.d. × hours
$$= 500 + 24$$
$$= 12\,000 \text{ kW h}$$

$$\text{Load factor} = \frac{\text{actual units per day}}{\text{units if m.d. is maintained}}$$

$$= \frac{4800}{12\,000} = 0.4 = 40\%$$

If load factor is improved to $66\frac{2}{3}\%$

$$\text{Units if m.d. maintained} = \frac{\text{units used}}{\text{load factor}}$$

$$= \frac{4800}{0.667} = 7200 \text{ kW h}$$

$$\therefore \text{ m.d.} = \frac{7200}{24} = 300 \text{ kW}$$

$\therefore$ Reduction in m.d. = 500 − 300 = 200 kW
$\therefore$ Saving = 200 × £10 = £2000

2. Power Factor (p.f.)

In an a.c. circuit
Power (watts) = volts × amps × power factor

i.e. $$P = VI \cos \phi \qquad (3.5)$$

With constant voltage V, it will be seen that a low power factor ($\cos \phi$) will require a high current (I) to flow for a given power, but I will be reduced if $\cos \phi$ is improved, i.e., brought nearer to unity. Thus a low power factor causes excessive current to be drawn for a given power and this in turn will require plant and equipment of a higher current rating. It is for this reason that plant and equipment are rated in kV A and not kW. To enable plant rating to be kept within reason and also have spare capacity available for other consumers, the supply authority encourages consumers to improve their power factor by having the m.d. charge a per kV A instead of per kW

$$kW = kV A \times p.f.$$

Thus, for a given kW power demand, a low power factor will give a high kV A maximum-demand charge.

This is the usual method of including power factor into the tariff, but sometimes the tariff will include a penalty clause for poor power-factor working, and sometimes a kilovar meter will be installed and a charge made

41

for reactive kilovolt amperes. Improving the power factor will obviously reduce this charge.

EXAMPLE

A 50 hp, 415 V, three-phase motor operates on full load at 0.7 p.f. lagging at an efficiency of 85%. What will be the kV A demand and the current taken from the supply? By how much will the kV A demand and the current be reduced if the power factor is improved to 0.95 lagging?

$$\text{Output in kW} = \frac{50 \times 746}{1000} \qquad = 37.3\,\text{kW}$$

$$\text{Input} \qquad = \frac{37.3}{0.85} \qquad = 43.9\,\text{kW}$$

$$\text{kV A} = \frac{\text{kW}}{\text{p.f.}} \quad = \quad \frac{43.9}{0.7} \qquad = 62.6\,\text{kV A}$$

$$\text{Current } I = \frac{\text{kV A} \times 1000}{1.73\,V}$$

$$= \frac{62.6 \times 1000}{1.73 \times 415} = 87\,\text{A}$$

If p.f. is improved to 0.95

then
$$\text{kV A} = \frac{43.9}{0.95} \qquad = 46.2\,\text{kV A}$$

$$\text{Current } I = \frac{46.2 \times 1000}{1.73 \times 415} = 64.3\,\text{A}$$

$\therefore$ Reduction in kV A $= 62.6 - 46.2 \quad = 16.4\,\text{kV A reduction}$

Reduction in current $= 87 - 64.3 \quad = 22.7\,\text{A reduction}$

Note: If the maximum demand charge is £10 per kV A then the improvement in power factor in this case would give a saving of £164.

Charge *b* is a running charge depending upon energy used in kWh. When electricity is used by a consumer, fuel is consumed at the generating plant. It is the cost of this fuel and associated running costs that is recovered by charge *b* in the tariff.

The basis of charges *a* and *b* can be summarized as follows:

(a) Fixed costs.

    (i) Interest and depreciation on capital cost of generating plant, buildings, transmission and distribution systems.

    (ii) Rents, rates and taxes.

(iii)   Most of the salaries and wages.

(iv)   Small amount of fuel to supply auxiliaries, etc.

(b)   Running costs.

(i)   Almost all the fuel cost.

(ii)   Small amount of salaries and wages.

3.2   Application of the two-part tariff

For small domestic and commercial consumers, the installation of maximum-demand metering equipment is not justified; therefore the fixed charge a is made, depending upon some means of comparison such as the size of building, floor area, number of rooms, or an estimated m.d. based upon the electrical equipment installed.

There may be a fixed charge per quarter independant of units used or, as is more usual today, the units may be on a *sliding-scale tariff* in which the first block of units is at a higher rate in order to recover the fixed costs, after which additional units are at a lower rate. The number of units in the first block depends upon the type and size of premises. For example, a *domestic tariff* may be quoted as:

For the first 72 units a quarter   7p per unit

All additional units a quarter   2.8p per unit

For small industrial or commercial premises with loads up to about 50 kV A the maximum demand may be assessed and a tariff arranged as follows. The number of blocks in a sliding scale may vary; in this example it is three.

First 90 units per quarter per kV A of assessed m.d.   7p per unit

Next 300 „ „ „ „ „ „ „ „ „ „ „ „   3.8p per unit

All units in excess of 390 per quarter per kV A of assessed m.d. 2.8p per unit

The *industrial two-part tariff* is based upon a fixed charge per month or per year per kV A of maximum demand plus an additional charge per unit used. In this case, the maximum demand is metered. An example of this tariff would be:

£10 per kV A of maximum demand per year

plus 2.8p per unit used

For very large consumers, a special tariff may be drawn up by agreement. Very often, both the m.d. charge and the unit charge will be on a sliding scale and a coal clause or fuel adjustment clause included, so that the charge per unit can be adjusted if the price of coal, or other fuel, rises or falls.

When the supply is given at high voltage, the metering will also be on the high-voltage side and the cost of substation and transformer equipment and their losses is borne by the consumer. It follows that the tariff charges for a high-voltage supply will be somewhat smaller than for an equivalent medium-voltage supply.

EXAMPLE

A factory has a maximum demand of 2000 kV A when operating at a power factor of 0.7 lagging. If power-factor improvement equipment is installed to give a p.f. of 0.95, what will be the annual saving in the electricity charge? What will be the total electricity charge in one year after the power factor has been improved if the factory has a load factor of 50%? The tariff is

£10 per kV A of maximum demand per year
plus 2.5p per unit consumed

m.d. at 0.7 p.f. = 2000 kV A

∴ kW = kV A × p.f. = 2000 × 0.7 = 1400 kW

$$\text{At } 0.95 \text{ p.f. m.d.} = \frac{\text{kW}}{\text{p.f.}} = \frac{1400}{0.95} = 1474 \text{ kV A}$$

∴ Reduction in m.d. = 2000 − 1474 = 526 kV A

∴ Saving = 526 × £10 = £5260

m.d. charge at 0.95 p.f.
   = 1474 × £10 = £14 740

Load factor = 50%

∴ Average kW = kW m.d. × load factor
   = 1400 × 0.5 = 700 kW

∴ Number of units in 1 year (8760 hours)
   = 700 × 8760 = 6 132 000 kW h

∴ Unit cost = 6 132 000 × 2.5
   = 15 330 000p
   = £153 300

∴ Total annual cost = £14 740 + £153 300
   = £168 040

Note: A consumer requires his electricity account to be correct to the nearest penny. Therefore, in general, slide-rule accuracy is not sufficient for tariff calculations.

3.3 Power factor improvement

The large numbers of induction motors used in industry today mean that almost all factories operate at a lagging power factor. It has been seen already that a consumer with a low power factor is penalized by having to pay an excessive maximum demand charge as part of his tariff. The consumer is encouraged, therefore, to install equipment that will reduce this charge without affecting the factory output. Improving the power factor also reduces the current for a given output power, thereby reducing the kV A ratings of switchgear, transformers, cables, etc., in the circuit, or, alternatively, causing spare capacity to be available for additional loads.

Any load taking a leading power factor will improve the power factor of an inductive circuit, but in most cases a static capacitor is used. Consider the supply to the inductive load of Fig. 3.2.

The phasor diagram (a) shows the current I_1 lagging by an angle ϕ_1. The active and reactive components are $I_1 \cos \phi_1$ and $I_1 \sin \phi_1$, respectively. The

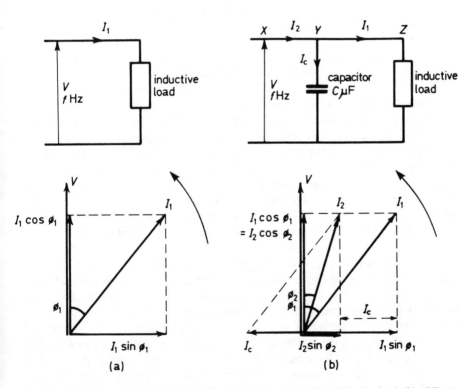

Fig. 3.2 Effect of capacitor in parallel with an inductive load: (a) an inductive load, (b) adding a capacitor

45

addition of the capacitor (diagram (b)) causes an additional current I_c to be drawn from the supply, but as this current is almost entirely reactive and leading the voltage by 90° it will reduce the reactive component $I_1 \sin \phi_1$ of the load to a smaller value $I_2 \sin \phi_2$. This means that the current I_2 taken from the supply has also been reduced and the new phase angle is ϕ_2, which gives an improved power factor, $\cos \phi_2$. It will be seen that the true power taken from the supply has not altered and $I_1 \cos \phi_1 = I_2 \cos \phi_2$. Also, I_2 is the resultant of the phasor sum of I_1 and I_c.

It can be seen also that the current I_2 flows from X to Y, that is, to the point at which the capacitor is connected, but beyond the capacitor, from Y to Z, the current and power factor are still the original values of I_1 and $\cos \phi_1$. Thus, the power factor is improved only on the supply side of the capacitor.

If a single capacitor is placed at the consumer's supply point then the improvement will affect only the metering, which is the main consideration, and the supply authority's equipment. It is usual to have the capacitor in several banks so that individual banks can be switched in or out of circuit either automatically or manually as the factory load changes, thereby keeping the power factor as near unity as possible.

Another method is to have a small capacitor at each machine which is switched with the machine so that control at the supply point is unnecessary. This method also reduces the current in the factory installation itself, although the installing of a large number of small capacitors at each machine will cost more than one large unit at the supply point.

If the capacitor connected to the motor terminals is too large there is the danger of creating an overvoltage. A synchronous generator supplying a capacitive load can generate a higher voltage on load than at no-load (Chapter 7). If the capacitance is large enough it can produce a reactance field which will cause self-excitation when the normal d.c. excitation is cut off and can produce voltages much higher than normal. Capacitors connected across the terminals of an induction motor can cause self-excitation in a similar way when the normal motor supply is switched off. The normal motor terminal voltage is the supply voltage but when the supply is switched off capacitors still connected could cause a sudden voltage increase if they were large enough. As the motor decreases speed, this voltage will be reduced but the initial surge may be sufficient to cause breakdown of equipment still connected to the terminals. The danger of these over-voltage surges is present only if the capacitor is too large and they can be avoided by matching the capacitor to the motor to ensure that it does not cause a leading current to be taken from the supply. A capacitor connected across the terminals of a motor should never be made large enough to improve the power factor of other adjacent circuits in addition to the motor itself.

The size of capacitor will depend upon the amount of improvement required, as it is not always economically sound to raise the power factor completely to unity. When the cost of additional equipment is taken into account, it may be found that the greatest saving is achieved at a power factor less than unity.

From Fig. 3.2(b) it is seen that

$$I_1 \sin \phi_1 = (I_1 \cos \phi_1) \tan \phi_1 \qquad (3.6)$$

$$I_2 \sin \phi_2 = (I_1 \cos \phi_1) \tan \phi_2 \qquad (3.7)$$

also
$$I_2 \cos \phi_2 = I_1 \cos \phi_1$$

Capacitor current $I_c = I_1 \sin \phi_1 - I_2 \sin \phi_2 \qquad (3.8)$

$$X_c = \frac{V}{I_c} = \frac{10^6}{2\pi f C} \qquad \text{where } C \text{ is in } \mu F$$

$$\therefore C = \frac{10^6 I_c}{2\pi f V} = \frac{10^6}{2\pi f X_c} \qquad \mu F \qquad (3.9)$$

EXAMPLE

A current of 35 A is taken from a 240 V, single-phase 50 Hz a.c. supply at a power factor of 0.75 lagging. If a capacitor is installed to improve the power factor to 0.96 lagging, find (1) the current taken from the supply, (2) the capacitor current, (3) the capacitance of the capacitor.

Original p.f. $= \cos \phi_1 = 0.75$ $\quad \therefore \phi_1 = 41.4°$ $\quad \sin \phi_1 = 0.6613$

Final p.f. $= \cos \phi_2 = 0.96$ $\quad \therefore \phi_2 = 16.2°$ $\quad \sin \phi_2 = 0.279$

In-phase component $I_1 \cos \phi_1 = 35 \times 0.75 = 26.25 \text{ A} = I_2 \cos \phi_2$

$$\therefore I_2 = \frac{I_2 \cos \phi_2}{\cos \phi_2} = \frac{26.25}{0.96} = 27.3 \text{ A}$$

1. $\therefore$ Current taken from supply after improvement $= 27.3$ A

2. Reactive component $I_1 \sin \phi_1 = 35 \times 0.661 = 23.1$ A

$$I_2 \sin \phi_2 = 27.3 \times 0.279 = 7.62 \text{ A}$$

$\therefore$ From Eq. (3.8)

Capacitor current $I_c = 23.1 - 7.62 = 15.48$ A

3. Using Eq. (3.9)

$$C = \frac{10^6 I_c}{2\pi f V} = \frac{10^6 \times 15.48}{2\pi \times 50 \times 240} = 205 \ \mu F$$

The student will be able to verify that the answers (1) and (2) can be found graphically by drawing the phasor diagram (Fig. 3.3) to scale.

If the current phasors of Fig. 3.3 are multiplied by $V/1000$ for single-phase circuits or $1.73 V/1000$ for three-phase circuits a power diagram (Fig.

47

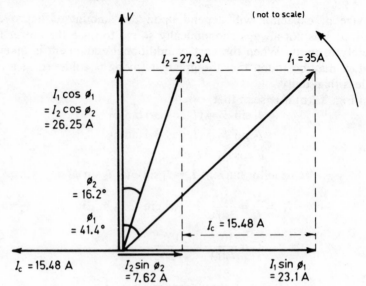

Fig. 3.3   Phasor diagram for worked example

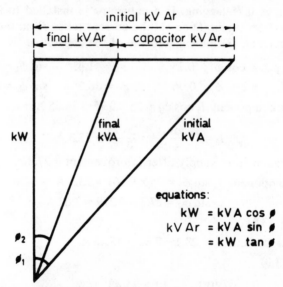

Fig. 3.4   Power factor improvement diagram

3.4) is produced. This is often the more convenient diagram to use for solving power factor improvement problems. The in-phase component is active power (kW), the quadrature component is reactive power (kV Ar), and the current phasor becomes apparent power (kV A).

48

EXAMPLE

A 415 V, three-phase, 50 Hz motor of 150 kW (200 hp) output operates on full load at a lagging power factor of 0.707 with an efficiency of 85.6%. Find the rating of a capacitor required to improve the power factor to 0.98 lagging and its capacitance per phase if it is delta-connected. If the maximum demand charge in the tariff is £8 per kV A per annum, what will be the annual reduction in the cost of electricity?

$$\text{Motor input} = \frac{\text{output}}{\eta} = \frac{150}{0.856} = 175 \text{ kW}$$

Initial p.f. $= \cos \phi_1 = 0.707$ $\therefore \phi_1 = 45°$ $\tan \phi_1 = 1$

Final p.f. $= \cos \phi_2 = 0.98$ $\therefore \phi_2 = 11.5°$ $\tan \phi_2 = 0.2035$

Initial kV Ar $= $ kW $\tan \phi_1 = 175 \times 1$ $= 175$ kV Ar

Final kV Ar $= $ kW $\tan \phi_2 = 175 \times 0.2035 = 35.6$ kV Ar

$$\therefore \text{Capacitor rating} = 175 - 35.6 = 139.4 \text{ kV Ar}$$

$$\text{Capacitor rating per phase} = \frac{139.4}{3} = 46.47 \text{ kV Ar}$$

Delta connection: $\therefore$ Volts across capacitor $= 415$ V.

$$\therefore \text{Capacitor current } I_c = \frac{\text{kV Ar} \times 1000}{V} = \frac{46.47 \times 1000}{415} = 112 \text{ A}$$

$\therefore$ Using Eq. (3.9)

$$\text{Capacitance } C = \frac{10^6 I_c}{2\pi f V} = \frac{10^6 \times 112}{2\pi \times 50 \times 415} = 859 \text{ } \mu\text{F per phase}$$

$$\text{Initial kV A} = \frac{\text{kW}}{\cos \phi_1} = \frac{175}{0.707} = 247.5 \text{ kV A}$$

$$\text{Final kV A} = \frac{\text{kW}}{\cos \phi_2} = \frac{175}{0.98} = 178.5 \text{ kV A}$$

$$\therefore \text{Reduction in kV A} = 247.5 - 178.5 = 69 \text{ kV A}$$

$$\therefore \text{Reduction in electricity cost} = £8 \times 69 = £552 \text{ per year}$$

There are other methods of improving the power factor instead of using a capacitor. For example, both the synchronous motor and synchronous-induction motor can be operated at a leading power factor by adjustment of the excitation, and if run continuously can be used to provide power factor improvement for the whole factory and at the same time drive a suitable load. The following example shows how such a power factor improvement calculation can be made. It is helpful to remember that active

49

power components (kW) can be added and reactive power components (kV Ar) can also be added algebraically, that is, a leading kV Ar must be treated as carrying a negative sign.

EXAMPLE

A factory has a load of 200 kW at a power factor of 0.8 lagging. A synchronous motor is to be added which will take a load of 50 kW from the supply. At what leading power factor must it be operated if it is to be used to improve the overall power factor to 0.9 lagging?

The method can be seen from Fig. 3.5 in which the phasor diagrams of the initial load and the synchronous motor are superimposed. If the

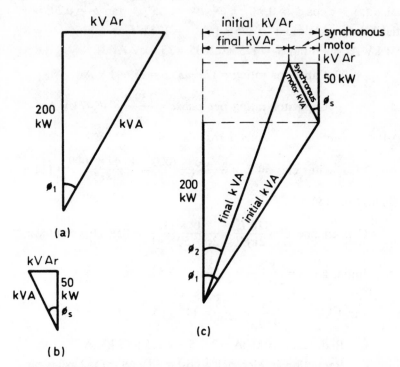

Fig. 3.5 Power factor improvement by synchronous motor: (a) initial load, (b) synchronous motor, (c) combined diagram

diagram is drawn to scale then ϕ_s can be measured and the leading power factor found.

$$\text{Initial p.f.} = \cos \phi_1 = 0.8 \qquad \therefore \ \phi_1 = 36.9° \qquad \tan \phi_1 = 0.75$$
$$\text{Final p.f.} \ = \cos \phi_2 = 0.9 \qquad \therefore \ \phi_2 = 25.8° \qquad \tan \phi_2 = 0.483$$

$$\therefore \text{ Initial kV Ar} = kW_1 \times \tan \phi_1 = 200 \times 0.75 = 150 \text{ kV Ar}$$
$$\text{Final kV Ar} = kW_2 \times \tan \phi_2 = 250 \times 0.483 = 121 \text{ kV Ar}$$

$$\therefore \text{ Synchronous motor leading kV Ar} = 150 - 121 = 29 \text{ kV Ar}$$

$$\tan \phi_s = \frac{\text{kV Ar}}{\text{kW}} = \frac{29}{50} = 0.58 \qquad \therefore \ \phi_s = 30.1°$$

$\therefore$ Synchronous motor leading power factor $= \cos 30.1° = 0.865$ leading.

Further increases of load can be included by adding the appropriate power triangle to the existing diagram. Unity power factor loads will be added as a straight line (kW), since there is no reactive component.

4. Generator and motor principles

4.1 Generator effect in a single loop

Figure 4.1 shows a loop of wire $ABCD$ rotating in a magnetic field about an axis XY. If the rotation is clockwise when viewed from end X then the direction of the induced e.m.f.s will be as shown. At the instant of Fig. 4.1(a) terminal P is positive and Q negative. The current in the external circuit will be from S to T.

Figure 4.1(b) shows the coil 180° later when terminal P has become negative and Q positive, with the external current flowing from T to S.

After 360° the condition will be as for Fig. 4.1(a) again, with the current flowing from S to T. Thus the e.m.f. generated in the rotating coil is alternating.

The effect will be the same if the field is rotating and the coil is fixed (see Chapter 7, Fig. 7.1).

Obviously the external circuit in Fig. 4.1 cannot be connected direct to terminals P and Q which are rotating with the coil. Current can be fed to the external circuit by *slip rings* (Fig. 4.2a). These consist of two copper rings attached to the shaft but insulated from it. Each end of the coil is attached to one of the rings so that one ring becomes terminal P and the other becomes terminal Q. Fixed carbon brushes make rubbing contact on to each ring. These brushes are connected to the external circuit to supply the alternating e.m.f. which produces an alternating current (a.c.) in this circuit.

If a unidirectional e.m.f. is required at the brushes to enable a direct current (d.c.) to flow in the external circuit then a *commutator* is required. In its simplest form, this consists of a single ring attached to the shaft, this ring being made up of two copper segments insulated from each other and from the shaft. One segment is connected to the end of the coil P, and the other to Q. Both segments are connected to the external circuit through brushes. The brushes are so positioned that their contact changes from one segment to the other at the instant the polarity of the segment changes. Thus one brush is always in contact with the segment which is positive at any particular instant and the other is always negative. The commutator

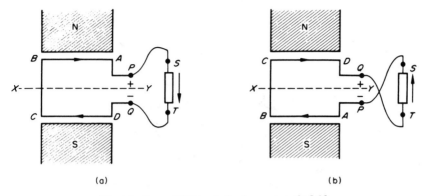

Fig. 4.1 Loop *ABCD* rotating in a magnetic field

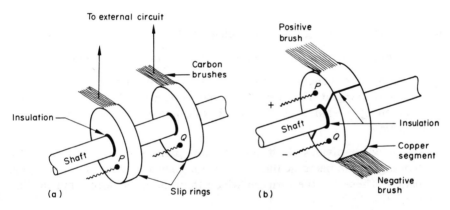

Fig. 4.2 Slip-rings and commutator: (a) slip-rings, (b) commutator

(Fig. 4.2b) acts like a changeover switch, ensuring that the current in the external circuit is d.c.

4.2 The ring armature

The general construction of a d.c. machine is shown in Chapter 5 (Fig. 5.1) but a simple method of showing the armature winding is as a continuous coil wound on an iron ring as shown in Fig. 4.3. The ring armature is now obsolete but it does serve to illustrate the basic principles of all armature circuits. It will be seen that the e.m.f.s are induced only in the outer conductors of each turn, since the inner conductors are magnetically screened by the ring itself.

From the diagram of the ring armature in Fig. 4.3 a number of features of

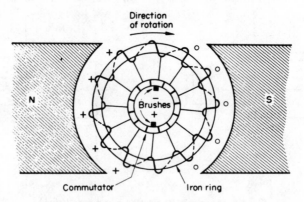

Fig. 4.3   The ring armature

a d.c. armature winding can be established:

1. The winding is uniformly wound on the ring and it is endless.

2. The e.m.f.s are generated in the conductors moving across the magnetic field in the air gap. The direction of the induced e.m.f. in each conductor is given by Fleming's Right Hand Rule and these are shown on the diagram.

3. The winding divides itself into natural paths (in this case two), the dividing points being at the turns in the magnetic neutral plain at that instant. These are the turns in which there is no induced e.m.f. at that instant.

4. Each turn or coil is connected to a commutator segment, making a multi-segment commutator necessary.

5. Brushes make contact with the commutator segments connected to the turns at the natural dividing points of item 3 above. Although the commutator is multi-segment, only two segments are in use at any one instant so its operation is, in effect, the same as the simple two-segment commutator.

6. The polarity of the machine is determined by the direction of rotation. In the case of Fig. 4.3 the lower brush is positive and the upper brush negative when the rotation is clockwise.

7. There are the same number of conductors in each parallel path in the armature, so the total e.m.f. will be the same in each path. This means that the net e.m.f. round the complete armature winding is zero, so there will be no circulating current in the armature under no-load conditions.

8. The e.m.f. across the brushes, that is the e.m.f. applied to the external circuit, will be the e.m.f. induced in *any one* of the armature paths. This is the sum of the e.m.f.s induced in all the conductors in series in that path.

9. The current supplied to the external circuit, that is, the total armature current, will be divided equally between all the parallel paths in the armature.

Thus:

$$\text{Current in any one conductor} = \frac{\text{Total armature current}}{\text{Number of parallel paths in armature}} \quad (4.1)$$

4.3 Lap and wave windings

In the modern d.c. machine the core of the armature is cylindrical and made up of iron stampings. It is called a drum armature. Unlike the ring armature, where the return or inner conductor has no e.m.f. induced in it, the return conductor of a coil on a drum armature is placed in an armature slot under a pole of opposite polarity from that of the first conductor of that coil. Thus the two conductors of each armature turn are in armature slots which are one pole pitch apart (i.e., the distance between the centres of two adjacent poles).

There are two main armature windings: (1) the lap winding, and (2) the wave winding. Figure 4.4 shows the arrangement of these windings with reference to two adjacent poles.

In the lap winding of Fig. 4.4(a) *ABCDEF* is one coil in which *BC* is one conductor under the N-pole and *DE* is the return conductor under the S-pole. The coil starts at a commutator segment at *A* and returns to finish at the adjacent segment at *F*, which is also the start of the next coil. The

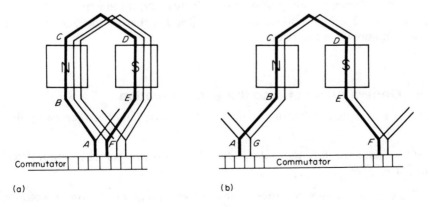

Fig. 4.4   Armature windings: (a) lap winding, (b) wave winding

winding continues in this way round the armature and is complete when it reaches the original starting point at A no matter how many poles there are.

Figure 4.4(b) shows the wave winding. Again $ABCDEF$ is one coil, but instead of the start and finish being at adjacent segments, the winding is taken forward each time so that commutator segments A and F are wide apart. When the winding has been taken once round the armature it will be connected to commutator segment G which is adjacent to A. G then becomes the start of the next series of coils round the armature. The winding continues in this way round and round the armature until every slot has been filled and the winding is complete when it returns to A once again.

The main differences between the lap and wave windings are:

1. In the lap winding the natural brush positions, where connection is made to coils in the magnetic neutral plane, occur at every gap between two poles. This gives two brushes (a positive and a negative) for every pair of poles, and makes the number of parallel paths in the armature the same as the number of poles; i.e., for a lap winding:

   Number of parallel paths = number of poles

   $$\text{and} \begin{Bmatrix} \text{Total current delivered} \\ \text{by armature} \end{Bmatrix} = \begin{Bmatrix} \text{current in each} \\ \text{armature conductor} \end{Bmatrix} \times \begin{Bmatrix} \text{no. of} \\ \text{poles} \end{Bmatrix} \quad (4.2)$$

2. In a wave winding there are only two parallel paths no matter how many poles there are; i.e., for a wave winding:

   Number of parallel paths = 2

   $$\text{and} \begin{Bmatrix} \text{Total current delivered} \\ \text{by armature} \end{Bmatrix} = \begin{Bmatrix} \text{current in each} \\ \text{armature conductor} \end{Bmatrix} \times 2 \quad (4.3)$$

3. In effect the lap winding is used for a heavy-current machine and a wave winding for a high-voltage machine, although there is no definite dividing line between the two.

4.4 Generated e.m.f. and the e.m.f. equation

Consider a single conductor rotating in a magnetic field between two poles, N and S.

If the magnetic flux per pole is Φ webers, then in one revolution it will cut 2Φ webers.

If there are p pairs of poles instead of one pair, then in one revolution the conductor will cut $2p\Phi$ webers.

If the speed of rotation is N rev/min, then in one second the conductor will cut $2p\Phi N/60$ webers per second.

But induced e.m.f. = rate of cutting flux in webers per second.

$$\therefore \text{ Induced e.m.f. in one conductor} = e = \frac{2p\Phi N}{60} \text{ volts} \qquad (4.4)$$

In a d.c. generator, the generated e.m.f. will be the sum of the e.m.f.s in all the conductors in series in any one armature path. If the number of conductors in series per armature path is Z_s, then

$$\text{Total e.m.f.} = Z_s \times \frac{2p\Phi N}{60} \text{ volts} \qquad (4.5)$$

If Z = total number of armature conductors, and c = number of parallel paths in the armature, then $Z_s = Z/c$, and the generated e.m.f. in a d.c. machine will be given by:

$$E = \frac{2Z}{c} \times \frac{p\Phi N}{60} \text{ volts} \qquad (4.6)$$

or

$$E = \frac{2Zp}{60c} \times \Phi N \text{ volts}$$

In a lap-wound machine $c = 2p$; in a wave-wound machine $c = 2$.

In the above equation Z, p and c are normally constant for a given machine.

Thus the term $2Zp/60c$ becomes a constant K_1.

If K_1 is known for a particular machine then the equation can be stated as

$$E = K_1\Phi N \text{ volts} \qquad (4.7)$$

or

$$E \propto \Phi N \qquad (4.8)$$

i.e., Generated e.m.f. $\propto$ magnetic flux $\times$ speed

In an a.c. generator it is the phase voltage which is calculated and Z will be the number of conductors in series *per phase*. The sum of the e.m.f.s in all the conductors in series will give the *average* value of the alternating e.m.f.

$$\therefore \text{ Average e.m.f. per phase} = \frac{2Zp\Phi N}{60} \text{ volts}$$

The generated e.m.f. is generally at a fixed frequency f, where $f = pN/60$ hertz.

$$\therefore \text{ Average e.m.f. per phase} = 2Zf\Phi \text{ volts}$$

57

Assuming a sine wave which has a form factor of 1.11

then $\qquad$ r.m.s. value = 1.11 average value

i.e., $$E_{\text{r.m.s.}} = 2.22Zf\Phi \text{ volts/phase} \qquad (4.9)$$

In practice, the windings of an a.c. machine are usually spread over several slots, and the e.m.f. will be slightly reduced so that a *distribution factor* k_d must be applied to the above equation. Sometimes a *span factor* k_p must also be used. This modifies the equation for the r.m.s. value of the generated e.m.f. per phase of an a.c. generator to:

$$E_{\text{r.m.s.}} = 2.22k_d k_p Zf\Phi \text{ volts/phase} \qquad (4.10)$$

4.5 Motor effect

The construction of a d.c. motor is similar to that of the generator, but in this case an external voltage is applied to the motor terminals. The resultant current in the armature conductors produces a torque which causes rotation. The direction of rotation is given by the *Left Hand Rule*. Although the current in the conductors produces the torque, the fact that they are rotating in a magnetic field means that there will be an e.m.f. generated in the conductors also. By applying the *Right Hand Rule* it will be seen that the e.m.f. generated in the armature of a motor opposes the e.m.f. applied from the external source. This generated e.m.f. is thus generally referred to as the *back e.m.f.* (E_b). The magnitude of this back e.m.f. is given by the generator equation, (4.6) or (4.7).

i.e., $$E_b = \frac{2Z}{c} \times \frac{p\Phi N}{60} = K_1 \Phi N \text{ volts} \qquad (4.11)$$

4.6 Generator and motor voltage equations

In Fig. 4.5(a) the generated e.m.f. E supplies a current to an external load. This results in an armature current I_a flowing through the conductors of the armature which has an armature resistance of R_a. Thus there will be a volt drop in the armature winding given by $I_a R_a$ and the terminal voltage V will be less than E by this amount.

i.e., $\qquad$ Terminal voltage $V = E - I_a R_a$ $\qquad$ for the generator

With the motor of Fig. 4.5(b) the terminal voltage V is the voltage applied to the motor from an external source. This causes an armature current I_a to flow, its magnitude being determined by the load on the motor. The terminal voltage V has to overcome the armature volt drop $I_a R_a$ in addition to the back e.m.f. E_b.

Thus $\qquad$ Terminal voltage $V = E + I_a R_a$ for the motor

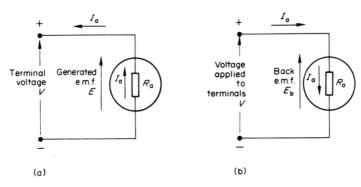

Fig. 4.5 Generator and motor voltages: (a) generator, (b) motor

The two voltage equations can be combined to give

$$V = E \pm I_a R_a \qquad (4.12)$$

where the positive sign is for a motor and the negative sign for a generator.

For a generator $\qquad V = E - I_a R_a$

from which $\qquad\qquad I_a = \dfrac{E - V}{R_a}$ amperes $\qquad (4.13)$

For a motor $\qquad\qquad V = E + I_a R_a$

from which $\qquad\qquad I_a = \dfrac{V - E}{R_a}$ amperes $\qquad (4.14)$

Since R_a is constant, the armature current depends upon the difference between V and E. Also, the direction of the armature current I_a depends upon whether the terminal voltage V is greater or less than the generated voltage E. If V is greater than E then the machine is a motor and the energy flow is into the machine from the supply. If E is greater than V then the machine is a generator and the energy flow is outwards.

4.7 Motor speed

From the above motor equation the back e.m.f. is given by

$$E_b = V - I_a R_a$$

Also, E_b is a generated e.m.f. given by Eq. (4.11),

i.e., $\qquad\qquad E_b = \dfrac{2Z}{c} \times \dfrac{p\Phi N}{60} = K_1 \Phi N$

$$\therefore K_1 \Phi N = V - I_a R_a$$

$$\therefore N = \dfrac{V - I_a R_a}{K_1 \Phi} \text{ rev/min} \qquad (4.15)$$

Since $K_1 = 2Z_p/60c$ is a constant for any particular machine,

$$\text{Speed } N \propto \frac{V - I_a R_a}{\Phi} \propto \frac{E_b}{\Phi} \qquad (4.16)$$

$$\therefore \text{ Speed} \propto \frac{\text{back e.m.f.}}{\text{magnetic flux}}$$

From Eq. (4.16) it can be seen that there are three possible methods by which the speed of a d.c. motor can be varied or controlled.

1. By varying the applied voltage V. Increasing voltage V will increase speed.

2. By adding resistance to the armature circuit, that is by increasing R_a. Increasing R_a reduces speed.

3. By adding resistance to the field circuit in order to reduce the field current, thereby reducing the magnetic flux Φ. Reducing Φ increases speed.

EXAMPLES

1. The armature of a six-pole d.c. generator is lap-wound with 840 conductors. The flux per pole is 20 mWb. Calculate the e.m.f. generated if the machine is driven at 1200 rev/min.
   Machine is lap-wound, therefore $c = 2p = 2 \times 3 = 6$; $Z = 840$; $p = 3$; $N = 1200$ rev/min; $\Phi = 20 \times 10^{-3} = 0.02$ Wb.

$$E = \frac{2Zp\Phi N}{60c} = \frac{2 \times 840 \times 3 \times 0.02 \times 1200}{60 \times 6} = 336 \text{ V}$$

2. What will be the terminal voltage of the above generator if the armature circuit resistance is 0.2 ohm and the current in each armature conductor is 20 A?
   This machine is six-pole lap-wound, so there are six armature paths in parallel.

$\therefore$ Total armature current $I_a = 6 \times 20 = 120$ A

$\therefore$ Terminal voltage $\quad V = E - I_a R_a$

$$= 336 - (120 \times 0.2)$$

$$= 336 - 24 = 312 \text{ V}$$

3. What will be the speed of the above machine if it is run as a motor connected to a 250 V supply and the motor is loaded to give a total armature current of 100 A? Assume the flux per pole is now 15 mWb.
   $V = 250$ V, $I_a = 100$ A, $R_a = 0.2\,\Omega$, $\Phi = 0.015$ Wb.

$$\text{Speed } N = \frac{(V - I_a R_a)60c}{2Zp\Phi} = \frac{[250 - (100 \times 0.2)] \times 60 \times 6}{2 \times 840 \times 3 \times 0.015}$$

$$= 1095.2 \text{ rev/min}$$

4. What would have been the generated e.m.f. if the above machine had been wave wound?
   For wave winding, $c = 2$.

$$E = \frac{2Zp\Phi N}{60c} = \frac{2 \times 840 \times 3 \times 0.02 \times 1200}{60 \times 2} = 1008 \text{ V}$$

4.8   Torque on a conductor rotating in a magnetic field

The force on an armature conductor when it is carrying a current is given by

$$F = BIl \text{ newtons}$$

If the armature diameter is d metres, then

$$\text{Torque } T = \text{force} \times \text{radius}$$

$$= BIl \times \frac{d}{2} \text{ newton metres}$$

The conductor is l metres long, therefore the area covered by *one* conductor in *one* revolution will be πdl square metres.

If there are p pairs of poles

$$\text{then} \quad \text{Area covered per pole} = a = \frac{\pi dl}{2p} \text{ square metres}$$

$$\text{but} \qquad B = \frac{\Phi}{a} = \frac{2p\Phi}{\pi dl} \text{ teslas}$$

$$\text{Torque } T = BIl \times \frac{d}{2}$$

$$= \frac{2p\Phi}{\pi dl} \times I \times l \times \frac{d}{2}$$

$$= \frac{p\Phi I}{\pi} \text{ newton metres per conductor} \quad (4.17)$$

4.9   Torque and output power of a d.c. motor

Equation (4.17) gives the torque per conductor.

If there are c parallel paths in the armature, then

$$\text{Current per conductor } I = \frac{I_a}{c}$$

where I_a = total armature current.

61

The armature has Z conductors each carrying the current I_a/c. Thus

$$\text{Total torque } T = \frac{Zp\Phi I_a}{\pi \times c} \text{ newton metres} \tag{4.18}$$

but for a practical machine Z, p, π, and c are constant.

$$\therefore T = \frac{Zp}{\pi \times c} \times \Phi I_a$$

$$= K_2 \Phi I_a \text{ newton metres} \tag{4.19}$$

where K_2 is a constant for the machine.

From this it is seen that

$$T \propto \Phi I_a \tag{4.20}$$

i.e.,   Total torque $\propto$ magnetic flux $\times$ armature current

By multiplying both numerator and denominator of Eq. (4.18) by $2N/60$ the back e.m.f. $E_b = 2Zp\Phi N/60c$ (Eq. 4.11) can be included in the torque equation.

i.e.,
$$T = \frac{2Zp\Phi N}{60c} \times \frac{60}{2\pi N} \times I_a$$

$$= \frac{60}{2\pi} \times \frac{E_b I_a}{N} \text{ newton metres}$$

$$= 9.55 \frac{E_b I_a}{N} \text{ newton metres} \tag{4.21}$$

But the equation for power in rotation is

$$P = \frac{2\pi NT}{60} \text{ watts} \tag{4.22}$$

from which
$$T = \frac{60}{2\pi} \times \frac{P}{N} = 9.55 \frac{P}{N} \text{ newton metres} \tag{4.23}$$

Comparing Eq. (4.21) and (4.23) above we can see that

$$\text{Output power } P = E_b I_a \text{ watts} \tag{4.24}$$

This is the *gross* power output and includes the rotational or mechanical losses in the motor.

If the gross power output is in horsepower the above equations become:

$$\text{Power } P = \frac{2\pi}{60} \times \frac{NT}{746} \text{ horsepower} \tag{4.22a}$$

$$\text{Torque } T = \frac{60}{2\pi} \times \frac{\text{hp} \times 746}{N} \text{ newton metres} \tag{4.23a}$$

The motor voltage equation (Eq. 4.12) is

$$V = E_b + I_a R_a$$

Multiplying this equation by I_a gives the power equation:

$$VI_a = E_b I_a + I_a^2 R_a$$

↓	↓	↓
Input	output including mechanical losses	copper loss

Thus $\quad VI_a$ = power input from supply

$E_b I_a$ = gross power output (including mechanical losses)

$I_a^2 R_a$ = electrical power loss (copper loss) in the armature

EXAMPLE

A four-pole d.c. motor has a wave-wound armature with 328 conductors. If the flux per pole is 30 mWb and the armature current is 40 A calculate the gross torque developed by the armature. Also calculate the power output if the speed of rotation is 800 rev/min. What will be the value of the back e.m.f. in the armature?

The armature is wave-wound, therefore $c = 2$; $Z = 328$; $p = 2$; $I_a = 40$ A; $\Phi = 30 \times 10^{-3} = 0.03$ Wb.

1. Torque $T = \dfrac{Zp\Phi I_a}{\pi \times c} = \dfrac{328 \times 2 \times 0.03 \times 40}{\pi \times 2}$

$$= 125.29 \text{ N m}$$

2. Power output $P = \dfrac{2\pi NT}{60} = \dfrac{2\pi \times 800 \times 125.29}{60}$

$$= 10\,496 \text{ W} = 10.496 \text{ kW}$$

3. But from Eq. (4.24) $P = E_b I_a$.

$\therefore$ Back e.m.f. $E_b = \dfrac{P}{I_a} = \dfrac{10\,496}{40} = 262.4$ V

5. D.C. machines

5.1 General construction

The general construction is shown in Fig. 5.1. The field windings are wound on inward-projecting poles attached to the yoke. The armature rotates between the poles, leaving a small air gap, and carries either a lap or a wave winding which is connected to the commutator. Contact to the external circuit is made through carbon brushes (not shown in the diagram) rubbing on the commutator segments.

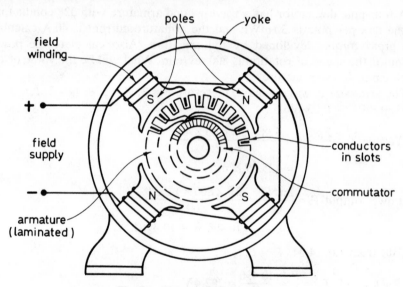

Fig. 5.1 D.C. machine construction

Typical materials used in the construction of a d.c. machine are:

Yoke. Cast steel or rolled steel.
Poles. High-permeability steel, usually laminated.
Armature. High-permeability, low-loss steel laminations or stampings. The laminations, which have a thin layer of insulation on one side, are necessary to stop the flow of eddy currents in the iron of the armature

parallel to the shaft. These eddy currents could cause overheating and serious energy loss.

Shaft. Mild steel forging.

Commutator. High-conductivity hard-drawn copper.

5.2 Types of machine

Direct-current machines are classified by the way in which the field circuit is connected. These are (1) separately excited machine, (2) shunt machine, (3) series machine, and (4) compound machine. Figure 5.2 shows the field connections. The current flow for generators is shown on the left hand side, and for motors on the right hand side. In the case of the generators the current I is the outgoing current from the terminals to the load, whereas for the motor current I is the current taken by the motor from the supply and depends upon the motor's mechanical load.

I_a is the armature current, I_f is the shunt field current, and I_s is the series field current.

The compound machine can be connected in one of two ways but basically the characteristics are the same for both types of connection. In the short-shunt connection (Fig. 5.2d) the shunt winding is connected directly across the armature, but in the long-shunt connection (Fig. 5.2e) the shunt winding is connected across both armature and series field.

5.3 D.C. machine characteristics

Generators

The generator characteristics are shown in Fig. 5.3. For comparison each machine is assumed to have the same terminal voltage at full load. In all types of generators there will be an additional small drop in generated e.m.f. due to armature reaction, which is dealt with in more detail in Sec. 5.4.

1. Separately Excited Generator. The field current is taken from a separate supply and will not affect the characteristic as I_f will be independent of the load. There will be a volt drop $I_a R_a$ in the armature which will be proportional to the load. This drop at full load is only about 2–3% of the no-load voltage so this is almost a constant voltage generator. This machine is not used for general supplies, as it requires a separate supply for its field. Its main use is in control systems where large variations of field currents are required independent of the armature circuit, as with the Ward–Leonard system of speed control.

2. Shunt-connected Generator. The armature volt drop $I_a R_a$ will cause a reduction of terminal voltage as the load increases. In this case the shunt field winding is supplied from the generator's own terminals so that an

65

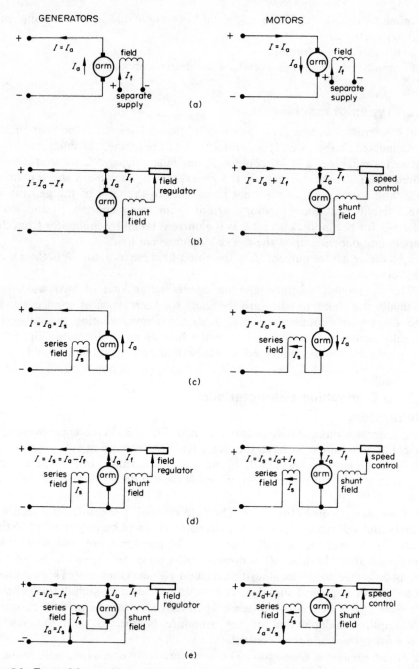

Fig. 5.2   Types of d.c. machines—field connections: (a) separate excitation, (b) shunt connection, (c) series connection, (d) compound connection–short shunt, (e) compound connection–long shunt

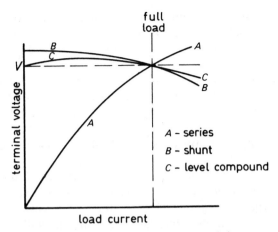

full
load

V — — — — —

terminal voltage

load current

A – series

B – shunt

C – level compound

Fig. 5.3   D.C. generator load characteristics

increase in load will reduce the p.d. across the field. This reduces the field current I_f which, in turn, reduces the magnetic flux Φ. This causes a further reduction in generated e.m.f. and terminal volts. The shunt generator characteristic is shown in Fig. 5.3, graph B, which indicates a reduction of terminal voltage with increase of load. The reduction is a little more than that of the separately excited generator, but even so the volt drop between no-load and full load is only about 3–4% of the no-load value. The shunt generator is almost a constant voltage machine, and in any case a field regulator is nearly always connected to enable the level of the generated e.m.f. to be adjusted or controlled.

3. Series-connected Generator. In this case the field current I_s is the same as the armature current I_a and also the load current I. Thus at no-load, $I = I_s = 0$, and the magnitude of the magnetic flux Φ will be due to the residual magnetism only. This will be so small that the generated e.m.f. will be a few volts only. A load connected to the terminals will cause a small load current I to flow which will also be the field current I_s. This increases Φ, causing a further increase of the generated e.m.f., thus giving a variable voltage characteristic as shown in Fig. 5.3, graph A. The difference between generated e.m.f. and the terminal voltage in this machine is due to the volt drop caused by the load current flowing through both armature and field, i.e., $V = E - I(R_a + R_s)$. The large variation of terminal voltage with changes of load limits the use of the series generator to special purposes (e.g., boosters).

4. Compound-connected Generator. This machine combines the characteristics of both shunt and series generators. The shunt winding produces the main field. The series winding is to give a voltage rise when load increases to compensate for the voltage drop which occurs in a normal

67

shunt generator. This gives a characteristic similar to graph C in Fig. 5.3. In this case the full-load terminal voltage is the same as the no-load value. This is called *level compounding*. Almost all large d.c. generators are compound-wound. Sometimes the series winding is made to give a higher terminal voltage at full load than at no-load. This is called *over-compounding* and is useful when the load is supplied by a long feeder. The additional over-voltage is then enough to compensate for the volt drop in the feeder so that the actual voltage at the load remains constant. If the series winding does not fully compensate for the drop in voltage between no-load and full load then the machine is said to be *under-compounded*.

In the above cases the series winding is assisting the shunt winding. This is called *cumulative compounding*. In special cases the series winding can be reversed so that its field opposes the shunt field. This is called *differential compounding* and gives a very large drop in volts with increase of load. Such a generator is ideal for welding supplies where a high voltage is required for striking the arc but a much reduced voltage for the actual welding.

Motors

Figure 5.4 shows the load characteristics of each type of motor, assuming that each machine operates at the same speed at full load and also that the supply voltage remains constant. The effect of load applied to the motor can be shown from the following equations (Eqs (4.16) and (4.20) of Chapter 4).

$$\text{Speed } N \propto \frac{V - I_a R_a}{\Phi} \quad \text{and} \quad \text{Torque } T \propto \Phi I_a$$

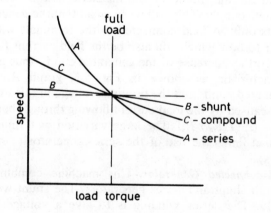

Fig. 5.4   D.C. motor load characteristics

1. Separately Excited Motor. Flux Φ is produced by an external source and remains essentially constant and does not affect either speed or torque. As the motor load increases I_a will increase. It will be seen from the above equations that this will cause an increase of torque and a reduction of speed. The reduction of speed at full load is only about 3–5% of no-load speed, so variation of speed with variation of load is quite small.

2. Shunt-connected Motor. The shunt field is connected directly across the supply which is constant. Thus I_f and Φ are constant and the shunt motor characteristic is similar to that of the separately excited motor, that is, there is only a small drop in speed with increase of load. In either type of motor any weakening of field due to armature reaction will tend to increase speed and will cancel out some of the effect of the load current I_a. Figure 5.4 graph *B* shows that the shunt motor is basically a constant-speed machine.

3. Series-connected Motor. At no-load field current I_s is equal to the load current I_a, which is zero. Thus, except for a little residual magnetism, flux Φ will be zero also. This gives infinite speed at no-load. As load increases, both I_a and Φ increase, giving a rapid fall in speed. Graph *A* of Fig. 5.4 shows a typical series motor characteristic. This type of characteristic is ideal where a quick drop in speed occurs when a sudden heavy load is applied, thus safeguarding the machine against serious mechanical stresses. However, no-load speeds can be dangerously high, so a series motor must never be used unloaded. It is ideal for traction and hoists where the motor is directly connected to the load at all times. Belt drives must not be used as the breaking of the belt will cause the motor to over-speed.

4. Compound-connected Motor. This motor has a variable speed characteristic (Fig. 5.4 graph *C*) similar to the series motor but the shunt winding restricts the no-load speed to a definite safe value. This type of motor is used generally for heavy duties, especially where sudden application of heavy loads may occur.

5.4 Armature reaction in a d.c. generator

In a d.c. armature, the induced e.m.f.s are in one direction under one pole and in the opposite direction under the other pole. Thus, when a current is flowing the armature is like a solenoid, producing a magnetic field in line with the brush positions, as shown in Fig. 5.5(a).

The natural position of the brushes is in the magnetic neutral axis. To give good commutation, the brushes should make contact with conductors in which no e.m.f. is being induced. The current in the armature produces a field with flux Φ_a at right angles to the main field with a flux Φ_f. The resultant field Φ is moved by an angle θ from the main field, thus causing distortion and causing the magnetic neutral axis to rotate by the angle θ.

69

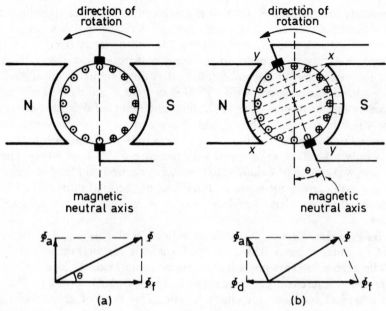

Fig. 5.5 Armature reaction in a d.c. generator: (a) before moving brushes, (b) after moving brushes

The brushes in their original position will now be making contact with conductors having e.m.f.s induced in them, and will cause poor commutation. For correct commutation, the brushes must be moved in the direction of rotation of the armature, as shown in Fig. 5.5(b). This causes some of the armature turns to produce a demagnetizing flux Φ_d which directly opposes the main field Φ_f. Thus, the resultant flux Φ will be reduced, giving a reduction in the e.m.f. generated. The distortion of the field also means that there is an increase of flux density at the trailing pole tips (x) and a decrease at the leading pole tips (y). This uneven distribution also results in a further reduction of flux due to saturation at one pole tip for a given field current.

This effect, due to the cross-magnetization caused by the armature current, is called *armature reaction*. The current in the armature is determined by the load. Therefore, it follows that the armature reaction effect also varies with the load. This means that for ideal commutation the brush position must be changed with changes of load. This, of course, is not very practicable, especially under constantly changing load conditions, although brushes mounted on rocker rings, adjustable to suit the load, are found in some machines.

It is seen that armature reaction results in a reduction of the magnetic

70

flux, which in turn causes a reduction of the generated voltage, since $e \propto \Phi N$ (see Chapter 4).

In the generator characteristics of Fig. 5.3, the terminal voltage at full load is V. There is a volt drop in the armature $I_a R_a$, so that the actual voltage generated is $E = V + I_a R_a$. This voltage, E, however, is somewhat less than would be generated for the same field current, but with no armature current, since armature reaction has reduced the flux Φ. Thus, the load characteristics are affected by both armature volt-drop and armature reaction. Figure 5.6 shows the effect upon the characteristic of a separately excited generator. The shunt generator will be similar, but with a further slight reduction in voltage, since field current will drop as the terminal voltage drops.

The characteristics of the series and compound generators will be affected in a similar way.

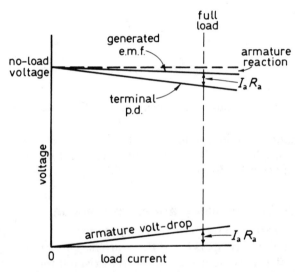

Fig. 5.6 Separately excited generator characteristics, showing effect of armature reaction

5.5 Armature reaction in a d.c. motor

Figure 5.7 shows the motor effect giving the same direction of rotation as in Fig. 5.5. To produce this rotation, the current in the armature conductors will be opposite that in the generator, thus giving a reaction field in the opposite direction. This causes a distortion of the magnetic flux, giving a decrease of flux density at the trailing pole tips x and an increase at the leading pole tips y. Figure 5.7(b) shows the brushes moved into the magnetic neutral axis for good commutation. In the case of the motor, it is

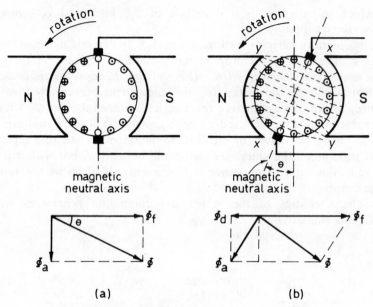

Fig. 5.7   Armature reaction in a d.c. motor

seen that the brushes must be moved in the opposite direction to the rotation.

Again, armature reaction causes a reduction of magnetic flux and, as seen from Eqs (4.20) and (4.16), this reduces the torque ($T \propto \Phi I_a$) but increases speed ($N \propto E_b/\Phi$).

5.6   Methods of minimizing armature reaction

It is seen, then, that armature reaction distorts the magnetic field, causing bad commutation, that is, sparking at the brushes. This can be improved by moving the brushes into the magnetic neutral axis, but this in turn causes a demagnetizing effect, thus reducing the generated e.m.f.

There are two ways in which a machine can be designed so that the effects of armature reaction are minimized. They are by increasing the air gap and by using compensating windings. The use of interpoles also helps by stabilizing the magnetic neutral axis and neutralizing the cross-magnetization, although it does not stop the field being distorted. However, as the main function of interpoles is to assist commutation, making the moving of the brushes unnecessary, they will be considered later.

1. Increasing the Air Gap. A long air gap considerably increases the reluctance of the magnetic circuit, thereby requiring a greater number of ampere-turns in the field to produce the necessary flux in the air gap. This means that the field ampere-turns will be much greater than the armature ampere-turns, so that the influence of armature reaction is minimized. If the gap at the pole tips is increased then the distortion of the main field is considerably reduced.

2. Compensating Windings. Armature reaction causes a distortion of the magnetic field, depending upon the load. Thus, sudden load changes will produce sudden changes of the flux distribution in the air gap and, since induced e.m.f. is proportional to the rate of change of flux, very high voltages may be induced in the armature windings. These high voltages can cause a flashover between commutator segments, and under severe load changes the arc may completely encircle the commutator, thus short-circuiting the brushes. Large machines, and especially those operating with small field currents as may be necessary with, say, Ward–Leonard control, would be unworkable unless compensating windings are fitted to eliminate this effect. These windings are coils wound between two adjacent poles, as shown in Fig. 5.8. They are connected in series with the armature and the

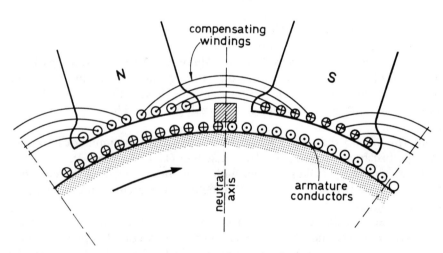

Fig. 5.8 Compensating windings in pole face

direction of current is opposite that in the armature conductors directly under the pole face. Thus, any sudden load change in the armature conductors produces an equal but opposing change in the compensating winding and the field distortion is avoided.

5.7 Commutation

Commutation is the action of transferring current from the armature conductors through the commutator segments and brushes to the external

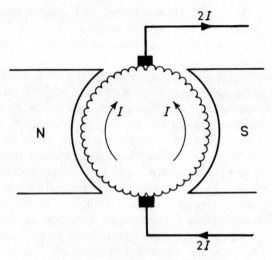

Fig. 5.9 Armature current flow

circuit. Consider Fig. 5.9, which represents the armature diagrammatically as two parallel paths between the brushes.

The total armature current $2I$ divides between the two parallel paths so that current I flows in a clockwise direction round the armature under the N-pole, and an equal current I flows anticlockwise under the S-pole. We will now look at just a few turns at a brush position. This is shown in Fig. 5.10.

(a), (b), and (c) show three stages during which the commutator moves so that the brush contact changes from segment (1) to segment (2).

At (a), the brush makes contact with segment (1) only and the current I in coil A is clockwise and in coil B anticlockwise, giving a total current in the brush of $2I$.

At (b), the armature has moved so that the brush now makes contact with segments (1) and (2), and thus short-circuits coil B, which will now carry no current. At this instant, coil B will be the coil in the magnetic neutral axis, so ideally it should have no e.m.f. induced in it and should not be affected by the shorting of the commutator segments. The current in the brush is received from coil A (clockwise) and coil C (anticlockwise).

At (c), the brush makes contact with segment (2) only, so that the current I in coil B is now clockwise and in coil C anticlockwise.

It will be seen that during commutation the current in coil B has reversed in direction, that is, there has been a total change of current of $2I$ in coil B. The time taken for the brush to pass from one segment to the next (t_c) will be quite small, possibly only $1/500$ s. Thus, the rate of change of current $2I/t_c$ may be large. Coil B is embedded in slots in the iron core of the armature, and will thus have a high inductance (L). The current

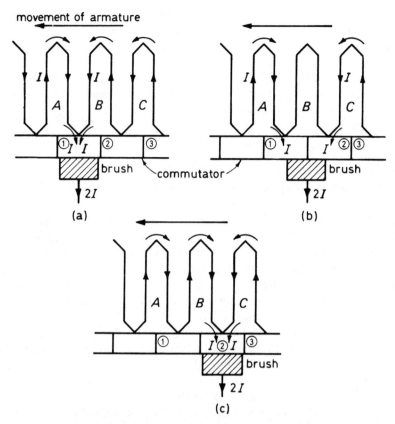

Fig. 5.10   Reversal of current in armature coil

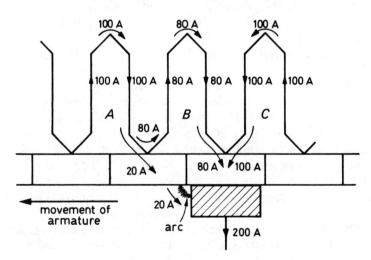

Fig. 5.11   Arc caused by incomplete reversal of current in coil *B* due to reactance voltage

75

change will cause an e.m.f. to be induced in the coil ($e = L \times 2I/t_c$). This is called the *reactance voltage*. This voltage opposes the current change so that, although the coil may be in the neutral axis, the change of current will not be complete by the time the brush leaves segment (1). The change can then only be completed by an arc between the segment and the brush (Fig. 5.11). This will cause very bad sparking at the brush, especially on heavy loads, and will also cause overloading of the trailing edge of the brush, with accompanying overheating of the brush and commutator.

5.8 Methods of improving commutation

1. Use of Carbon Brushes (Resistance Commutation). The fact that carbon brushes have a high contact resistance assists commutation, and this is one of the main reasons for using carbon. As the brush moves from one segment to the next, as in Fig. 5.10, the contact area with segment (1) becomes smaller and therefore the contact resistance becomes higher, whereas the contact area with segment (2) becomes greater and the resistance smaller. Thus, just before the trailing edge of the brush leaves segment (1) the current will be flowing through two parallel paths to the brush but the path through segment (1) will be of high resistance, whereas that through segment (2) will be of comparatively low resistance. This causes the larger part of the current to be diverted through segment (2), thereby assisting the process of commutation. The use of carbon brushes, although in itself it is unable to prevent sparking due to the reactance voltage, does assist in reducing the sparking.

2. Commutating e.m.f. Since the reactance voltage is the main cause of bad commutation, it is necessary to neutralize its effect. This can be done by inducing an e.m.f. in the short-circuited coil which will be equal and opposite to the reactance voltage. One method of doing this could be by moving the brushes as in the case of armature reaction but, in general, this is not practicable, as variations of load would require readjustment of the brush positions.

The usual way of producing the commutating e.m.f. is by means of *interpoles*. The brushes remain fixed and the short-circuited coil is in the neutral axis of the main field. The interpole is a narrow pole placed in this neutral axis of the main field and its polarity is such that it induces the commutating e.m.f. in the short-circuited coil to neutralize the reactance voltage. The position of the interpoles is shown in Fig. 5.12. It will be seen that in a generator the polarity of an interpole is the same as the next main pole in the direction of rotation, whereas in a motor the interpole polarity is opposite the next main pole in the direction of rotation.

The reactance voltage is proportional to the armature current, and so also must be the commutating e.m.f. Thus, the interpole flux must be

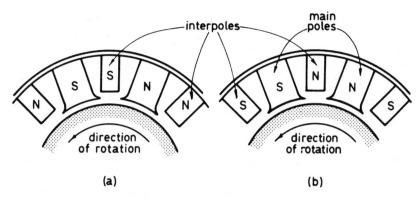

Fig. 5.12   Interpoles in a d.c. machine: (a) generator, (b) motor

proportional to the armature current, therefore the interpole winding is placed in series with the armature. Also, the reluctance of the magnetic path must be kept constant. This is achieved by making the interpole air gap large.

5.9   Care of the commutator and brushes

It has been seen that poor commutation resulting in bad sparking, overheating, and burning at the brushes and commutator can be due to armature reaction and the reactance voltage in the short-circuited coil. To overcome this, the brushes must be in the correct position and of the correct grade, and interpoles are used. Sparking can also be caused by badly worn or loosefitting brushes, an uneven commutator, an accumulation of conducting dust between the segments, or overloading which causes excessive heat at the brushes. A faulty armature winding would, of course, cause sparking, but provided the winding is healthy the sparking can be reduced by bedding the brushes onto the commutator by using a strip of fine abrasive cloth and by applying the correct brush tension as recommended by the manufacturer. The commutator should be kept clean and any irregularities smoothed out. As the commutator wears, the mica insulation between segments must be cut back by a special undercutting tool or a broken hacksaw blade, to keep the commutator surface smooth, In cases of a very badly worn commutator, the armature may have to be removed and the commutator turned in a lathe.

The grade of brush to give the best results will be recommended by the manufacturer. There are a number of grades but these fall into four general categories. *Normal carbon* brushes are the cheapest and can be used where extreme operating conditions are not likely to be met. They have a higher coefficient of friction than other types, but this tends to cause the mica insulation to wear evenly with the copper, making this type of brush suitable for the high-voltage machine with flush mica insulation between segments.

Natural graphite brushes are a soft material having very good natural lubricating properties. Their coefficient of friction is less than carbon and they make extremely good electrical contact with the commutator segments. They are suitable for high-speed commutators, giving silent running and a long life.

Electrographite brushes are made from carbon which is formed into an artificial graphite by heating in an electric furnace. This produces a brush which is soft but very tough. It has a low coefficient of friction but is capable of carrying very heavy currents. This brush is suitable for severe working conditions where a machine may be subjected to very heavy overloads and mechanical shock and high-speed running.

Copper–carbon brushes are made of a combination of these two materials, giving low resistance and a high current density. These brushes have a fairly low coefficient of friction. They are generally used for low-voltage, heavy-current d.c. machines as, for example, for electroplating supplies.

5.10 D.C. motor starter

Consider the following example:

Calculate the current in the armature of a d.c. shunt motor having a resistance of $0.1\,\Omega$ at the moment of start if it is connected direct to the supply of 250 V.

$$I_a = \frac{V - E_b}{R_a}$$

At the moment of start the armature is stationary so the generated back e.m.f. E_b will be zero.

$$\therefore \; I_a = \frac{V}{R_a} = \frac{250}{0.1} = 2500 \text{ A}$$

Obviously, this current is excessive and a means of reducing the starting current must be introduced by a starter. This takes the form of a variable resistance in the armature circuit, this resistance being gradually taken out as the motor increases speed and the back e.m.f. E_b builds up.

If the starting current of the above motor must be reduced to 100 A then the armature circuit resistance must be:

$$R_a = \frac{V}{I_a} = \frac{250}{100} = 2.5\,\Omega$$

The armature resistance is 0.1 Ω.

$$\therefore \text{ Starter resistance} = 2.5 - 0.1 = 2.4 \, \Omega$$

The starter resistance is connected in circuit as shown in Fig. 5.13(a).

It will be seen from Fig. 5.13(a) that as the motor runs up to normal speed the starter resistance is removed from the armature circuit and is added to the field circuit. The field circuit has a much higher resistance

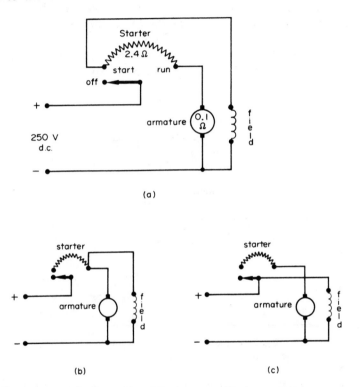

(a)

(b)   (c)

Fig. 5.13   D.C. motor starter circuit: (a) correct connection, (b) and (c) incorrect connections

(probably around 200 Ω), so adding the starter resistance of 2.4 Ω to this circuit has neglibible effect. Also, it can be seen that when the motor is switched off and is running down, the armature, field, and starter form a closed series circuit through which the highly inductive field can safely discharge its e.m.f. against a slowly reducing back e.m.f. in the armature.

There are two other possible ways of connecting the starter with reference to the field but both have drawbacks and should not be used. These are shown in Fig. 5.13(b) and (c).

In Fig. 5.13(b) the field is connected to the starter resistor at the same

79

point as the armature. Since the object of the starter is to reduce the voltage across the armature to a small value the voltage across the field will be reduced to the same value. Thus the field current and the flux will be so small that the torque may not be sufficient to start the motor.

With the connection of Fig. 5.13(c) the field will be connected directly across the supply even before the starter is operated. This will enable the motor to start when the starter is operated but when the motor is stopped and the supply switch opened there is no path through which the induced e.m.f. in the field can be safely discharged. This could result in a dangerous high-voltage flashover at the switch contacts.

Figure 5.14 shows the circuit of a typical faceplate starter for a d.c. shunt motor and includes overload and no-voltage protective devices.

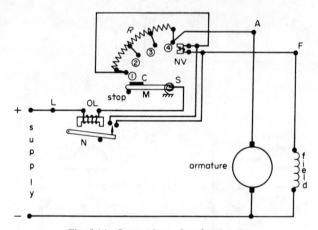

Fig. 5.14   Starter for a d.c. shunt motor

The positive of the d.c. supply is connected through the overload coil OL to the starter arm M, which is an open switch when in the 'stop' position. When M is moved to stud 1 the starter resistor R is connected in the armature circuit and full supply voltage is applied to the shunt field. The motor starts and as it increases speed the back e.m.f. builds up and M can be moved slowly to stud (2), then (3), and finally to stud (4), when the motor will have attained its normal speed. The starter resistor has now been transferred from the armature circuit to the field circuit. The electro-magnet NV is in series with the field and will be energized sufficiently to hold the starter arm on stud (4), that is, in the 'run' position, by means of a piece of soft iron C attached to M. NV is called the no-volt release and if

80

its coil loses its supply the starter arm will be released and pulled back to the stop position by the spring S. This would occur if the d.c. supply failed. The no-volt release is a safety device to ensure the motor does not restart when supply is restored without the normal starting procedure being carried out.

The full motor current flows through the overload coil OL. The energized electromagnet exerts a pull on the pivoted arm N. N is adjusted by means of a spring or by varying the air gap so that it is not attracted to the electromagnet until the motor current reaches a predetermined value. This will probably be around 50% over full-load current so that it only operates if the motor is overloaded or if a fault occurs. When OL operates two contacts are closed, causing the no-volt coil NV to be short-circuited. NV thus loses its supply and releases the starter arm which falls back to the stop position, and the motor is safely shut down.

5.11 Tests to find the efficiency of a d.c. machine

1. Brake Test for a D.C. Motor. For this test, the load is applied to the motor by means of a rope or belt 'brake'. The force F applied by adjusting the brake is measured in newtons by a spring balance, or the difference between two balance readings, depending upon the type of brake. The effective radius r from the centre of the motor shaft to the point of application of the force is measured in metres. The torque T can then be calculated:

$$T = F \times r \text{ newton metres}$$

The 'brake' may also be applied electrically by means of a dynamometer or an eddy-current brake and, since for any particular 'brake' the radius will be constant, the balance may be calibrated directly as torque in newton metres. A voltmeter and ammeter are connected in the motor circuit to measure the supply voltage and the current taken from the supply. After the motor has been running for a while to allow the field windings to reach normal running temperature, the load is applied in steps up to 30–50% over full load. At each step, the current, voltage, torque, and speed are recorded. Note that when testing a series motor there must always be some load on the machine, since no-load speed may be dangerously high. In this case, it may be an advantage to start with heavy loads, taking readings as the load is reduced and stopping when the speed starts to become excessive. The results should be tabulated and the necessary calculations made as indicated by the table heading shown here. Graphs of efficiency, speed, power, or current against torque can be plotted.

Input			Output			
Pressure	Current	Power input	Torque	Speed	Power output	Efficiency
V	I	$P_1 = VI$	$T = F \times r$	N	$P_2 = \dfrac{2\pi NT}{60}$	$= \dfrac{P_2}{P_1}$
volts	amps	watts	newton metres	rev/min	watts	p.u.

In the brake test all the power output is wasted in the form of heat, which means that it is normally limited to small motors.

2. *Swinburne Test.* This test is for shunt or compound machines, and enables the efficiency of the machine to be calculated for any load when running as either a motor or a generator, from data obtained by a no-load test as a motor. The mechanical and iron losses are found by the no-load test, and it is assumed that these losses are constant at all loads. This assumption is not quite true, so that the Swinburne test gives calculated efficiencies which are somewhat higher than the true values.

The test is carried out as follows. The armature resistance (R_a') is measured by ammeter–voltmeter method, using a current comparable with the load current of the machine. This resistance must include all series and interpole windings. The shunt field resistance (R_f') is also measured. Both these measurements are made when the machine is cold. If we assume a 50–55°C rise in temperature under load conditions, the resistance of the hot windings can be calculated. A close approximation of the 'hot' value can be obtained by taking 1.2 times the 'cold' value. Thus

$$R_a = 1.2\, R_a' \qquad R_f = 1.2\, R_f'$$

The machine is now connected as in Fig. 5.15 and run light as a motor at normal speed and with normal voltage.

After the bearings and field windings have been allowed to warm up by running light for 10–15 minutes, the supply voltage V, armature current I_a and field current I_f are measured.

At no-load   Armature current $= I_0$

∴ at no-load   Input to armature $= VI_0$

This is the power required to overcome the iron loss and the mechanical loss, together with an armature copper loss, which is usually so small it can be neglected.

$$\therefore \text{ Iron loss} + \text{mechanical loss} = VI_0 = P_0 \qquad (5.1)$$

The field copper loss is also constant at all loads and is given by $I_f^2 R_f$.

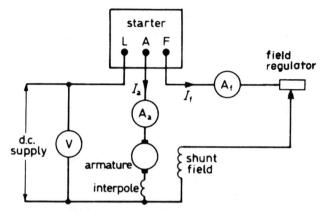

Fig. 5.15 Circuit for Swinburne test

Thus $\qquad$ Constant losses at all loads $= P_0 + I_f^2 R_f$ $\qquad$ (5.2)

When the machine is running the armature copper loss, including series and interpole windings, will be $I_a^2 R_a$ $\qquad$ (5.3)

$\therefore$ total loss for any armature load current I_a is given by:

$$P_L = P_0 + I_f^2 R_f + I_a^2 R_a \qquad (5.4)$$

For a motor, input $= V(I_a + I_f)$.

$$\therefore \text{ Efficiency for a motor} = \frac{\text{input} - \text{losses}}{\text{input}} = \frac{V(I_a + I_f) - P_L}{V(I_a + I_f)} \qquad (5.5)$$

For a generator, output $= V(I_a - I_f)$.

$$\therefore \text{ Efficiency for a generator} = \frac{\text{output}}{\text{output} + \text{losses}} = \frac{V(I_a - I_f)}{V(I_a - I_f) + P_L} \qquad (5.6)$$

EXAMPLE

A 250 V d.c. shunt machine has an armature resistance (including interpoles) of 0.5 Ω and a shunt field resistance of 125 Ω, both values at working temperature. When it is running light as a motor, the current taken from the supply is 5 A. Calculate the efficiency of the machine (1) when taking a current of 52 A from the supply as a motor, and (2) when delivering a current of 35 A as a generator.

On no-load $\qquad I_f = \dfrac{V}{R_f} = \dfrac{250}{125} = 2 \text{ A}$

$$\therefore I_0 = I - I_f = 5 - 2 = 3 \text{ A}$$

$\therefore$ Iron and mechanical losses $P_0 = VI_0 = 250 \times 3 = 750$ W

Field copper loss $= I_f^2 R_f = 2 \times 2 \times 125 = 500$ W

$\therefore$ Constant loss $= 750 + 500 = 1250$ W

$$= 1.25 \text{ kW}$$

1. *As a motor*: Input $= VI = 250 \times 52 = 13\,000$ W $= 13$ kW.

$$I_a = 52 - 2 = 50 \text{ A}$$

$\therefore$ Armature copper loss $= I_a^2 R_a = 50 \times 50 \times 0.5 = 1250$ W $= 1.25$ kW

$\therefore$ Total losses $P_L = 1.25 + 1.25 = 2.5$ kW

$$\text{Efficiency} = \frac{\text{input} - \text{losses}}{\text{input}} = \frac{13 - 2.5}{13} = 0.808 = 80.8\%$$

2. *As a generator*: Output $= VI = 250 \times 35 = 8750$ W $= 8.75$ kW.

$$I_a = I + I_f = 35 + 2 = 37 \text{ A}$$

$\therefore$ Armature copper loss $= I_a^2 R_a = 37 \times 37 \times 0.5 = 685$ W $= 0.685$ kW

$\therefore$ Total losses $P_L = 1.25 + 0.685 = 1.935$ kW

$$\text{Efficiency} = \frac{\text{output}}{\text{output} + \text{losses}} = \frac{8.75}{8.75 + 1.935} = 0.819 = 81.9\%$$

3. Hopkinson Test. The Swinburne test gives no indication of the behaviour of the machine when it is loaded, especially with regard to temperature rise, sparking at the brushes, etc. The Hopkinson test enables a large shunt machine to be tested fully loaded without a serious waste of energy, but it does require a second similar machine. The two machines are coupled

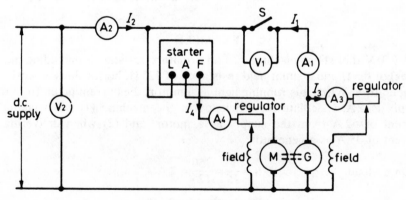

Fig. 5.16 Hopkinson test

together so that one runs as a motor driving the other as a generator. The circuit arrangement is shown in Fig. 5.16.

The motor M is started with switch S open. The field current of generator G is adjusted until voltmeter V_1 reads zero, then switch S is closed. The generator voltage can now be raised by adjusting its field current I_3 and this causes current I_1 to be taken by the motor in addition to its no-load current. Thus, by adjusting the fields both machines can be loaded, one as a motor, the other as a generator. This load current I_1 circulates between the two machines so that they operate at any desired load, yet the only current taken from the supply is that to supply the losses, that is, the current I_2.

Assume the same efficiency for both machines $= \eta$.

$$\text{Generator output} = VI_1 \text{ watts}$$

$$\text{Motor input} = V(I_1 + I_2) \text{ watts}$$

$$\text{Motor output} = \eta V(I_1 + I_2) = \text{generator input}$$

$$\therefore \text{ Generator output} = \eta^2 V(I_1 + I_2) = VI_1$$

$$\therefore \eta^2 = \frac{VI_1}{V(I_1 + I_2)} = \frac{I_1}{I_1 + I_2}$$

$$\therefore \text{ Efficiency } \eta = \left(\frac{I_1}{I_1 + I_2}\right)^{1/2} \tag{5.7}$$

The armature and field currents of the two machines will not be the same, therefore their losses will be different, so the above equation is only approximate. For a more accurate figure, the losses of each machine must be calculated separately.

6. Transformers

6.1 Outline of basic principles

Basically, a single-phase transformer consists of two windings, primary and secondary, electrically insulated from each other but wound on a common laminated magnetic core. To minimize magnetic leakage, primary and secondary windings are wound close to each other on both limbs of the iron core, forming either a sandwich or a concentric arrangement. For simplicity, however, the windings can be shown on separate limbs, as in Fig. 6.1.

The a.c. supply voltage V_p will produce an alternating magnetic flux Φ in the iron core and, assuming no magnetic leakage, Φ will also link with the secondary winding. This flux Φ links with both primary and secondary windings and will induce the same value of e.m.f. in each turn (v).

$$\therefore \quad \frac{\text{Induced e.m.f. in primary}}{\text{Induced e.m.f. in secondary}} = \frac{N_p v}{N_s v} = \frac{N_p}{N_s}$$

The no-load current of a transformer is very small causing negligible volt drop, so the induced e.m.f. in the primary will be almost equal to the supply voltage V_p and the induced e.m.f. in the secondary will be the secondary terminal voltage V_s.

$$\therefore \quad \frac{V_p}{V_s} \simeq \frac{N_p}{N_s} \tag{6.1}$$

For all practical purposes, it can be said that the voltage ratio of a single-phase transformer is the same as the turns ratio.

The transformer is a highly efficient machine, with extremely small losses. Thus the output is almost equal to the input,

i.e., $$I_p V_p \cos \phi_p \simeq I_s V_s \cos \phi_s \tag{6.2}$$

But primary and secondary power factors are almost the same.

$$\therefore \quad I_p V_p \simeq I_s V_s$$

$$\frac{I_p}{I_s} \simeq \frac{V_s}{V_p} \simeq \frac{N_s}{N_p} \tag{6.3}$$

For practical purposes, the current ratio is inversely proportional to the turns ratio.

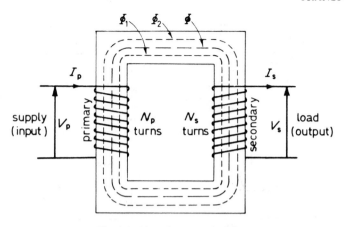

Fig. 6.1 Transformer principle

When a load is connected to the secondary, a current I_s will flow in the secondary winding which tends to produce an additional magnetic flux Φ_2. Φ_2 is a demagnetizing flux which weakens the main flux Φ. The primary voltage, however, is fixed by the supply voltage V_p. Thus, the primary winding must draw a current I_p from the supply so that it produces a flux Φ_1 equal and opposite to Φ_2. So, whatever the load, Φ_1 and Φ_2 always cancel each other out, and therefore never exist as separate fluxes. This means that the magnetic flux Φ is constant at all loads, so the iron loss also will be constant at all loads and will be the no-load value.

6.2 Transformer construction

Windings. To minimize magnetic leakage, the l.v. and h.v. windings are wound close to each other on the same limb. If the windings are spread over two limbs, there will be half of each winding on each limb. The windings may be wound in a concentric form or a sandwich form, as shown in Fig. 6.2.

Iron Core–Single-phase Transformers. The *core-type* transformer is the type most commonly used, and consists of a single magnetic circuit with two limbs (Fig. 6.3a). This is constructed of laminated iron, which gives a near-circular cross-section. Half of each winding is placed on each limb.

Figure 6.3(b) shows the *shell-type* construction. In this case, all the windings are on the centre limb, which has double the cross-section of the outer limbs. The reactance of this type of transformer is somewhat less than the core type, and is more suitable for dealing with very heavy currents, although it is not so easy to dismantle in the event of breakdown. It is mainly used to supply electric furnaces.

87

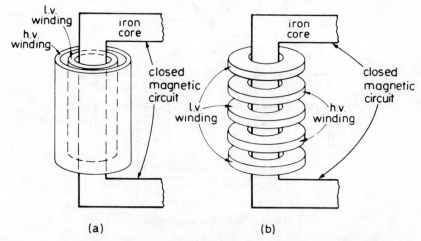

Fig. 6.2   Types of transformer windings: (a) concentric winding, (b) sandwich winding

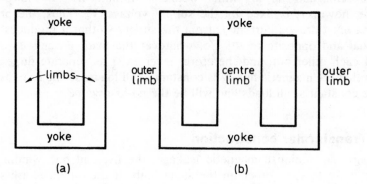

Fig. 6.3   Single-phase transformer cores: (a) core type—windings on both limbs, (b) shell type—windings on centre limb only

Iron   Core–Three-phase   Transformers. Three   single-phase,   core-type transformers could be used for three-phase working, but it is generally cheaper and more convenient to have a single unit. The core has three equal limbs, as in Fig. 6.4, and each limb carries both l.v. and h.v. windings for one phase.

There is also a five-limb core construction in which the three centre limbs carry all the windings. This construction allows a reduction in the height of each limb and therefore in the height of the transformer. It is only used in cases where a reduction in the height is essential.

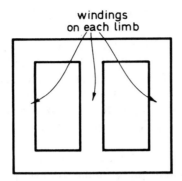

Fig. 6.4   Three-phase transformer core

6.3   The transformer on no-load

The ideal transformer is one in which there are no losses; it can be represented as in Fig. 6.5(a).

The applied voltage V_p will produce a magnetizing current I_m which

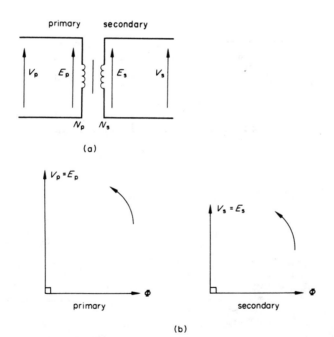

Fig. 6.5   The ideal transformer on no-load: (a) circuit, (b) phasor diagram
E_p = primary induced e.m.f.; V_s = secondary terminal voltage
V_p = primary applied voltage; E_s = secondary induced e.m.f.;

produces the magnetic flux Φ which will lag V_p by 90°, as shown in the phasor diagram of Fig. 6.5(b). Since this is an ideal transformer, the theoretical value of I_m is zero and thus is not shown. The flux Φ induces an e.m.f. E_p in the primary which leads Φ by 90° and will be equal and in phase with V_p. An e.m.f. E_s is induced in the secondary, which will lead Φ by 90° also. The terminal voltage V_s will be equal to and in phase with E_s. The ratio E_s/E_p will depend upon the transformer turns ratio N_s/N_p. The phasor diagram is shown in Fig. 6.5(b), the primary and secondary phasors being shown separate.

In practice the magnetizing current I_m will not be zero but will flow in the primary and will lag behind the terminal voltage V_p by 90°. This current produces the flux Φ; since Φ is alternating there will be eddy current and hysteresis losses in the iron core which produce heat, and thus a power loss which can be represented by a current I_w in phase with V_p. So the transformer will have a no-load current I_0 in the primary which will be the phasor sum of I_m and I_w. Since I_m lags 90° behind V_p it can be represented by a current flowing through an inductance L_0. I_w is in phase with V_p, so it

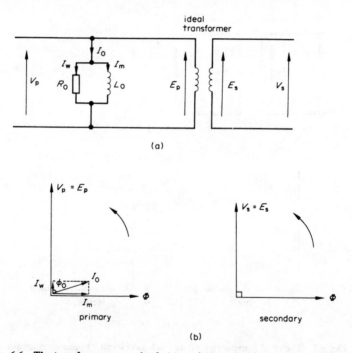

(a)

(b)

Fig. 6.6 The transformer on no-load: (a) equivalent circuit, (b) phasor diagram

can be represented by a current through a resistance R_0. L_0 and R_0 can be shown as a parallel group, with a resultant current I_0 taken from the primary supply, giving the equivalent no-load transformer circuit of Fig. 6.6(a). The phasor diagram is given in Fig. 6.6(b) where ϕ_0 is the no-load phase angle and $\cos \phi_0$ will be the no-load power factor. The resistance and inductance of the transformer windings themselves have been omitted at this stage.

6.4 The transformer on load

The equivalent circuit for a transformer on load is shown in Fig. 6.7. It was seen in Sec. 6.1 that the flux Φ remains constant at all loads so that I_0 remains constant and independent of the load. Thus the equivalent circuit

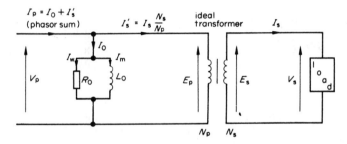

Fig. 6.7 Equivalent circuit of a transformer on-load (neglecting winding impedance)

will contain the parallel group of R_0 and L_0, as in the no-load diagram. The load takes a secondary current I_s which causes a current I_s' to flow in the primary of the ideal transformer where $I_s' = I_s(N_s/N_p)$. I_s' is called *the secondary current referred to the primary*. The primary current I_p will be the phasor sum of I_s' and I_0.

The secondary phase angle ϕ_s and the load power factor $\cos \phi_s$ will be determined by the load. The secondary current referred to the primary I_s' will be in phase with I_s. Figure 6.8 gives the phasor diagrams for the three cases of lagging, unity, and leading power-factor loads. The phasor diagrams show that, theoretically, there is a difference between the primary and secondary phase angles but, except for small transformers, in practice I_0 is generally so small compared with the load current that its effect can be ignored and it is usually assumed that the primary and secondary phase angles are the same.

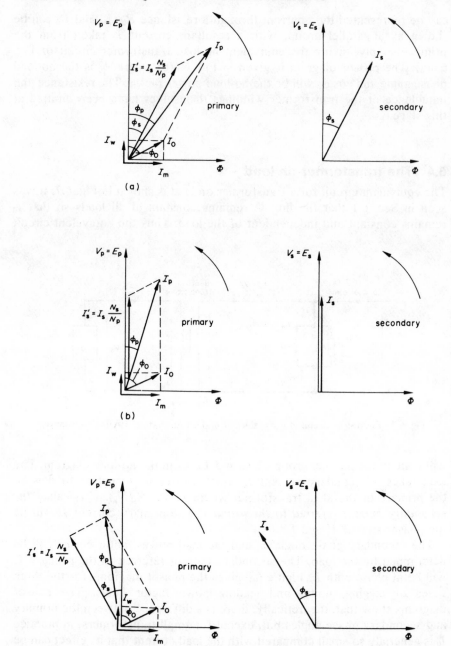

Fig. 6.8 **Phasor diagrams for various loads (neglecting winding impedance): (a) lagging power factor load, (b) unity power factor load, (c) leading power factor load**

6.5 Example of a transformer on load

Consider a 3600/240 V step-down transformer with a no-load current of 1 A at a power factor of 0.2 lagging. It is required to find the primary current and power factor when the secondary load current is 150 A at a power factor of 0.9 lagging. The impedance of the windings will be ignored.

The phasor diagram will be similar to Fig. 6.8(a).

$$\text{Turns ratio } \frac{N_s}{N_p} = \frac{E_s}{E_p} = \frac{240}{3600} = \frac{1}{15}$$

given $I_s = 150$ A.

$$\therefore \text{ Referred to primary } I'_s = I_s \frac{N_s}{N_p} = \frac{150}{15} = 10 \text{ A}$$

$$\text{Secondary power factor} = \cos \phi_s = 0.9 \text{ lagging}$$

$$\therefore \text{ Load phase angle } \phi_s \quad = 25.84°$$

$$\text{No-load current } I_0 \quad = 1 \text{ A}$$

$$\text{No-load power factor} \quad = \cos \phi_0 = 0.2 \text{ lagging}$$

$$\therefore \text{ No-load phase angle } \phi_0 = 78.46°$$

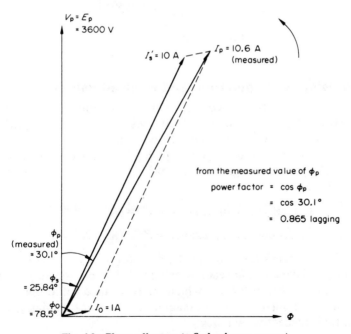

Fig. 6.9 Phasor diagram to find primary current

93

With this information the phasor diagram can now be drawn to scale and the resultant primary current I_p and its phase angle ϕ_p can be measured, and the power factor $\cos \phi_p$ found. Since the secondary current has been referred to the primary, only the primary phasor diagram need be drawn. The student should draw this diagram *to scale* as large as possible to obtain the greatest accuracy and check the results with the information given on Fig. 6.9. It must be pointed out, however, that of necessity, the book diagram has to be kept small and is not to scale.

The measured values on the phasor diagram of Fig. 6.9 can be checked by calculation by adding the in-phase and the quadrature components of I_0 and I'_s.

In-phase components:

$$I_p \cos \phi_p = I_0 \cos \phi_0 + I'_s \cos \phi_s$$
$$= (1 \times 0.2) + (10 \times 0.9) = 9.2 \text{ A}$$

Quadrature components:

$$I_p \sin \phi_p = I_0 \sin \phi_0 + I'_s \sin \phi_s$$
$$= (1 \times 0.98) + (10 \times 0.436) = 5.34 \text{ A}$$
$$\therefore \ I_p = (9.2^2 + 5.34^2)^{1/2} = 10.637 \text{ A}$$
$$\text{p.f.} = \cos \phi_p = \frac{9.2}{10.637} = 0.865 \text{ lag}$$

$$\text{Phase angle } \phi_p = 30.13°$$

6.6 Transformer impedance and referred values

In the above sections the impedance of the transformer windings has been ignored. However, each winding will have resistance, R_p in the primary and R_s in the secondary. There is bound to be some leakage flux, that is, flux which links only with the winding in which it is produced. So each winding will have self-inductance, giving a primary reactance X_p and a secondary reactance X_s. Thus

$$\text{Primary impedance} = Z_p = (R_p^2 + X_p^2)^{1/2}$$

$$\text{Secondary impedance} = Z_s = (R_s^2 + X_s^2)^{1/2}$$

Figure 6.10(a) shows the equivalent circuit for a transformer on load with the winding resistances and reactances added. The phasor diagram for this circuit is shown in Fig. 6.10(b) in which the resistance volt drops are shown in phase with the current and the reactance volt drops leading the current by 90° in their respective windings.

For the purpose of calculations involving transformers, it is more con-

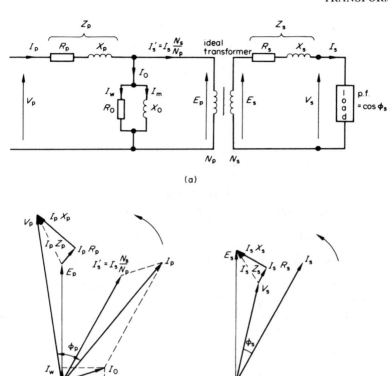

Fig. 6.10 Transformer on load, including winding impedance: (a) equivalent circuit, (b) phasor diagram

venient to bulk all the resistance and reactance in either the primary or the secondary circuit.

The secondary resistance R_s can be transferred to the primary circuit to give the *referred resistance* $R_s(N_p/N_s)^2$. Similarly, the referred value of R_p in the secondary will be $R_p(N_s/N_p)^2$. The reactances are transferred in the same way.

The *total* resistance or reactance in the primary or the secondary is called the *equivalent value*.

The equivalent values in the primary will be

$$R_{ep} = R_p + R_s\left(\frac{N_p}{N_s}\right)^2 \qquad (6.4)$$

$$X_{ep} = X_p + X_s\left(\frac{N_p}{N_s}\right)^2 \qquad (6.5)$$

95

also
$$Z_{ep} = (R_{ep}^2 + X_{ep}^2)^{1/2} \tag{6.6}$$

The equivalent values in the secondary will be

$$R_{es} = R_s + R_p\left(\frac{N_s}{N_p}\right)^2 \tag{6.7}$$

$$X_{es} = X_s + X_p\left(\frac{N_s}{N_p}\right)^2 \tag{6.8}$$

also
$$Z_{es} = (R_{es}^2 + X_{es}^2)^{1/2} \tag{6.9}$$

EXAMPLE

A 500/200 V single-phase transformer has the following particulars:

Primary: Resistance 0.5 Ω; reactance 2.5 Ω

Secondary: Resistance 0.03 Ω; reactance 0.15 Ω

Find the equivalent values of resistance, reactance, and impedance referred to (1) the primary, and (2) the secondary.
$R_p = 0.5$ Ω; $X_p = 2.5$ Ω; $R_s = 0.03$ Ω; $X_s = 0.15$ Ω. Turns ratio $N_p/N_s =$ voltage ratio $= 500/200 = 5/2$.

1. *Primary circuit*

$$R_{ep} = R_p + R_s\left(\frac{N_p}{N_s}\right)^2 = 0.5 + 0.03\left(\frac{5}{2}\right)^2 = 0.6875 \text{ Ω}$$

$$X_{ep} = X_p + X_s\left(\frac{N_p}{N_s}\right)^2 = 2.5 + 0.15\left(\frac{5}{2}\right)^2 = 3.4375 \text{ Ω}$$

$$Z_{ep} = (R_{ep}^2 + X_{ep}^2)^{1/2} = (0.6875^2 + 3.4375^2)^{1/2} = 3.5 \text{ Ω}$$

2. *Secondary circuit*

$$R_{es} = R_s + R_p\left(\frac{N_s}{N_p}\right)^2 = 0.03 + 0.5\left(\frac{2}{5}\right)^2 = 0.11 \text{ Ω}$$

$$X_{es} = X_s + X_p\left(\frac{N_s}{N_p}\right)^2 = 0.15 + 2.5\left(\frac{2}{5}\right)^2 = 0.55 \text{ Ω}$$

$$Z_{es} = (R_{es}^2 + X_{es}^2)^{1/2} = (0.11^2 + 0.55^2)^{1/2} = 0.56 \text{ Ω}$$

Figure 6.11 shows the development of the equivalent circuit with all values transferred to the primary. In the final diagram, Fig. 6.11(b), there is only one value for resistance and one for reactance. These are the equivalent referred values. The no-load circuit of R_0 and X_0 can be transferred to the incoming supply terminals, since any error introduced by doing this is negligible. The ideal transformer can be omitted and replaced

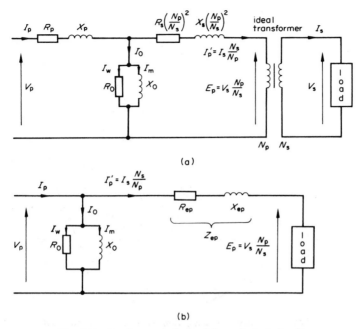

Fig. 6.11 Development of complete equivalent circuit

by the secondary load with a voltage across it of $E_p = V_s(N_p/N_s)$, where E_p is the primary voltage for the ideal transformer.

6.7 Voltage regulation

The *voltage regulation* of a transformer is defined as the arithmetic difference between the secondary no-load voltage E_s and the terminal voltage V_s at a specified load and power factor (usually full load), the primary supply voltage remaining constant. That is, regulation, stated as a voltage, is equal to $E_s - V_s$, although it is generally expressed as a fraction or as a percentage of the no-load voltage.

$$\therefore \text{ Fractional regulation } = \frac{E_s - V_s}{E_s} \tag{6.10}$$

$$\therefore \text{ Percentage regulation} = \frac{E_s - V_s}{E_s} \times 100 \tag{6.11}$$

To calculate voltage regulation the primary winding resistance and reactance are referred to the secondary; the equivalent values are used to construct the secondary phasor diagram as shown in Fig. 6.12, in which the load current is I_s with a lagging phase angle ϕ_s.

97

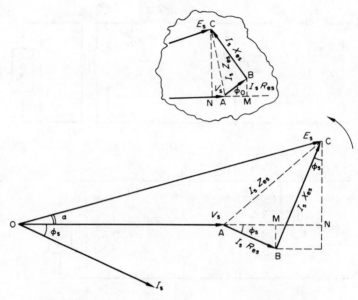

Fig. 6.12 Secondary phasor diagram for a transformer on load

I_s = secondary load current; $R_{es} = R_s + R_p\left(\dfrac{N_s}{N_p}\right)^2$

ϕ_s = load phase angle; $X_{es} = X_s + X_p\left(\dfrac{N_s}{N_p}\right)^2$

Transformers are highly efficient and losses are small. Thus the impedance triangle ABC will be small compared with the voltages E_s and V_s. The angle α will be so small that, for practical purposes, it can be said that $OC = ON$.

$$\therefore \ E_s - V_s = OC - OA = ON - OA = AN$$

but $$AN = AM + MN$$

$$= I_s R_{es} \cos \phi_s + I_s X_{es} \sin \phi_s$$

$$= I_s(R_{es} \cos \phi_s + X_{es} \sin \phi_s) \tag{6.12}$$

If the load phase angle ϕ_s is leading the triangle ABC will be in the position shown in the inset of Fig. 6.12, which shows that for a leading phase angle $AN = AM - MN$,

i.e., $$E_s - V_s = I_s(R_{es} \cos \phi_s - X_{es} \sin \phi_s) \tag{6.13}$$

Combining Eqs (6.12) and (6.13), the fractional regulation will be given by:

$$\text{Regulation} = \frac{E_s - V_s}{E_s} = \frac{I_s(R_{es} \cos \phi_s \pm X_{es} \sin \phi_s)}{E_s} \tag{6.14}$$

the negative sign being used when the load power factor is leading.

EXAMPLE

The 500/200 V transformer in the example in Sec. 6.6 provides a 2.4 kW load at a lagging power factor of 0.8. What will be the regulation at this loading? What would the regulation be if the power factor had been 0.8 leading?

The load is supplied at 200 V, i.e., $V_s = 200$ V.

$$V_s I_s \cos \phi_s = 2400 \text{ W}$$

$$\therefore I_s = \frac{2400}{200 \times 0.8} = 15 \text{ A}$$

1. *With 0.8 lagging p.f.*

$$E_s - V_s = I_s(R_{es} \cos \phi_s + X_{es} \sin \phi_s)$$
$$= 15[(0.11 \times 0.8) + (0.55 \times 0.6)]$$
$$= 15(0.088 + 0.33) = 15 \times 0.418 = 6.27 \text{ V}$$

$$\therefore E_s = V_s + 6.27 = 206.27 \text{ V}$$

$$\therefore \text{Regulation} = \frac{6.27}{206.27} = 0.0304 \text{ (fractional)}$$
$$= 3.04\%$$

2. *With 0.8 leading p.f.*

$$E_s - V_s = I_s(R_{es} \cos \phi_s - X_{es} \sin \phi_s)$$
$$= 15(0.088 - 0.33) = 15 \times (-0.242)$$
$$= -3.63 \text{ V}$$

$$\therefore E_s = V_s - 3.63 = 196.37 \text{ V}$$

$$\therefore \text{Regulation} = \frac{-3.63}{196.37} = -0.0185 \text{ (fractional)}$$
$$= -1.85\%$$

The negative sign in the answer to (2) shows that there is actually a *voltage rise* in the transformer instead of a voltage drop and that it is possible for a leading power factor load to cause V_s to be greater than E_s.

6.8 Transformer losses

A transformer has no moving parts, therefore there are no friction or windage losses. The only losses are magnetic and electrical, and with good design these can be quite small, so that the transformer becomes a very efficient machine with efficiencies in the region of 97–98%.

Losses in a transformer are as follows.

1. Iron loss or core loss (P_i). Since the magnetic flux Φ is constant at all loads, this loss is constant.

2. Copper loss (P_c). This loss is due to the current flowing through the winding resistance and is given by

$$P_c = I_p^2 R_p + I_s^2 R_s = I_s^2 R_{es}$$

where R_{es} is the whole of the primary and secondary winding resistances referred to the secondary and is given by Eq. (6.7).

3. Additional losses. These additional losses are due to eddy currents set up by the leakage flux in the transformer casing, tank, bolts, etc., and in large-section copper windings, but these are usually kept so small by good design that in general they can be neglected. In any case, if the transformer resistance is measured by an a.c. method instead of a d.c. method, these losses will show up by causing an apparently slightly higher value of resistance to be obtained. If this value of resistance is used in calculating the copper loss P_c, then these additional losses will have been allowed for.

6.9 Transformer tests

The efficiency of a transformer can be found by directly loading it. With ammeters, voltmeters, and wattmeters connected in both primary and secondary circuits, the efficiency and power factor can be calculated for any load. However, this method is wasteful of energy, and therefore is suitable only for small transformers.

To obtain data from which the efficiency can be calculated, two tests are necessary—the open-circuit test and a short-circuit test.

The Open-circuit Test. The circuit for this test is shown in Fig. 6.13.

The no-load current (I_0) of a transformer is at a low power factor, so, for accuracy, a low-power-factor wattmeter should be used. I_0 provides the

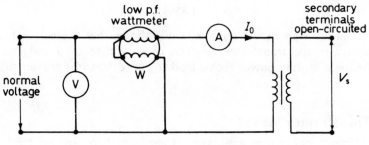

Fig. 6.13   Open-circuit test

magnetizing current and the iron-loss current and will be constant at all loads. Thus, the iron loss P_i will be constant at all loads.

From the test: Wattmeter reading = iron loss P_i watts

$$\text{No-load power factor } \cos \phi_0 = \frac{P_i}{V_p I_0}$$

The Short-circuit Test. Figure 6.14 shows the connections for this test. The wattmeter takes a high current at a low voltage in this case. Unless the reading is corrected for wattmeter losses, the method shown for connecting the instruments will give the minimum error.

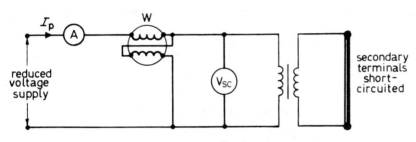

Fig. 6.14   Short-circuit test

The current I_p may be any suitable value, but it is generally more convenient to make it the normal full-load value. The applied voltage V_{sc} is slowly increased until the full-load current I_p is obtained. Since the secondary is short-circuited, the voltage V_{sc} will be quite small, usually about 5% of normal voltage. At this voltage, any iron loss will be so small that it can be neglected.

The secondary is short-circuited. Therefore, the secondary terminal voltage will be zero.

Thus, the primary voltage passes the current I_p through the primary as though all the transformer impedance is in the primary.

$$\therefore \text{ Equivalent impedance } Z_{ep} = \frac{V_{sc}}{I_p} \qquad (6.15)$$

Wattmeter reading = copper loss at full load = P_c

$$\text{Equivalent resistance in primary} = R_{ep} = \frac{P_c}{I_p^2} \qquad (6.16)$$

Also, X_{ep} can be calculated:

$$X_{ep} = (Z_{ep}^2 - R_{ep}^2)^{1/2} \qquad (6.17)$$

The equivalent referred values in the secondary circuit can be found by

101

multiplying by $(N_s/N_p)^2$ or $(V_s/V_p)^2$,

e.g.,
$$R_{es} = R_{ep} \times \left(\frac{V_s}{V_p}\right)^2 \tag{6.18}$$

The above two tests can be carried out from either the h.v. or l.v. side, whichever is more convenient. The data obtained can be used to find the efficiency and the regulation of a transformer.

6.10 Transformer efficiency

The *ordinary* or *commercial efficiency* of a transformer is given by

$$\text{Efficiency } \eta = \frac{\text{power output}}{\text{power input}}$$

$$= \frac{\text{output}}{\text{output} + \text{losses}} \text{ (p.u. value)} \tag{6.19}$$

$$\text{Power output} = P = V_s I_s \cos \phi_s \text{ watts}$$

$$\text{Total copper loss} = P_c = I_s^2 R_{es} \text{ watts}$$

$$\text{Iron loss} = P_i \text{ watts}$$

$$\text{Total loss} = P_c + P_i = I_s^2 R_{es} + P_i$$

$$\therefore \text{Power input} = \text{output} + \text{losses} = P + P_c + P_i$$

$$\text{Efficiency } \eta = \frac{P}{P + P_c + P_i}$$

$$= \frac{V_s I_s \cos \phi_s}{V_s I_s \cos \phi_s + I_s^2 R_{es} + P_i} \tag{6.20}$$

Note that P_c is proportional to I_s^2 so if P_c is the copper loss at full load then at

$$\tfrac{1}{4}\text{f.l. copper loss} = (\tfrac{1}{4})^2 \times P_c = \frac{P_c}{16}$$

$$\tfrac{1}{2}\text{f.l. copper loss} = (\tfrac{1}{2})^2 \times P_c = \frac{P_c}{4}$$

$$\tfrac{3}{4}\text{f.l. copper loss} = (\tfrac{3}{4})^2 \times P_c = \frac{9P_c}{16}$$

$$1\tfrac{1}{2}\text{f.l. copper loss} = (\tfrac{3}{2})^2 \times P_c = \frac{9}{4} P_c \quad \text{etc.}$$

Equations (6.19) and (6.20) can be used for mathematical and calculator solutions but when using a slide rule greater accuracy is obtained if the equations are changed as follows.

$$\eta = \frac{\text{output}}{\text{input}} = \frac{\text{input} - \text{losses}}{\text{input}} = 1 - \frac{\text{losses}}{\text{input}}$$

$$= 1 - \frac{\text{losses}}{\text{output} + \text{losses}} \qquad (6.21)$$

$$\therefore \ \eta = 1 - \frac{P_c + P_i}{P + P_c + P_i}$$

$$= 1 - \frac{I_s^2 R_{es} + P_i}{V_s I_s \cos \phi_s + I_s^2 R_{es} + P_i} \qquad (6.22)$$

For a three-phase transformer, V_s and I_s will be *line values*. R_{es} will be the equivalent resistance *per phase*, and I_{phs} will be the phase current and will depend upon the type of connection (star or delta). P_i will be the *total* iron loss.

$$\text{Three-phase power output} = P = 1.73 \times V_s I_s \cos \phi_s$$

$$\text{Total loss} = 3 I_{phs}^2 R_{es} + P_i$$

$$\text{Efficiency } \eta = \frac{\text{output}}{\text{input}}$$

$$= \frac{\text{output}}{\text{output} + \text{losses}}$$

$$= \frac{1.73 \times V_s I_s \cos \phi_s}{1.73 V_s I_s \cos \phi_s + 3 I_{phs}^2 R_{es} + P_i} \qquad (6.23)$$

Using the alternative equation:

$$\text{Efficiency } \eta = 1 - \frac{\text{losses}}{\text{output} + \text{losses}}$$

$$= 1 - \frac{3 I_{phs}^2 R_{es} + P_i}{1.73 V_s I_s \cos \phi_s + 3 I_{phs}^2 R_{es} + P_i}$$

$$(6.24)$$

EXAMPLE

A 100 kV A, 2200/400 V, single-phase transformer is shown to have an iron loss of 850 W when open-circuit tested. From a short-circuit test the effective resistance in the secondary was found to be 0.0144 Ω. Find the efficiency of the transformer when it is delivering: (1) full load at unity p.f., (2) half full-load at unity p.f., (3) full load at 0.8 p.f. lagging, and (4) half full-load at 0.8 p.f. lagging.

$$\text{f.l. current } I_s = \frac{kV A \times 1000}{V_s} = \frac{100 \times 1000}{400} = 250 \text{ A}$$

$$\text{f.l. copper loss} = P_c = I_s^2 R_{es} = 250 \times 250 \times 0.0144 = 900 \text{ W}$$

$$\text{Iron loss} = P_i = 850 \text{ W}$$

1. *Unity p.f. at f.l.:*

$$\text{Output } P = kV A \times \text{p.f.} = 100 \times 1 = 100 \text{ kW}$$

$$\text{Total loss at f.l.} = P_c + P_i = 900 + 850 = 1750 \text{ W} = 1.75 \text{ kW}$$

Using Eqs (6.21), (6.22):

$$\eta = 1 - \frac{\text{losses}}{\text{output} + \text{losses}}$$

$$= 1 - \frac{P_c + P_i}{P + P_c + P_i} = 1 - \frac{1.75}{101.75} = 0.9828 = 98.28\%$$

2. *Unity p.f. at $\frac{1}{2}$ f.l.:*

$$\text{Output} = 50 \text{ kW}$$

$$\text{Copper loss} = (\tfrac{1}{2})^2 \times 900 = 225 \text{ W} = 0.225 \text{ kW}$$

$$\text{Iron loss is constant} = 850 \text{ W} = 0.85 \text{ kW}$$

$$\text{Total loss} = 0.225 + 0.85 = 1.075 \text{ kW}$$

$$\eta = 1 - \frac{\text{losses}}{\text{output} + \text{losses}} = 1 - \frac{1.075}{51.075} = 0.9789 = 97.89\%$$

3. *0.8 p.f. at f.l.:*

$$P = kV A \times \text{p.f.} = 100 \times 0.8 = 80 \text{ kW}$$

$$\text{Total loss as for unity p.f.} = 1.75 \text{ kW}$$

Using Eq. (6.19):

$$\eta = \frac{\text{output}}{\text{input}} = \frac{\text{output}}{\text{output} + \text{losses}} = \frac{80}{81.75} = 0.9786 = 97.86\%$$

4. *0.8 p.f. at $\frac{1}{2}$ f.l.:*

$$kV A \times \text{p.f.} = 50 \times 0.8 = 40 \text{ kW}$$

$$\text{Total loss at } \tfrac{1}{2} \text{ f.l.} = 1.075 \text{ kW}$$

$$\eta = \frac{\text{output}}{\text{output} + \text{losses}} = \frac{40}{41.075} = 0.9738 = 97.38\%$$

Note that the efficiency is affected by the power factor.

6.11 Operation of a three-phase transformer

The windings on each limb of a three-phase transformer are like the windings of a single-phase transformer. The flux Φ produced by the primary voltage also links with the secondary winding, inducing an e.m.f.

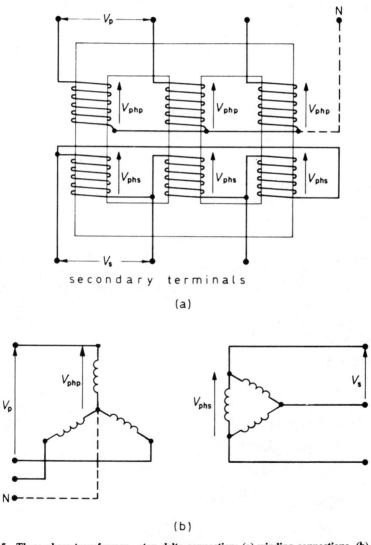

Fig. 6.15 Three-phase transformer—star–delta connection: (a) winding connections, (b) circuit diagram

105

proportional to the turns ratio. The phase of the secondary voltage will also be related to the primary phase. The three primary phases (one on each limb) will have a 120° phase difference from each other. It follows that the secondary windings on each limb will also have a 120° phase difference from each other and can be connected to give a three-phase supply. It is important to note, however, that it is the *phase* voltage ratio which is proportional to the turns ratio of the windings on one limb.

Both primary and secondary windings may be connected either star or delta. Figure 6.15(a) shows a transformer with the primary winding connected star and the secondary connected delta. In circuit diagrams it is usual to show the phase windings spaced 120° apart, as indicated in Fig. 6.15(b).

V_p and V_s are the primary and secondary *line* voltages, respectively. Since the primary is star-connected, the phase voltage $V_{php} = V_p/1.73$, but with the secondary delta-connected the line and phase voltages are the same.

Thus

$$\text{Turns ratio } N_s/N_p = V_{phs}/V_{php} = 1.73 V_s/V_p$$

In this case, the turns ratio does not give the line voltage ratio, that is, the ratio of the transformer terminal voltages.

EXAMPLE

A three-phase, 415 V load takes a line current of 800 A from a 3300/415 V delta–star transformer. The 3300 V system is supplied from an 11 000/3300 V star–star transformer. Draw the circuit diagram and, assuming no losses, find both line and phase values of voltages and currents in each part of the circuit. What will be the turns ratios of both transformers?

The circuit will be as shown in Fig. 6.16.

Voltages: $V_4 = 415$ V

$$V_{ph4} = \frac{V_4}{1.73} = \frac{415}{1.73} = 240 \text{ V}$$

$$V_3 = 3300 \text{ V}$$

$$V_{ph3} = V_3 = 3300 \text{ V}$$

$$V_2 = V_3 = 3300 \text{ V}$$

$$V_{ph2} = \frac{V_3}{1.73} = \frac{3300}{1.73} = 1905 \text{ V}$$

$$V_1 = 11\,000 \text{ V}$$

$$V_{ph1} = \frac{V_1}{1.73} = \frac{11\,000}{1.73} = 6350 \text{ V}$$

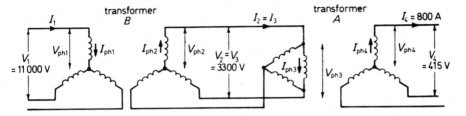

Fig. 6.16 Three-phase circuit

Turns ratios: Transformer A turns ratio $= \dfrac{V_{ph3}}{V_{ph4}} = \dfrac{3300}{240} = 13.75:1$

Transformer B turns ratio $= \dfrac{V_{ph1}}{V_{ph2}} = \dfrac{6350}{1905} = 3.33:1$

Currents: $I_4 = 800$ A

$I_{ph4} = I_4 = 800$ A

$I_{ph3} = \dfrac{I_{ph4}}{\text{turns ratio } A} = \dfrac{800}{13.75} = 58.2$ A

$I_2 = I_3 = 1.73 \times I_{ph3} = 1.73 \times 58.2 = 100.8$ A

$I_{ph2} = I_2 = 100.8$ A

$I_{ph1} = \dfrac{I_{ph2}}{\text{turns ratio } B} = \dfrac{100.8}{3.33} = 30.2$ A

$I_1 = I_{ph1} = 30.2$ A

Check (neglecting losses): Assume unity p.f., which will be the same for both input and output.

$$\text{Input} = 1.73 V_1 I_1 \cos \phi_1 = 1.73 \times 11\,000 \times 30.2 \times 1 = 575\,000 \text{ V A}$$
$$= 575 \text{ kV A}$$

$$\text{Output} = 1.73 V_4 I_4 \cos \phi_4 = 1.73 \times 415 \times 800 \times 1 \quad = 575\,000 \text{ V A}$$
$$= 575 \text{ kV A}$$

Thus

$$\text{Input} = \text{output}$$

6.12 Three-phase transformer connections

Star Connection. A star-connected winding has a voltage across it of only 0.58 (i.e., 1/1.73) of the line voltage. This enables its insulation to be reduced to a minimum for a given supply voltage and makes it the most economic connection for a high-voltage winding. The star point is available if a fourth wire is required. A third-harmonic e.m.f. (see Chapter 16) induced in the phase windings will produce a third-harmonic current in the fourth wire. In a three-wire system, where the star point is not solidly earthed, the third-harmonic e.m.f.s, while not appearing in line voltage, will make the neutral unstable.

Delta Connection. This must be insulated for the full line voltage, but will only carry 0.58 of the line current. Thus it is the most economical connection for a low-voltage winding. Its main drawback is that there is no neutral point and, therefore, it is unsuitable for general four-wire supplies. The closed circuit formed by the delta connection produces a circulating third-harmonic current. This eliminates the third-harmonic e.m.f.s from the external circuit and also improves the magnetic flux wave in the core, so that third-harmonic effects become negligible in the other winding, which may be star-connected. The delta winding is more effective for unbalanced load conditions.

A number of the more common transformer connections are given below with their main uses.

Star–Star. Economical for h.v. transformer, but neutral unstable if not solidly earthed. Not suitable for general supplies with unbalanced load. Generally used for small balanced power loads.

Delta–Delta. Economical for l.v. transformer. Third harmonics are damped out. Large unbalanced loads can be supplied, but this connection is not often used as there is no neutral point and a four-wire supply cannot be given.

Star–Delta. Delta winding damps out the third harmonic e.m.f.s and stabilizes the star point of primary. There is no secondary neutral and four-wire supplies cannot be given. The main use is as a stepdown transformer to supply balanced three-phase motor loads.

Delta–Star. This is the most commonly used connection for general supplies, although, as a stepdown transformer, the windings are not the most economical. The secondary star point can be earthed and a four-wire supply given. Since there is a delta winding (primary), the third-harmonic e.m.f. is damped and both balanced and unbalanced loads can be supplied.

Interconnected-star Winding. This is a special secondary winding in which half of each phase winding is placed on a different limb so that the induced e.m.f.s in each half are produced by two separate primary phases. The e.m.f.s induced in each half are 60° out of phase, so for a given phase voltage 15% more turns will be required. For a given rating a transformer with an interconnected star winding will be physically larger and more expensive than a normal star winding. However, this connection reduces the third-harmonic current, while it has the advantage, when supplying an unbalanced four-wire load, of reducing the out-of-balance in the primary winding. It is also used on extensive supply systems to give a 30° phase shift, which may be required for paralleling purposes. Figure 6.17 gives a diagram of the interconnected-star or zigzag connection.

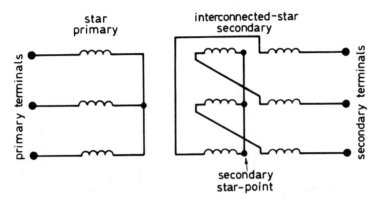

Fig. 6.17 Star–interconnected star connection

Tertiary Winding. This is a third, delta-connected winding sometimes provided in a transformer. Although it can be used to supply additional power, the tertiary winding generally has no external connection. Its main purpose is to absorb the third-harmonic current and stabilize the neutral of the main star windings. It also assists in restoring balance when an unbalanced load is being supplied by a four-wire star-connected secondary. It may be necessary, for interconnection purposes, to install a star–star transformer in a system. A tertiary delta winding would then be necessary to enable this to be done.

6.13 Terminal markings

Transformers can be used for both stepping down and stepping up the voltage. In one case the h.v. winding will be the primary and in the other case the l.v. winding will be the primary. To avoid confusion, it is normal practice to speak of the h.v. winding and the l.v. winding.

The terminals of the h.v. winding of a three-phase transformer are marked by capital letters—*A*, *B*, *C* for the phases, *N* for the neutral. Lower-case letters are used for the l.v. terminals—*a*, *b*, *c* for the phases, *n* for the neutral.

The student will be familiar with the single-phase transformer phasor diagram (see Fig. 6.5). As either winding could be the primary it is better, from the point of view of terminal markings and winding connections, to consider the induced e.m.f. in both windings produced by a common

109

magnetic flux Φ, irrespective of which winding is producing the flux. Figure 6.18 shows the h.v. and l.v. windings, both linked by flux Φ. If Φ is increasing, the induced e.m.f. will be in the same direction in both windings as shown, making the top terminals of each winding positive at that instant. These two terminals will be given the same suffix number, i.e., A_1 and a_1. The other terminals will be A_2 and a_2. The associated phasor diagrams are shown.

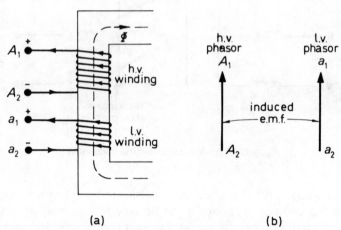

(a)　　　　　　　　　　　(b)

Fig. 6.18　Terminal markings (a), and phasor diagram (b)

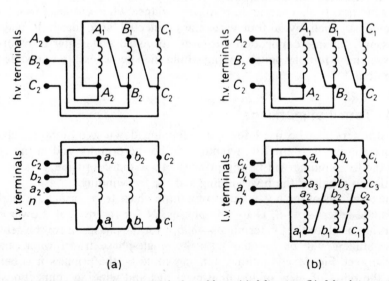

(a)　　　　　　　　　　　(b)

Fig. 6.19　Three-phase transformer terminal markings: (a) delta–star, (b) delta–interconnected star

If the winding is tapped then the terminals are marked A_1, A_2, A_3, A_4, etc., in order of their separation from terminal A_1. The full winding will be connected between terminal A_1 and the terminal with the highest suffix number.

With a star connection, points A_1, B_1, and C_1 may be made common inside the transformer and the common connection brought out to a single terminal marked N. The other terminals will be A_2, B_2, and C_2.

Figure 6.19 shows examples of terminal markings for two different types of transformer.

6.14 Transformer groupings

It has been seen (Fig. 6.18) that the h.v. and l.v. induced e.m.f.s for windings on the same limb are in the same phase but the phase relationship at the terminals of a three-phase transformer will depend upon the type of connection. For example, the h.v. and l.v. terminal voltages will still have the same phase, that is, there will be no phase displacement, if the transformers are connected star–star or delta–delta. If the connections are delta–star or star–delta, there will be a phase shift between h.v. and l.v. terminal voltages of ±30°. Also, reversing the l.v. terminal connections will give a phase shift, or displacement of 180°. Thus, three-phase transformers can be placed in four groups, depending upon the phase displacement between h.v. and l.v. sides. These groups are given clock representation, e.g., no displacement (0 o'clock), 180° displacement (6 o'clock), −30° (1 o'clock) and +30° (11 o'clock). Symbols are used for the star and delta

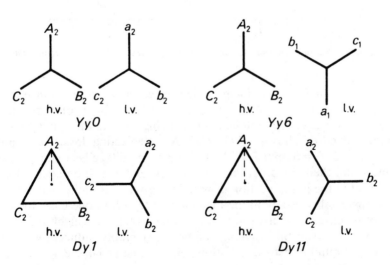

Fig. 6.20 Examples of three-phase transformer phasor diagrams

111

windings: Y and D for h.v. connection, y and d for l.v. connection, and z for l.v. interconnected star. Transformers in each group are:

Group 1: no displacement   *Yy*0, *Dd*0, *Dz*0

Group 2: 180° displacement   *Yy*6, *Dd*6, *Dz*6

Group 3: −30° displacement   *Dy*1, *Yd*1, *Yz*1

Group 4: +30° displacement   *Dy*11, *Yd*11, *Yz*11

The phasor diagram with the associated terminal markings is shown for one type of transformer in each group in Fig. 6.20.

These standards for transformers are laid down in BS 171, which the student should consult.

6.15 The auto-transformer

The auto-transformer has only one winding for both primary and secondary. The secondary is supplied by means of a tapping, which usually gives a secondary voltage slightly less or slightly more than the primary voltage. Figure 6.21 shows the general arrangement.

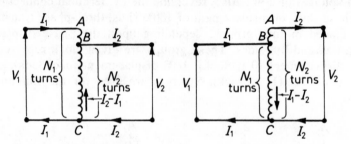

Fig. 6.21   The auto-transformer: (a) step-down connection, (b) step-up connection

This is a transformer principle; therefore, unlike a resistance potentiometer, the voltages are determined by the number of turns and a secondary voltage can be obtained which is higher than the applied voltage. In both the cases shown, $V_1/V_2 = N_1/N_2$. Neglecting losses and power factor, input $I_1 V_1 =$ output $I_2 V_2$. If the change in voltage between V_1 and V_2 is quite small then the difference between I_1 and I_2 will be small also. So the current in the larger section of winding between B and C will be small, being considerably less than the load current ($I_2 - I_1$ in one case and $I_1 - I_2$ in the other case). The cross-section, and therefore the weight and cost, of this common part of the winding, can be considerably reduced, whereas in the double-wound transformer both windings must be large enough to carry their respective currents.

Weight of copper $\propto NI$

if current density and mean length of turn remain constant.

$\therefore$ For the double-wound transformer

Total weight of copper $W_D \propto (N_1 I_1 + N_2 I_2)$

With the stepdown auto-transformer

Weight of copper in section $AB \propto (N_1 - N_2) I_1$

Weight of copper in section $BC \propto N_2 (I_2 - I_1)$

$\therefore$ Total weight of copper $W_A \propto (N_1 - N_2) I_1 + N_2 (I_2 - I_1)$

$$\propto (N_1 - 2N_2) I_1 + N_2 I_2$$

$$\therefore \quad \frac{W_A}{W_D} = \frac{(N_1 - 2N_2) I_1 + N_2 I_2}{N_1 I_1 + N_2 I_2}$$

Dividing both numerator and denominator by $N_2 I_1$,

$$\frac{W_A}{W_D} = \frac{(N_1/N_2) - 2 + (I_2/I_1)}{(N_1/N_2) + (I_2/I_1)}$$

but

$$\text{Turns ratio } m = \frac{N_1}{N_2} = \frac{I_2}{I_1}$$

$$\therefore \quad \frac{W_A}{W_D} = \frac{m - 2 + m}{m + m} = \frac{2m - 2}{2m} = 1 - \frac{1}{m} = 1 - k \qquad (6.25)$$

where $k = (N_2/N_1) = (V_2/V_1)$, i.e., ratio of secondary volts to primary volts.

So if V_2 is $1/10 \, V_1$ then $\dfrac{W_A}{W_D} = 1 - 1/10 = 0.9$ i.e., saving of 10%;

but if V_2 is $9/10 \, V_1$ then $\dfrac{W_A}{W_D} = 1 - 9/10 = 0.1$ i.e., saving of 90%.

So, for a small lowering or raising of the voltage, the saving is considerable. The smaller current in the winding also means that the copper loss will be less, leading to a higher efficiency for an auto-transformer. In practice, the overall saving will not be quite as good as indicated by the above theoretical values, and very little saving is achieved if the voltage ratio is greater than $3:1$.

The main disadvantage of the use of the auto-transformer is that the h.v. and l.v. sides are connected together by the common winding and a fault could cause the full high-voltage to be applied to the low-voltage circuit. This would be particularly dangerous if the difference in the voltages was large. In an installation, the use of the auto-transformer is restricted to

113

special applications, such as a motor starter, power factor improvement circuits, discharge lighting circuits, etc. They must never be used to give an extra-low voltage supply from a mains supply (e.g., for bell circuits). In the supply system, auto-transformers are used for transforming between the Grid voltage (132 kV) and the Super Grid (275 kV).

EXAMPLE

How much more copper will be required for a double-wound transformer than for an auto-transformer of the same rating if the secondary voltage is three-quarters of the primary voltage?

$$\frac{W_A}{W_D} = 1 - k = 1 - \tfrac{3}{4} = \tfrac{1}{4}$$

$\therefore$ Four times more copper is required by the double-wound transformer.

EXAMPLE

An auto-transformer is used to reduce the voltage from 500 V to 440 V to supply a load of 20 kW at unity p.f. Neglecting losses and the magnetizing current, find the currents in each part of the transformer winding.

The circuit is as Fig. 6.21(a)

$$I_1 = \frac{P}{V_1 \cos \phi_1} = \frac{20\,000}{500 \times 1} = 40 \text{ A}$$

$$I_2 = \frac{P}{V_2 \cos \phi_2} = \frac{20\,000}{440 \times 1} = 45.45 \text{ A}$$

Current in winding A to $B = I_1 = 40$ A

Current in winding B to $C = I_2 - I_1 = 45.45 - 40 = 5.45$ A

6.16 Instrument transformers

In a.c. circuits, measuring instruments are not always connected directly into the circuit, but are supplied by means of instrument transformers. This is especially the case when high voltages or heavy currents have to be measured. The transformer primary carries the current or the voltage to be measured, and the instrument is connected to the secondary so that it measures a small current or voltage which is proportional to the main circuit values.

There are several advantages of using instrument transformers:

1. The secondary is wound for low voltage, which simplifies the insulation of the measuring instrument and makes it safe to handle.
2. One point in the secondary is always earthed so that the secondary

circuit and the instrument are always kept at a low potential, even when measuring high voltages.

3. The transformer isolates the instrument from the main circuit.
4. The measuring instrument can be connected by long leads to the transformer and can be placed in the most convenient position for reading.
5. The secondary voltage or current can be standardized (usually 110 V for potential transformers or 5 A for current transformers), which simplifies instrument changes.

Potential or Voltage Transformer (PT or VT). The construction is similar to a power transformer and has a special low-loss iron core. The secondary is connected to a voltmeter, the voltage coil of a wattmeter or energy meter, or a voltage-operated relay, depending upon its particular use. The current taken will be quite small and the voltage is usually standardized at 110 V. The reading of the 110 V voltmeter must be multiplied by the transformer ratio to give the voltage of the main circuit, or the instrument may be calibrated to give a direct reading. Figure 6.22 shows the circuit for a potential transformer.

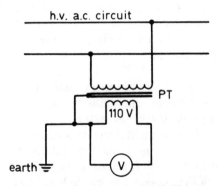

Fig. 6.22   Use of a potential transformer

Current Transformer (CT). The operation of this transformer is different from that of the power transformer. It will be seen from Fig. 6.23(a) that the CT primary must consist of a small number of turns (N_1) in series with the main circuit load and therefore will have only a small voltage drop across it. The secondary consists of a larger number of turns (N_2) and it is connected to an ammeter, the current coil of a wattmeter or energy meter, or relay, etc. The ammeter is of low impedance and so constitutes almost a short circuit across the secondary, keeping the secondary voltage small. The current is usually standardized at 1 A or 5 A and the transformer ratio

115

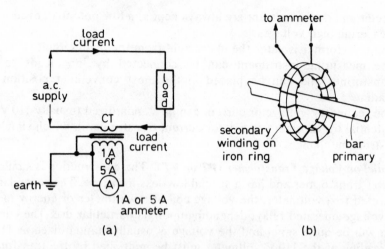

Fig. 6.23　The current transformer: (a) CT circuit, (b) bar-primary CT

chosen so that the 1 A or 5 A flows when the main circuit carries full-load current. The ammeter reading can be multiplied by the transformer ratio or it can be calibrated to give a direct reading. When heavy currents are being measured, one turn on the primary may be sufficient. In this case, the conductor carrying the main current or the busbar may be used as a single turn and the CT may consist of a secondary winding on a ring core which is threaded onto the conductor or busbar. This is called a bar-primary (Fig. 6.23b).

With a power transformer, a secondary load is necessary to cause a primary current to flow, and this maintains the magnetic flux at a constant value. With a CT the primary current is the main circuit current and will flow whether the secondary is connected or not. However, the secondary current through the ammeter is necessary to stabilize the magnetic flux. If the ammeter is removed, the voltage across the secondary terminals could reach a dangerously high value and may cause breakdown of the insulation. Also, with no secondary current there is no means of stabilizing the magnetic flux, the iron core will become saturated, and the accuracy of the CT destroyed. Thus, a CT must *never* be operated with its secondary terminals open-circuited. If the ammeter has to be removed then the terminals must first be short-circuited. This will preserve the CT, will in no way harm it, and will prevent a dangerous situation arising.

Burden. This is the name given to the rating of an instrument transformer and is in volt amperes (V A). The use of an instrument transformer can introduce some errors (ratio error and phase-angle error). With a correctly designed and calibrated transformer, these errors can be minimized and are usually negligible when operated at its designed burden. It is important that

116

an instrument connected to an instrument transformer should create the correct burden, otherwise errors will be introduced. Care must be taken to see that the burden is correct if an instrument transformer is used to supply more than one instrument, and also when long leads are used, as this can alter the V A loading.

For example, a CT with a rated burden of 15 V A and a rated secondary current of 5 A will have a secondary voltage of 3 V. The impedance of the load circuit, therefore, should be

$$\frac{V}{I} = \frac{3}{5} = 0.6 \ \Omega$$

This must include the leads between the CT and its instrument. Thus if

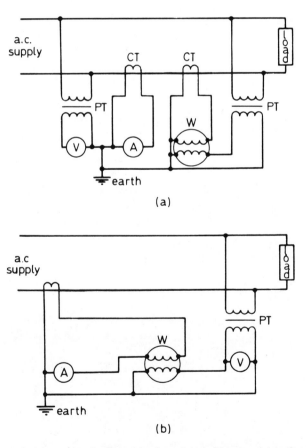

(a)

(b)

Fig. 6.24 Use of instrument transformers: (a) using separate instrument transformers, (b) using one current transformer and one potential transformer

long leads are required they will increase the impedance of the circuit and it may be necessary to use a CT having a higher burden.

For PTs the standard rated burdens are:

$$10, 15, 50, 100, \text{ and } 500 \text{ V A per phase}$$

For CTs the standard rated burdens are:

$$2\tfrac{1}{2}, 5, 7\tfrac{1}{2}, 15, 30, \text{ and } 50 \text{ V A per phase}$$

Figure 6.24 shows alternative methods of using instrument transformers for measuring voltage, current, and power.

7. The three-phase a.c. generator

7.1 Construction

Nowadays, almost all large generating plant is a.c., employing the a.c. *synchronous generator* or, as it is still often known, the alternator. Generating voltages of 11 kV and 33 kV are now quite common, supplying currents of over 1000 A.

A loop rotating in a magnetic field produces an alternating e.m.f. which can feed current to an external circuit by means of slip-rings. To produce very high voltages in this way would require a large number of turns and it would also be necessary to have considerable insulation for this voltage. If heavy currents were to be fed from the machine also, then conductors of a large cross-section would be required. These large coils and the iron core on which they would be mounted would become unwieldly, creating serious problems when run at high speeds. Collecting such currents at these high voltages would also create difficulties. Thus, for an a.c. generator it is essential, in order to overcome these difficulties, to have the armature coils stationary where weight and size are of no great consequence, and have the magnetic field rotating. By using this method of construction, it is possible to have conductors of large cross-section with adequate insultation for the large currents and high voltages demanded by the modern supply system. The slip-rings are also eliminated in the armature circuit and heavy bolted connections can be made.

Thus, the armature of almost all a.c. synchronous generators, except the very smallest, is the outer fixed winding and is called the *stator*. The field, which requires only a small amount of power supplied by d.c. through slip-rings, is the rotating part and is called the *rotor*.

7.2 The stator

Figure 7.1 shows a single stator coil $A-A_1$ and the field as a rotating bar magnet. The e.m.f. induced in coil $A-A_1$ will be the same as that produced in a coil rotating in a magnetic field, that is, it will produce an alternating voltage with a sine wave.

If two more coils, $B-B_1$ and $C-C_1$, are added so that their start points A, B, and C are spaced 120° apart, the arrangement shown in Fig. 7.2 will be

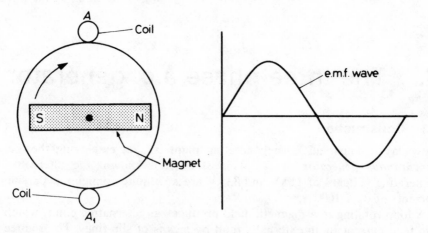

Fig. 7.1   E.M.F. induced in a single turn

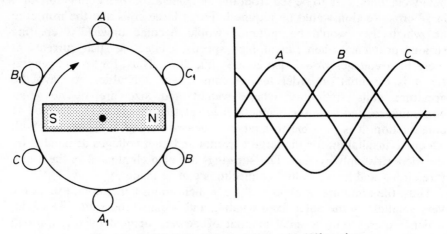

Fig. 7.2   E.M.F.s induced in three turns with 120° spacing

formed. Since the coils are 120° apart the positive maximum or peak value of the induced e.m.f.s will occur at 120° intervals. This gives a simple three-phase arrangement of the coils. The sine wave e.m.f. produced in each coil is shown in the diagram.

In practice, multiturn coils are used, and instead of being placed at one point on the stator, they are spread over several slots of a laminated steel stator core. The slots are evenly spaced round the stator, as shown in Fig. 7.3, and each of the three phases makes use of a third of the slots (Fig. 7.4). Each phase winding is separate, and the coils extend over a pole span, or,

120

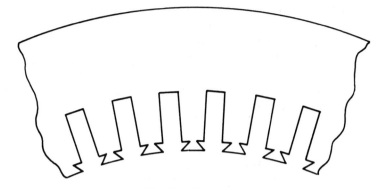

Fig. 7.3   Stator slots

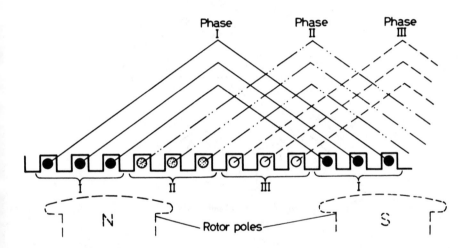

Fig. 7.4   Arrangement of three-phase distributed windings in stator slots

in order to improve the e.m.f. wave, just short of a pole span. This is a distributed winding.

7.3   The rotor

The rotor provides the field and its coils are supplied by d.c. through slip-rings. A small d.c. generator is usually coupled to the rotor shaft to provide this supply, and is known as an *exciter*.

There are two types of rotor construction. Low-speed machines generally employ the *salient-pole* type, and high-speed rotors are of the *cylindrical-* or *round-rotor* type.

121

The salient-pole rotor consists of outward projecting poles, each pole wound with a concentrated field winding. For low-speed machines of up to about 125 rev/min, the rotor is of large diameter with the poles attached to the rim of a spider wheel, as shown in Fig. 7.5. For speeds up to 500 rev/min, the poles may be fixed by studs to a magnet wheel as shown in Fig. 7.6. When the generator is engine-driven, this magnet wheel acts like a flywheel to give smooth running.

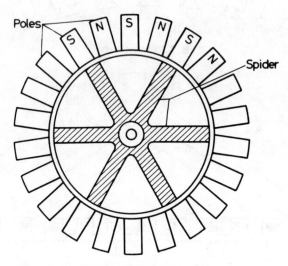

Fig. 7.5   Salient pole rotor

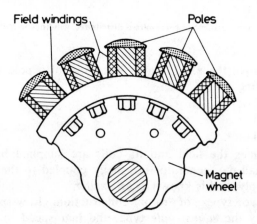

Fig. 7.6   Poles with stud fixing to magnet wheel

122

At higher speeds, the tendency is for the rotor diameter to become less and the axial length to increase to minimize the effect of centrifugal force. The rotor body may be of cast steel, with cast steel or laminated poles fixed to the body by studs or keyed to the rotor, as in Fig. 7.7. Hydro-electric generators with a waterwheel drive are of this construction, but their rotor diameters are less and their axial lengths greater than a steam-driven generator of similar output. Such a generator may run at

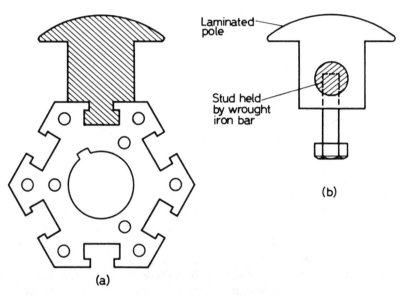

Fig. 7.7 Methods of fixing poles to rotor: (a) pole keyed to rotor, (b) stud fixing

500 rev/min, but if the load is suddenly removed when it is working with a large head of water there may be an overspeed of as much as 80% before the governor can act. This type of machine must have a rotor constructed to withstand these overspeeds. In addition, the rotor is often constructed to incorporate a flywheel to absorb energy in the event of overspeed.

Salient-pole rotors are rarely used for speeds over 1000 rev/min. The modern synchronous generator is generally a two-pole machine driven by a steam turbine at a speed of 3000 rev/min. At this speed, the centrifugal force is high, and to minimize its effect the rotor must be kept as small as possible in diameter with an increase in axial length. To give an idea of the forces involved, a mass of $\frac{1}{2}$ kg at the circumference of a rotor of 1 m diameter rotating at 3000 rev/min has a force acting on it of almost 20 kN. Thus, at these speeds the salient-pole construction is a disadvantage and

123

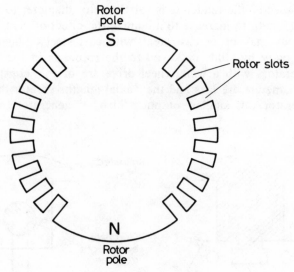

Fig. 7.8   Cylindrical rotor

the cylindrical or round rotor is used. Figure 7.8 shows the two-pole construction of this rotor. Slots are evenly spaced round the rotor, except for two blank areas opposite each other. These form the rotor poles. The windings in the slots are wound like a solenoid, having semicircular sides instead of the usual parallel sides. Although not very common, a four-pole version of the cylindrical rotor may also be found. This would operate at 1500 rev/min, but the higher speed of 3000 rev/min is preferred for the modern steam turbine-driven plant, giving a supply frequency of 50 Hz.

7.4   Excitation supply

A d.c. supply is required to energize the rotor field coils. Usually, for the lower-speed machines and generators of medium size, the supply is obtained from a directly coupled d.c. generator known as an *exciter*. For machines of higher speeds, the exciter may be driven through a reduction gear so that its speed is kept at 1000 rev/min or less. The exciter voltage may be in the range of 100–400 V and its output up to 2% of the main stator output. The supply is fed to the rotor through slip-rings. The exciter output can be controlled by a field regulator, and this controls the generated voltage of the synchronous machine. The basic circuit arrangement is shown in Fig. 7.9.

An a.c. exciter can also be used to feed d.c. to the slip-rings through a silicon controlled rectifier.

124

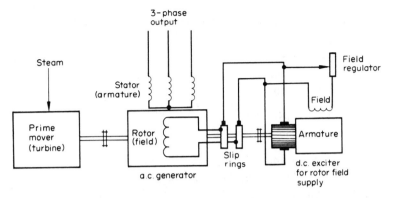

Fig. 7.9 A.C. generator—basic circuit arrangement

Another type of synchronous generator is the *brushless alternator*. In this the exciter consists of a rotating-armature synchronous generator on the main generator shaft. This supplies the main rotor winding through rectifiers which are mounted on and rotate with the rotor shaft. The general circuit arrangement is shown in Fig. 7.10.

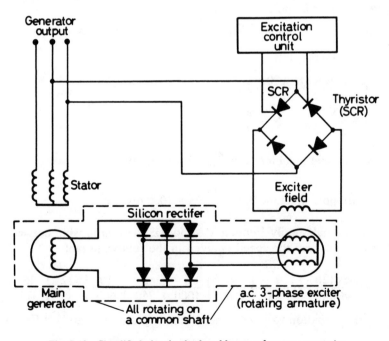

Fig. 7.10 Simplified circuit of a brushless synchronous generator

125

7.5 Relationship between number of poles, speed, and frequency

When a two-pole rotating magnet has completed one revolution, then a stator conductor has had one cycle of alternating e.m.f. induced in it. A four-pole field will produce two cycles, and so on.

Thus: ONE cycle is produced by ONE PAIR of poles.
    If there are p pairs of poles
        then in one revolution there will be p cycles
        and in N revolutions there will be pN cycles
        if N is rev/min then there will be pN cycles/min
    But frequency f is in cycles per second (hertz)

$$\therefore f = \frac{pN}{60} \text{ hertz} \tag{7.1}$$

EXAMPLE

A two-pole synchronous generator is driven at a speed of 3000 rev/min. What will be its output frequency? At what speeds must a four-pole and a six-pole machine be run in order to provide the same output frequency?

2 poles = 1 pair of poles $\therefore p = 1$

(Note: Be careful to understand that p is pairs, *not* number of poles.)

$N = 3000$ rev/min

$$\therefore f = \frac{pN}{60} = \frac{1 \times 3000}{60} = 50 \text{ Hz}$$
$$f = \frac{pN}{60} \qquad \therefore N = \frac{60f}{p}$$

$\therefore$ for a four-pole machine $N = \dfrac{60 \times 50}{2} = 1500$ rev/min

for a six-pole machine $N = \dfrac{60 \times 50}{3} = 1000$ rev/min

For our normal supply frequency of 50 Hz, the relationship between the number of poles and the speed is given in the following table:

No. of poles ($2p$)	2	4	6	8	10	12	16	20
Speed rev/min	3000	1500	1000	750	600	500	375	300

The e.m.f. equation for an a.c. generator is given in Chapter 4 Eq. (4.10):

$$E_{rms} = 2.22 \, k_d k_p Zf\Phi \text{ volts/phase}$$

7.6 Synchronous generator characteristics

From the operating engineer's point of view, the most important factor about a generator is the way the terminal voltage varies with changes of load, and, with an a.c. machine, with changes of power factor. When current is being supplied by a synchronous generator, there will be a voltage 'drop' in the machine due to its impedance. This *impedance* is made up of three items:

1. The *resistance* of the machine windings, R (ohms).
2. The *leakage reactance* of the windings, X_L (ohms).
3. The effect of armature reaction which causes a change in the magnetic field with changes of load and power factor. This causes the e.m.f. generated for a given excitation to be different on load than at no-load. The effect, however, is similar to that caused by the reactance and so it is often called the '*fictitious reactance*' or the *armature reaction reactance*, X_A.

The effects of items (2) and (3) are similar so they are usually added together and called the *synchronous reactance, X_s*:

$$\text{Synchronous reactance } X_s = X_L + X_A \qquad (7.2)$$

The resistance R and synchronous reactance X_s together form the *synchronous impedance* of the machine.

$$\text{Synchronous impedance } Z_s = (R^2 + X_s^2)^{1/2} \qquad (7.3)$$

The synchronous generator can be represented by the circuit given by Fig. 7.11.

When supplying a load, the load current I causes a volt-drop within the

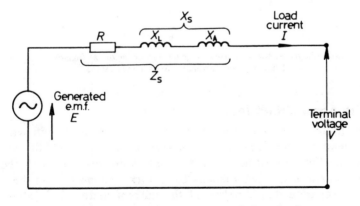

Fig. 7.11 Synchronous generator equivalent circuit

machine IR in phase with the current due to the resistance, and a drop IX_s leading the current by 90° due to the synchronous reactance.

This can be represented by the phasor diagrams of Fig. 7.12. Diagram (a) is for a lagging power factor load (I lags ϕ behind V), and diagram (b) is for a leading power factor load (I leads V by ϕ). It will be seen that, for a leading power factor, it is possible for the voltage drop in the machine IZ_s to become, in effect, a voltage rise, making the terminal voltage V greater in magnitude than the generated e.m.f. E.

There are two tests which can be carried out on a synchronous generator to enable information to be obtained from which the machine performance can be ascertained. These are the *open-circuit test* and the *short-circuit test*.

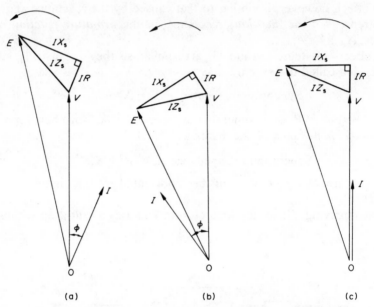

Fig. 7.12 **Phasor diagrams for synchronous generator on load: (a) lagging power factor, (b) leading power factor, (c) unity power factor**

7.7 The open-circuit test

An open-circuit test for any generator is a test carried out in which the actual generated e.m.f. is measured for various values of field or excitation with the machine operating at normal speed on no-load. With the synchronous generator the field (usually the rotor) is supplied from the exciter or from a separate d.c. supply and the current increased in steps from zero. At each step the *phase* voltage (i.e., the generated e.m.f.) in the stator winding is measured. The circuit for the test is shown in Fig. 7.13(a). If the star point is not available then the voltmeter must be connected across the terminals of two of the phases (i.e., line voltage) and the reading divided by 1.73.

The *open-circuit characteristic* is a graph of *phase* e.m.f. against excitation current (Fig. 7.13(b)). As can be seen this is a typical B–H type curve and it is sometimes called a *magnetization characteristic*.

The open-circuit characteristics of d.c. generators are similar and they

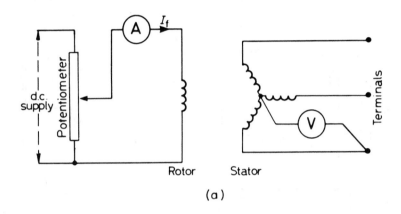

(a)

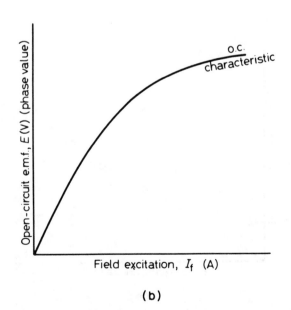

(b)

Fig. 7.13   Open-circuit test: (a) circuit, (b) open-circuit characteristic

are obtained in the same way by isolating the field from the armature circuit and supplying the field from a separate d.c. supply. Most d.c. generators have their fields supplied from their own armatures so it is important not to confuse the open-circuit characteristic with the no-load condition when the machine is connected for normal use.

7.8 The short-circuit test

With the terminals of the synchronous generator short-circuited, the e.m.f. produced will circulate a short-circuit current I_{sc} throught the impedance Z_s

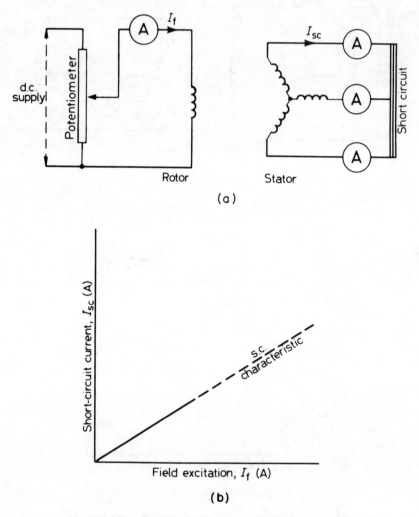

Fig. 7.14 The short-circuit test: (a) circuit, (b) characteristic

of the machine. Only a small excitation current is required to produce a large short-circuit current. The circuit for this test is given in Fig. 7.14(a).

The short-circuit current I_{sc} is read on one of the ammeters (three ammeters are used only to balance the circuit) for varying values of excitation current until the short-circuit current reaches about twice normal full-load value. This excitation will be quite small, nowhere near its normal working value, but since the magnetic circuit will be far below saturation, the graph can be extended as a straight line to cover the normal excitation range. Figure 7.14(b) shows the short-circuit characteristic.

7.9 Regulation

Regulation is the term given for the change in terminal voltage between no-load and load conditions (usually full-load).

In practice, the terminal voltage of a synchronous generator is usually kept constant by means of an automatic voltage regulator. Therefore, regulation for this type of machine is generally defined in terms of the full-load terminal voltage rather than the no-load voltage.

Thus, regulation of a synchronous generator is the *rise* in terminal voltage when full load is thrown off, the speed and excitation current remaining constant. This is usually expressed as a percentage.

If V = terminal p.d. on full load, and E = terminal p.d. on no-load for the same speed and excitation, then

$$\text{Regulation } \% = \frac{E - V}{V} \times 100 \qquad (7.4)$$

There are several methods used to determine the regulation of the synchronous generator, but one of the simplest is the *synchronous impedance method*. For this, the synchronous impedance must be found from the open-circuit and short-circuit characteristics. This assumes that the synchronous reactance is entirely true reactance, which strictly is incorrect, and this leads to values of impedance which are not quite accurate. The errors, however, generally give calculated values of regulation somewhat higher than those found from an actual load test. Thus, if this method is used it can be assumed that the machine will actually be better than the calculation indicates.

If the open-circuit and short-circuit characteristics are drawn on the same graph, then the synchronous impedance can be calculated for each value of excitation and its graph drawn. Assuming the e.m.f. causing the current I_{sc} to flow through the impedance Z_s is that produced by the same excitation on open circuit, then

$$Z_s = \frac{E}{I_{sc}} \qquad (7.5)$$

131

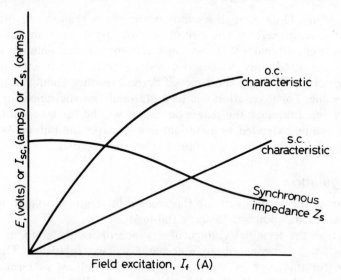

Fig. 7.15 **Method of finding synchronous impedance Z_s from the o.c. and s.c. characteristics**

It will be seen from the graph (Fig. 7.15) that Z_s is not a constant and the value used will depend upon the excitation.

The resistance per phase (R) of the machine can be found using the ammeter–voltmeter method and the synchronous reactance X_s can be calculated:

$$X_s = (Z_s^2 - R^2)^{1/2} \qquad (7.6)$$

The resistance of most synchronous generators is small compared with the reactance so that in practice $X_s \simeq Z_s$.

Consider the generator phasor diagram for a lagging power factor load, with V drawn horizontal (Fig. 7.16).

I = load current lagging ϕ behind terminal p.d. V
E = no-load e.m.f. for the same excitation

From triangle OAB $\qquad AB = V \sin \phi = CD$

and $\qquad\qquad\qquad OB = V \cos \phi$

From triangle ODF $\qquad (OF)^2 = (OD)^2 + (DF)^2$

i.e. $\qquad\qquad\qquad E^2 = (OB + BD)^2 + (CD + CF)^2$

$$= (V \cos \phi + IR)^2 + (V \sin \phi + IX_s)^2$$

$$\therefore E = [(V \cos \phi + IR)^2 + (V \sin \phi + IX_s)^2]^{1/2} \quad (7.7)$$

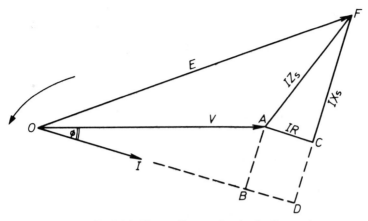

Fig. 7.16   Phasor diagram (lagging load)

If the power factor is leading then $DF = CF - CD$, that is, the term $V \sin \phi$ becomes negative. Since the negative sign is eliminated when $(CF - CD)$ is squared, it is usual to make the term IX_s negative for leading power factors, giving the equation for the open-circuit e.m.f. as:

$$E = [(V \cos \phi + IR)^2 + (V \sin \phi \pm IX_s)^2]^{1/2} \qquad (7.8)$$

This value of E can then be used in the Eq. (7.4), i.e.,

$$\text{Regulation } \% = \frac{E - V}{V} \times 100$$

With a leading power factor it is possible for V to be greater than E, giving negative regulation. This means that there is a drop in volts when the load is thrown off, instead of a rise.

EXAMPLE

A 50 kV A, 440 V, three-phase, star-connected synchronous generator gave a terminal p.d. of 440 V for a given excitation current on open-circuit test. From a short-circuit test, the estimated current for the same excitation was 282 A. The resistance between terminals was found to be 0.4 Ω. Using the synchronous impedance method, find the regulation at full load when the power factor is (1) 0.8 lagging, and (2) 0.8 leading.

$$\text{Full-load current } I = \frac{\text{kV A} \times 1000}{1.73\, V_L} = \frac{50 \times 1000}{1.73 \times 440} = 65.6 \text{ A}$$

Use phase values:

$$\text{Phase voltage } V = \frac{440}{1.73} = 254 \text{ V}$$

Resistance between terminals is the resistance of two phase windings in series.

$$\therefore \text{ Resistance per phase } R = \frac{0.4}{2} = 0.2 \ \Omega$$

$$\text{Impedance per phase } Z_s = \frac{V}{I_{sc}} = \frac{254}{282} = 0.9 \ \Omega$$

$$\text{Reactance per phase } X_s = (Z_s^2 - R^2)^{1/2} = (0.9^2 - 0.2^2)^{1/2} = 0.878 \ \Omega$$

$$\text{Resistance drop} = IR = 65.6 \times 0.2 = 13.12 \text{ V}$$

$$\text{Reactance drop} = IX_s = 65.6 \times 0.878 = 57.6 \text{ V}$$

In both cases, the power factor is 0.8

$$\therefore \cos \phi = 0.8 \quad \text{and} \quad \sin \phi = 0.6 \ (\phi = 36°52')$$

$$V \cos \phi = 254 \times 0.8 = 203.2 \ V$$

$$V \sin \phi = 254 \times 0.6 = 152.4 \ V$$

1. *p.f. 0.8 lagging*

$$E = [(V \cos \phi + IR)^2 + (V \sin \phi + IX_s)^2]^{1/2}$$
$$= [(203.2 + 13.12)^2 + (152.4 + 57.6)^2]^{1/2}$$
$$= (216.32^2 + 210^2)^{1/2} = (90\ 890)^{1/2} = 301.5 \text{ V}$$

$$\text{Regulation } \% = \frac{E - V}{V} \times 100 = \frac{301.5 - 254}{254} \times 100$$

$$= \frac{47.5}{254} \times 100 = 18.7\%$$

2. *p.f. 0.8 leading*

$$E = [(V \cos \phi + IR)^2 + (V \sin \phi - IX_s)^2]^{1/2}$$
$$= [(203.2 + 13.12)^2 + (152.4 - 57.6)^2]^{1/2}$$
$$= (216.32^2 + 94.8^2)^{1/2} = (55\ 781)^{1/2} = 236.2 \text{ V}$$

$$\text{Regulation } \% = \frac{E - V}{V} \times 100 = \frac{236.2 - 254}{254} \times 100$$

$$= \frac{-17.8}{254} \times 100 = -7\%$$

It will be seen that in the leading p.f. case the regulation is negative, that is, there will be a voltage drop as load is removed. The regulation may appear to be rather high, but with large modern machines it may be much higher. This is not as great a drawback as it would seem, since such machines have their terminal voltage kept constant by automatic regulators and the high value of reactance is a safeguard against short-circuit faults. Many modern synchronous generators are designed to have a high reactance, which enables them to withstand even a short circuit close to their terminals without damage.

7.10 Load characteristics

It has been seen that there will be a voltage drop as a lagging load is applied to a synchronous generator, and it is possible to have a voltage rise for some leading power factor loads.

If the resistance of the machine is neglected, which in most cases is justified since it is small compared with the reactance, the accompanying simplified phasor diagrams (Fig. 7.17) show the cases for unity power factor load and the extremes of zero power factor lagging and leading loads. In each case, the reactance volt drop IX_s will lead the load current by 90°, and will be proportional to the load current. If the excitation is kept constant, then the no-load e.m.f. E will be constant in each case.

If load increases, the value of IX_s will increase, and this will affect the value of the terminal p.d. V as follows:

Case (1): zero p.f. load lagging; V is considerably reduced.

Case (2): unity p.f. load; V is reduced as indicated by the broken line diagram.

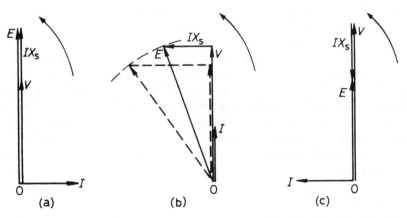

Fig. 7.17 Phasor diagrams—effect of power factor: (a) zero p.f. load lagging, (b) unity p.f. load, (c) zero p.f. load leading

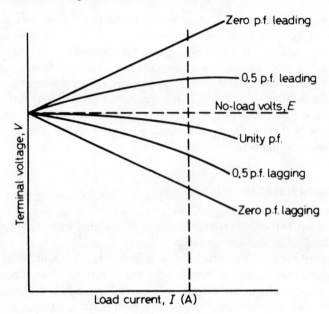

Fig. 7.18 Synchronous generator load characteristics

Case (3): zero p.f. load leading; V is considerably increased.

It will be seen from this that the load characteristic, that is, the graph showing the effect of load upon the terminal voltage, will depend upon the power factor as well as upon the load current. There will be, in fact, a series, or family, of load characteristics for different power factors. These are shown in Fig. 7.18.

Increasing the excitation will increase the no-load e.m.f. E. This will raise the level of the whole characteristic and increase the value of the terminal p.d. for each particular load.

The power input to a synchronous generator is applied by a prime mover, in most cases a steam turbine. This input is related to the output. If output is increased, more power must be applied by the prime mover, otherwise speed will drop, causing a drop of output voltage and frequency. Increasing the prime-mover power (e.g., increasing the steam supply to the driving turbine) without an increase of generator output will cause an increase of speed, resulting in an increase of both terminal voltage and frequency.

8. The three-phase synchronous motor

8.1 The synchronous motor—principle

The construction of the synchronous motor is the same as the synchronous generator, in fact the same machine may be used as either a generator or a motor. In both cases a d.c. supply is required for the rotor field, usually from a small d.c. exciter connected to the machine shaft. The rotor has concentrated windings which produce fixed rotor poles. These are shown as salient poles in Fig. 8.1.

The stator has a three-phase distributed winding (see Fig. 7.4) and, when the machine operates as a motor, this will be connected to a three-phase supply. As will be seen in Chapter 9, this will produce a rotating magnetic field in which there are no physical poles but the magnetic flux will rotate round the stator at synchronous speed. Consider this stator field rotating clockwise (Fig. 8.1) and its effect upon the salient poles of the rotor. The letters N and S on the stator indicate the position of the rotating stator poles at one particular instant.

Suppose the rotor is stationary. The stator field will be rotating at synchronous speed, therefore each rotor pole will be subject to both an attractive force and a repelling force every cycle of the supply frequency as it is passed by two stator poles of opposite polarities. The inertia of the rotor will not allow it to move in either direction; therefore when the rotor is stationary the resultant torque is zero. Thus, the synchronous motor is not self-starting.

If the rotor is made to rotate at or near the same speed as the stator field, that is, synchronous speed, then stator and rotor poles of opposite polarity will 'lock' together, producing a torque which will cause the rotor to continue rotating at synchronous speed. If the rotor slows down it will fall out of step, i.e., out of synchronism, with the stator, the torque will be reduced to zero, and the rotor will stop. The synchronous motor can run only at synchronous speed. The relationship between number of poles, speed, and frequency is the same as that for the generator given in Sec. 7.5 (Eq. 7.1).

$$f = pN/60 \quad \text{from which speed } N = 60f/p \text{ rev/min} \quad (8.1)$$

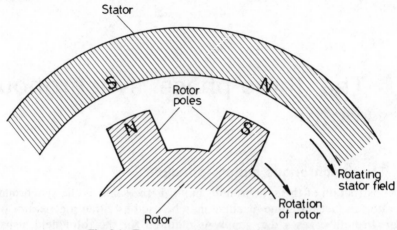

Fig. 8.1   Torque produced by synchronous motor

The synchronous speeds for motors of different numbers of poles operating at a supply frequency of 50 Hz are given in the table at the end of Sec. 7.5.

8.2   Starting a synchronous motor

A synchronous motor is not self-starting, therefore provision must be made to run the machine up to synchronous speed and then switch the supply by that part of the starting procedure known as *synchronizing*. Two methods of bringing the motor up to synchronous speed are as follows:

1. Pony Motor. This is a small motor, usually an induction motor which is self-starting, coupled to the synchronous motor shaft. This drives the main motor up to or near synchronous speed on no-load. The excitation is then switched on and the machine synchronized (see Sec. 8.3) with the three-phase supply. The induction motor can then be switched off and the load applied to the main machine. Owing to *slip* (see Chapter 9), the induction motor will drive the synchronous machine at a speed a little less than synchronous speed but, unless it is a large machine, the main motor will be pulled into synchronism when the supply is switched on. However, to enable synchronous speed to be reached, the induction motor may have two poles less than the synchronous motor so that its synchronous speed will be higher than that of the main machine. This will take the main motor right through its own synchronous speed and allows it to be synchronized at its correct speed.

A development of this method is to connect the stator windings of the induction motor and the synchronous motor in series as shown in Fig. 8.2. The machine then becomes self-synchronizing.

138

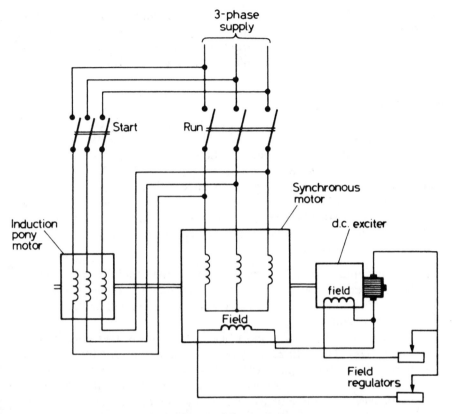

Fig. 8.2 Self synchronizing synchronous motor

When the 'start' switch is closed, the induction motor drives the main machine and passes its starting current through the stator windings of the synchronous motor, producing a weak rotating field. As synchronous speed is reached, this rotating field will be strong enough to lock the rotor, whose excitation will also have become stronger with increase of speed. Thus the motor synchronizes itself and the rotor continues to rotate at synchronous speed. The 'run' switch can now be closed, the 'start' switch opened, and load applied to the motor. This method will allow light-load starting.

2. *Induction Starting.* In this case, the motor is designed so that it starts as an induction motor, which allows starting on light loads. The rotor poles carry a cage-type winding called a 'damper winding'. With the excitation off and the rotor windings short-circuited, the motor is started like an induction motor with direct-on-line starting for small machines, and auto-transformer or star–delta starting for larger machines. When maximum speed has been attained, which will be at a little under synchronous speed,

139

the normal d.c. excitation is switched on and the motor will be pulled into synchronism. This means a sudden increase in speed to synchronous speed, which causes a heavy current to be drawn from the supply for a short time. Starters must be capable of withstanding this current surge.

8.3 Synchronizing

When a synchronous motor is being run up to speed it will be operating like a generator and a three-phase e.m.f. will develop at the terminals. Thus short-circuit conditions could occur if the incoming supply is fed into these terminals at this stage without checks being made. The operation of connecting a synchronous machine to an existing supply is called *synchronizing*. This applies not only to a synchronous motor but also to a synchronous generator being connected in parallel with an existing supply.

There are three conditions to be met before a machine can be synchronized with the supply:

1. The machine voltage must be the same as the supply voltage. This can be checked by voltmeter. A small difference in voltage will produce circulating currents and a large voltage variation will be equivalent to a fault or short circuit.
2. The voltages of the two lines to be connected together must be in the same phase. The voltages may be equal, satisfying condition (1), but if they are in different phases there will still be a voltage between them. This, too, would give a condition equivalent to a fault. This applies particularly to a three-phase circuit in which the phase sequence must be correct, otherwise there will be a 120° displacement between two of the phases.
3. The frequency of the machine must be the same as the supply frequency, in order to maintain the correct phase-to-phase conditions. This means that the machine speed must be correct.

8.4 Methods of synchronizing

1. Lamps Dark Method. The machine is run up to speed by its driving machine or pony motor but with the supply switch S open. In each phase there are two lamps in series connected across the open switch. (Using two lamps is a safeguard against over-voltage.) The circuit is shown in Fig. 8.3.

As the machine builds up speed and starts to generate, the lamps will flicker, the flickering becoming slower as the speed increases until the lamps brighten and dim very slowly when synchronous speed is almost reached. This indicates that the speed and the frequency are almost correct. The fact that all the lamps are either bright or dim at the same time indicates a correct phase rotation. By adjusting the excitation the voltages

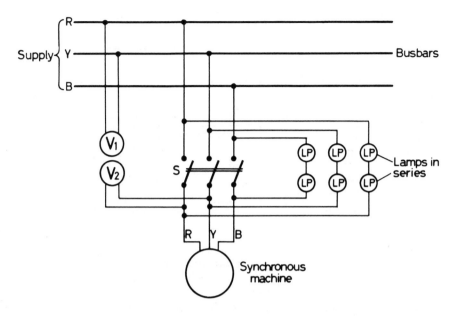

Fig. 8.3 Synchronizing—lamps dark method

as indicated on V_1 and V_2 are made equal. The lamps will dim very slowly, become dark, and then brighten again. When they are dark this is an indication that the voltage between both sides of each pole of the switch is zero and the switch can be closed. The machine is now synchronized and connected to the supply; the pony motor can be shut down, and load applied to the synchronous motor.

2. Lamps in Sequence Method. The circuit is shown in Fig. 8.4. It will be seen that two sets of lamps are cross-connected between phases. By this method the lamps vary in brightness in sequence and the particular sequence will indicate if the machine is running too fast or too slow. When speed and voltage have been adjusted, the switch S can be closed when one set of lamps (A in the diagram) is dark and the other two sets are of equal brightness.

3. Synchroscope. This instrument is designed for synchronizing and is usually preferred instead of lamps—especially for h.v. machines, when its operation is through instrument transformers. The instrument consists of a rotor and a stator, one connected to the machine to be synchronized, the other to the supply. The pointer connected to the rotor will rotate if the frequencies are different; anticlockwise rotation indicates that the frequency and therefore the speed of the incoming machine is too slow,

141

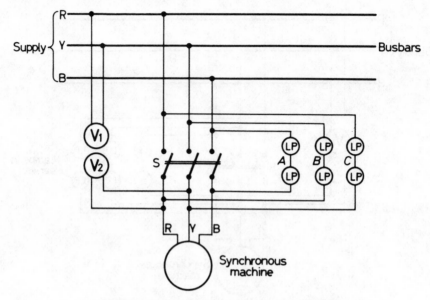

Fig. 8.4   Synchronizing—lamps in sequence method

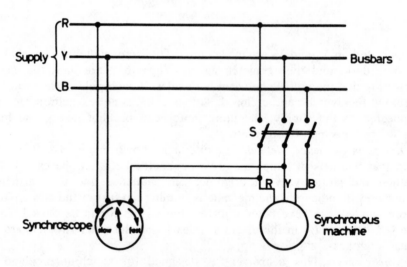

Fig. 8.5   Use of the synchroscope

and clockwise rotation indicates too fast a speed. When the frequency is correct the pointer is stationary, and when the voltages and phases are correct the pointer remains in the vertical position and the supply can be switched on to the machine. Figure 8.5 shows the circuit.

142

8.5 Synchronous motor phasor diagram

When a synchronous machine is running, it generates an e.m.f. E proportional to the excitation flux Φ and therefore almost proportional to the excitation current I_f. If the machine operates as a generator then the terminal voltage will be V and the outgoing load current will be I (see Fig. 7.11). If the machine operates as a motor then the load current will be incoming from the supply and the terminal voltage will be the supply voltage V. The generated e.m.f. E will become a back e.m.f. opposing the supply voltage V. The voltage diagram will be as Fig. 8.6(a). There will also

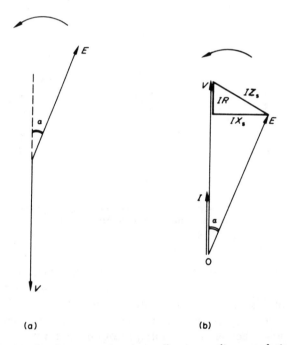

(a)   (b)

Fig. 8.6 Synchronous motor phasor diagram—unity power factor

be voltage drops owing to the resistance and synchronous reactance of the machine itself. To show this, it is more convenient to draw the phasors E and V as shown in Fig. 8.6(b) where IZ_s is shown as the difference of V and E. In this case, the volt-drop triangle has been shown with the resistance drop IR in phase with V. Thus, I will also be in phase with V, that is, this is the unity power factor case (compare with Fig. 7.12).

As in the case of the generator, the resistance of a synchronous motor is

143

usually small enough to be neglected for practical purposes compared with its synchronous reactance, so that $IX_s \simeq IZ_s$ and the current I will lag IX_s by 90°. The simplified phasor diagrams for unity, lagging, and leading power factor cases will be as shown in Fig. 8.7.

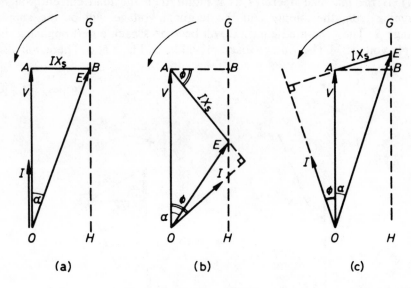

Fig. 8.7 Synchronous motor simplified phasor diagrams: (a) unity power factor, (b) lagging power factor, (c) leading power factor

Now, the supply voltage V produces the rotating field in the stator. The generated or back e.m.f. E is produced in the stator windings by the rotor field. When load is applied to the motor the rotor poles tends to drop back slightly from their associated stator poles. The larger the load, the greater becomes the angle between associated rotor and stator poles. This angle, in electrical degrees, is called the *load angle* α. (180° electrical is the angle between two adjacent poles, i.e., half a cycle of an a.c. wave.) This will also be the phase angle between V and E, as shown in the diagram. If the load becomes excessive, the angle becomes so large that torque cannot be maintained; the machine will fall out of synchronism and come to a standstill. The torque at which this occurs is called the *pull-out torque*.

It will be seen in Fig. 8.7 that the volt drop IX_s leads the current I by 90° and is also proportional to I. Therefore IX_s can be used as a measure of the current I and the angle it makes with the horizontal AB through V will be the phase angle ϕ. ϕ will be lagging when it is below the horizontal and leading when above.

144

Horizontal $AB = IX_s \cos\phi \propto I\cos\phi$

but the supply voltage V is normally constant.

$$\therefore \ AB \propto VI\cos\phi \propto \text{power input to the motor}$$

Thus AB to scale becomes a measure of power input, and if a vertical line GH is drawn through B then GH will represent a line of constant power.

The phasor diagram can be used to form the load diagram of Fig. 8.8.

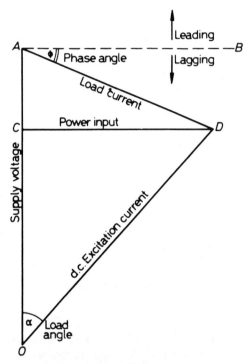

Fig. 8.8 Synchronous motor diagram

OA is drawn vertical to represent the supply voltage V. AB is drawn horizontal as a unity power factor line. OD is the back e.m.f. E, and therefore represents the excitation current to a suitable scale. AD is the reactance drop IX_s and can represent the current I to scale, the angle between AB and AD being the phase angle. CD is $IX_s\cos\phi$ and therefore represents the power input to scale. Load angle α is the angle at O.

8.6 Operating a synchronous motor with fixed excitation

Figure 8.9 is a diagram for a motor with supply voltage OA and the excitation fixed at OD. Lines of constant power are shown. Whatever the

145

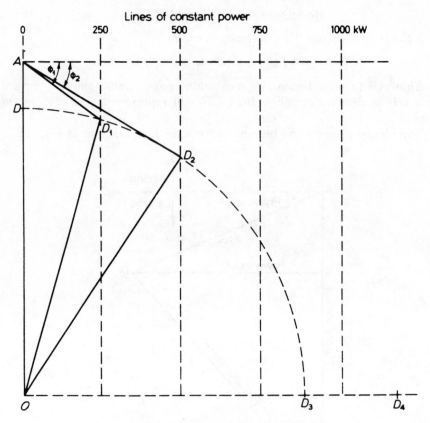

Fig. 8.9   Operation with fixed excitation

load, the operating point will be on an arc of radius *OD*. Take an example where the power input is 250 kW. The current will be AD_1 (to scale) and the power factor cos ϕ_1 lagging. If the input increases to, say, 500 kW, the current increases to AD_2 with a slightly better power factor cos ϕ_2. The best power factor will occur when *AD* is a tangent to the excitation arc. The machine will become unstable at about 900 kW at D_3 for this excitation, after which the motor will fall out of synchronism. If the load on the motor is to be increased beyond this point, the excitation must be increased to, say, OD_4. A limit will be reached when either the stator or the exciter circuit becomes overloaded.

8.7   Operating a synchronous motor at constant power

Suppose the load on the motor is constant, giving a constant input power of 500 kW as indicated in Fig. 8.10. With excitation OD_1 the current will be

146

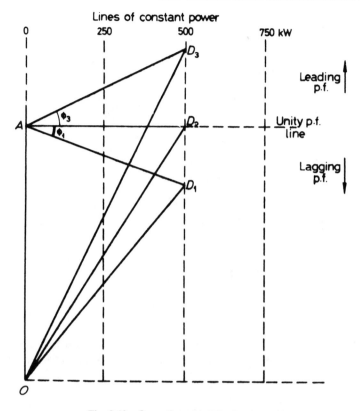

Fig. 8.10 Operation at constant power

AD_1 and the power factor cos ϕ_1 lagging. If the excitation is increased to OD_2 so that AD_2 is horizontal, the power factor will now be unity and the current AD_2 will have been reduced to its minimum value for this power. Increasing the excitation further to OD_3 increases the current again to AD_3, but now at a leading power factor cos ϕ_3. Thus, by varying the excitation a synchronous motor can be operated at any desired power factor, either lagging or leading, subject to either the stator or excitation windings not becoming overloaded. This property of the synchronous motor is very useful for purposes of power factor improvement.

8.8 Synchronous motor V-characteristics

It is seen above that for constant power the current at a lagging power factor at first decreases as excitation increases, becomes a minimum at unity power factor, and increases again as the power factor becomes leading. Thus, if the current is plotted against excitation the graph is in the

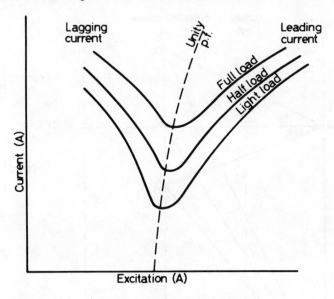

Fig. 8.11 The V-characteristic

form of a V. This is known as the *V-characteristic* and a family of such characteristics could be drawn for different loadings, as in the graph of Fig. 8.11.

8.9 Use of synchronous motors

The use of the synchronous motor is severely limited by the fact that it is not self-starting. It is generally used where starting is infrequent and where the load is removed or is very much reduced at start. Such a motor is usually operated over a considerable period of time without being stopped. By varying the excitation current the synchronous motor can be operated at different power factors and its main advantages are that it runs at constant speed and also has the ability to operate at a leading power factor, thereby giving power factor improvement to the system it is connected to. Its main uses are for driving ventilation and pumping machinery where continuous running is required.

8.10 Synchronous motor examples

1. A 100 hp (74.6 kW), 415 V, three-phase, star-connected synchronous motor has a synchronous reactance per phase of 0.5 Ω. Its resistance can be neglected. With its excitation adjusted to 4 A it operates on full load at 0.85 p.f. lagging. Assuming linear magnetization, find the

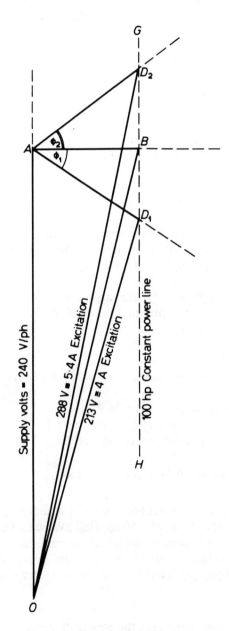

Fig. 8.12 Motor excitation—graphical solution

excitation current required to run the motor (a) at unity power factor and (b) at 0.8 p.f. leading. The motor runs at an efficiency of 92%. The example can be solved graphically (Fig. 8.12).
Use phase values.

$$\therefore\ V = \frac{415}{1.73} = 240\ \text{V}$$

Draw OA vertical $= 240$ V to scale.
Current at unity p.f.

$$I = \frac{\text{hp} \times 746}{1.73 \times E \times \eta} = \frac{100 \times 746}{1.73 \times 415 \times 0.92} = 113\ \text{A}$$

$\therefore$ At unity p.f.

$$IX_s = 113 \times 0.5 = 56.5\ \text{V}$$

Draw $AB = IX_s = 56.5$ V to scale horizontal from A.
Through B draw GH vertical to represent the constant-power line of 100 hp output [or $(100 \times 746)/(0.92 \times 1000) = 81.1$ kW input].
For p.f. $\cos \phi_1 = 0.85$ $\phi_1 = 31.8°$
Draw AD_1 at angle $31.8°$ below AB for lagging p.f.
OD_1 is the generated or back e.m.f. and is found, by measurement, to be 213 V, which represents 4 A excitation.
(a) OB (measured) $= 247$ V to give unity p.f.

$$\therefore\ \text{Excitation for unity p.f.} = 4 \times \frac{247}{213} = 4.64\ \text{A}$$

(b) For p.f. $\cos \phi_2 = 0.8$ leading $\phi_2 = 36.9°$.
Draw AD_2 at angle $36.9°$ above AB for leading p.f.
OD_2 (measured) gives a generated voltage of 288 V.

$$\therefore\ \text{Excitation for 0.8 p.f. leading} = 4 \times \frac{288}{213} = 5.4\ \text{A}$$

2. A factory has a three-phase load of 600 kV A at a power factor of 0.7 lagging. An additional load of 250 hp (187 kW) can be met by the installation of a synchronous motor which operates at an efficiency of 90%. This motor is also used to improve the power factor of the factory to 0.95 lagging. At what leading power factor must the motor be operated?

Figure 8.13 (not to scale) represents the power diagram.

Initial p.f. $\cos \phi_1 = 0.7$ $\therefore\ \sin \phi_1 = 0.714$

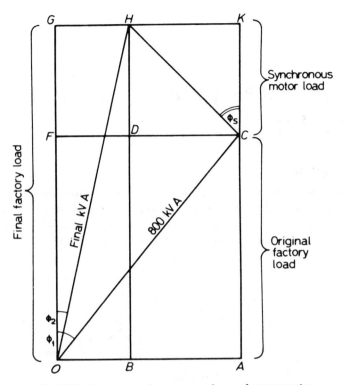

Fig. 8.13 Power factor improvement by synchronous motor

$$\therefore \text{ kW} = \text{kV A} \times \cos \phi_1 = 600 \times 0.7 = 420 \text{ kW} = OF$$
$$\text{kV Ar} = \text{kV A} \times \sin \phi_1 = 600 \times 0.714 = 428 \text{ kV Ar} = OA$$

$$\text{Synchronous motor load} = \frac{250 \times 746}{1000 \times 0.9} = 207.2 \text{ kW} = FG = CK$$

$$\therefore \text{ Final power} = 420 + 207.2 = 627.2 \text{ kW} = OG$$

Final p.f. $\cos \phi_2 = 0.95 \qquad \therefore \text{ } \tan \phi_2 = 0.3288$

$$\therefore \text{ Final kV Ar} = \text{kW} \times \tan \phi_2 = 627.2 \times 0.3288 = 206.2 \text{ kV Ar} = OB$$

$\therefore$ Synchronous motor leading kV Ar $= OA - OB$
$$= 428 - 206.2 = 221.8 \text{ kV Ar} = CD$$

$$\tan \phi_3 = \frac{HK}{CK} = \frac{CD}{FG} = \frac{221.8}{207.2} = 1.07$$

$$\therefore \cos \phi_3 = 0.6828$$

$\therefore$ Synchronous motor operates at a power factor of 0.6828 leading.

9. The three-phase induction motor

9.1 Construction

The Stator. The three-phase induction motor has a stator similar to that of a synchronous machine in which a three-phase distributed winding is placed uniformly in slots around the stator (Fig. 9.1). Generally the stator is made up of laminations of silicon steel with thin insulated covering to

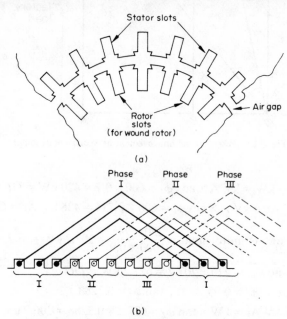

(a)

(b)

Fig. 9.1   Three-phase induction motor construction: (a) stator and wound rotor construction, (b) three-phase winding arrangement

reduce eddy current losses. Each phase winding consists of multiturn coils spread over several slots as indicated in Fig. 9.1(b).

The Cage or Squirrel-cage Rotor. There are two forms of rotor, the cage type being the simplest. Figure 9.2(a) shows the general construction. For simplicity the diagram shows only a small number of conductors. The rotor

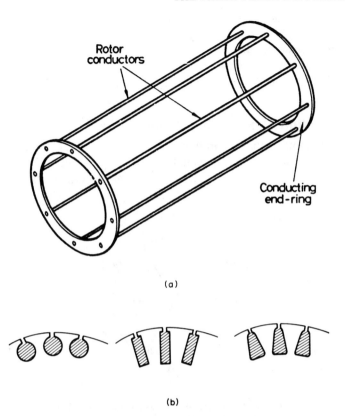

Rotor
conductors

Conducting
end-ring

(a)

(b)

Fig. 9.2 Cage rotor construction: (a) conductor arrangement, (b) types of conductor shapes

conductors consist of solid copper bars which are short-circuited at each end by end-rings. This gives the appearance of a circular cage, hence the name. The conductors are lightly insulated and they are placed in slots in a laminated iron rotor core. Better starting and quieter running are obtained if these slots are skewed. Conductors can be of a variety of shapes, some of which are shown in Fig. 9.2(b). The shape of the conductor affects starting performance and the type of conductor used is determined mainly by the starting requirements in a particular situation. Sometimes, especially for the smaller motors, aluminium is used for the conductors. It will be seen that with this type of rotor there are no external connections, which eliminates the use of slip-rings and brushes. This type of construction provides a cheap, reliable, and efficient motor.

The Wound Rotor. With this type of rotor there are phase windings in slots. The rotor is constructed of silicon steel laminations with a cross-section similar to that shown in Fig. 9.1(a). The distributed three-phase winding is

153

similar to that of the stator and it is usually connected star with the ends of each phase brought out to three slip-rings. The slip-rings are used to add external resistance to the rotor circuit, particularly for starting, but for normal running the slip-rings are short-circuited. Thus, the principle of operation is the same for both cage- and wound-rotor machines.

9.2 Production of a rotating magnetic field

Consider the simple stator winding of Fig. 9.3, in which three single-turn coils AA', BB', and CC' are spaced 120° apart, A, B, and C being the *start* of each coil for the positive direction of current. When the current is in the

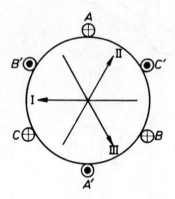

Fig. 9.3   Three single-turn coils and associated flux

positive direction in each coil, AA' produces a magnetic flux in direction I, BB' in direction II, and CC' in direction III. The magnitude and direction of each flux will depend upon the magnitude and direction of the current in each coil but they will always be in the same position in space, as shown in the diagram. The three individual fluxes combine to form a resultant flux which will be the phasor addition of the three.

Suppose the three coils are connected to a three-phase supply the waveform of which is shown in Fig. 9.4. Coils A, B, and C are connected to phases I, II, and III, respectively and form fluxes I, II, and III, respectively.

Take instant (a). The current in coil A is maximum positive, while the currents in coils B and C are both 0.5 maximum and are both negative. Thus flux I will be maximum in the direction shown in Fig. 9.3 and fluxes II and III will be 0.5 maximum value and in a direction opposite to that of Fig. 9.3. The phasors of fluxes for instant (a) are shown in Fig. 9.4. The resultant flux Φ is in the direction shown and its magnitude is 1.5 times the maximum value of any individual flux I, II, or III.

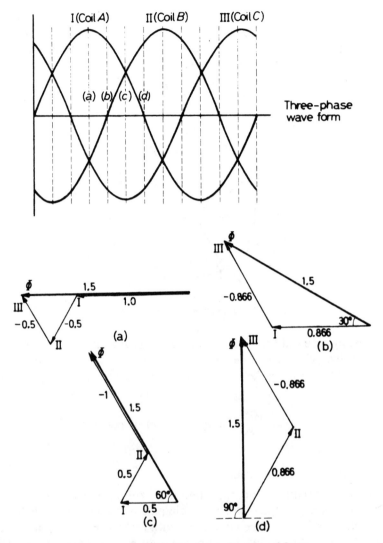

Fig. 9.4 **Rotating field—phasor diagrams of fluxes**

At instant (b) flux I will be positive and 0.866 of its maximum value, flux II will be zero, and flux III will be 0.866 of maximum but negative. The phasor diagram shows that resultant flux Φ is still 1.5 times the maximum of I, II, or III but it has turned clockwise through 30°.

The phasor diagrams for instances (c) and (d) are shown and it will be seen that after each case the resultant flux Φ rotates through 30°, but its magnitude remains constant at 1.5 times the maximum of I, II, or III.

155

It is now obvious that if instances are considered covering the whole cycle a two-pole field of constant magnitude has been produced which rotates at the same rate as the frequency, that is, at synchronous speed.

If there are two coils to each phase as shown in Fig. 9.5, each coil having a span of 90° instead of 180°, then a four-pole field is produced as indicated for the instant (a) of Fig. 9.4. $AA'aa'$ are two coils of one phase, the other

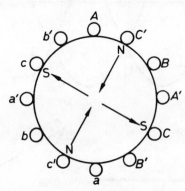

Fig. 9.5 Production of a four-pole field

phases being marked similarly. Thus by splitting the phases round the stator rotating fields of any desired numbers of poles can be produced and the speed of this rotating field will be the synchronous speed N_s as given in Eq. (8.1);

i.e., $$N_s = \frac{60f}{p} \text{ where } p \text{ is pairs of poles.}$$

9.3 Production of torque

Consider one conductor on the stationary rotor of Fig. 9.6(a) and the three-phase supply to the stator producing a clockwise rotating field.

The relative motion of the conductor with reference to the field is to the left. If the direction of flux is from stator to rotor then an e.m.f. will be induced in the conductor, producing a current which will be outwards as shown (Fleming's Right Hand Rule). The current in the conductor will produce a concentric anticlockwise field round the conductor (Fig. 9.6b). These two fields will be superimposed, causing a strengthening of the field to the left of the conductor and a weakening of the field to the right (Fig. 9.6c). Thus a force will be applied to the conductor in the same direction as the rotating field. Similar forces are applied to all the conductors on the rotor, so that a torque is produced causing the rotor to rotate. The direction of rotation is reversed by reversing the connections to any two phases.

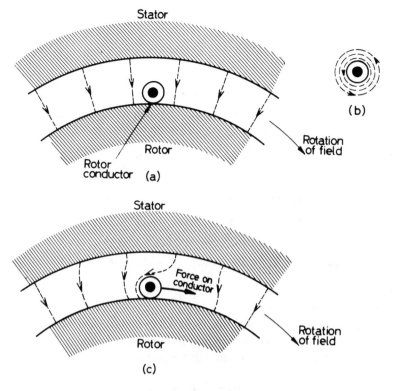

Fig. 9.6   Production of torque

9.4 Slip

It has been seen that torque is produced by inducing an e.m.f. in the rotor conductors, owing to the relative motion between the conductors and the rotating field. The torque produces rotation in the same direction as the field and the rotor increases speed. If the rotor reached synchronous speed, then the conductors would be moving with the field, there would be no relative movement between conductors and field, no e.m.f. would be induced, and there would be no torque produced. Thus, it is impossible for a normal induction motor to run at synchronous speed. If torque is to be produced, the induced e.m.f. is necessary, therefore the rotor must run at something less than synchronous speed. The difference between the actual speed N and synchronous speed N_s is called the *slip speed*.

$$\therefore \text{ Slip speed} = N_s - N \tag{9.1}$$

It is more usual to speak of *slip* of an induction motor as a fractional value which is given the symbol s.

157

Thus $$\text{Slip } s = \frac{N_s - N}{N_s} \qquad (9.2)$$

Also, the percentage slip will be $\dfrac{N_s - N}{N_s} \times 100$ (9.3)

EXAMPLE

A four-pole induction motor operated on a 50 Hz supply runs at a speed of 1425 rev/min. What will be its slip?

$$\text{Synchronous speed } N_s = \frac{60f}{p} = \frac{60 \times 50}{2} = 1500 \text{ rev/min}$$

$$\text{Slip speed} = N_s - N = 1500 - 1425 = 75 \text{ rev/min}$$

$$\text{Slip } s = \frac{N_s - N}{N_s} = \frac{75}{1500} = 0.05$$

As a percentage this will be 5%.

9.5 Rotor constants

Rotor E.M.F. When an induction motor is stationary, the stator and rotor windings form the equivalent of a transformer as shown in Fig. 9.7(a). Thus, the rotor e.m.f. at standstill will be given by

$$E_2 = \frac{N_2}{N_1}E_1 = nE_1 \qquad (9.4)$$

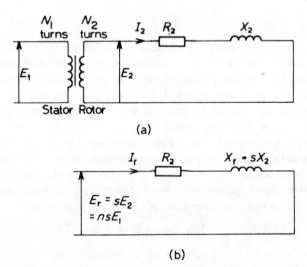

Fig. 9.7 Rotor circuit constants: (a) at standstill, (b) when running

where E_1 is the supply voltage per phase to the stator and n is the equivalent rotor–stator turns ratio.

If the slip-rings of a stationary wound-rotor machine are open-circuited, a voltmeter will measure the rotor voltage across the slip-rings when the stator supply is switched on. The rotor voltage will depend upon whether the rotor is star- or delta-connected.

When the motor is running (Fig. 9.7b), the induced e.m.f. in the rotor will become less, since the relative movement between conductors and rotating field becomes less. The induced e.m.f. is proportional to this movement, therefore it must be proportional to the slip s.

$\therefore$ When motor is running.

$$\text{Rotor e.m.f. per phase} = E_r = sE_2$$

$\therefore$ from Eq. (9.4) $$E_r = nsE_1 \qquad (9.5)$$

Rotor Frequency. The rotor e.m.f. is induced by an alternating flux and the rate at which this flux passes the conductors is the *slip speed*. Thus, the frequency of the rotor e.m.f. will be given by

$$f_r = (N_s - N)\frac{p}{60}$$

$$= \frac{N_s - N}{N_s} \times \frac{N_s p}{60}$$

but $$\frac{N_s - N}{N_s} = \text{slip } s$$

and $$\frac{N_s p}{60} = \text{supply frequency } f$$

$$\therefore f_r = sf$$

Rotor Resistance. The resistance of the rotor winding is affected by neither the frequency nor the slip. Therefore, ignoring any temperature effect,

Rotor resistance per phase $= R_2$ and this remains constant.

Rotor Reactance. The reactance depends upon the frequency of the rotor current.

At standstill (Fig. 9.7a)

$$\text{Reactance per phase } X_2 = 2\pi f L$$

When running (Fig. 9.7b)

$$\text{Reactance per phase} = X_r = 2\pi f_r L = 2\pi sfL = sX_2 \qquad (9.6)$$

Rotor Impedance. The impedance can be calculated from the resistance and reactance values.

159

$\therefore$ Rotor impedance per phase $= Z_r = [R_2^2 + (sX_2)^2]^{1/2}$ \hfill (9.7)

At standstill $s = 1$, so that the standstill value is

$$Z_2 = (R_2^2 + X_2^2)^{1/2}$$

9.6 Rotor current

The equations for rotor current per phase at standstill (I_2) and when running (I_r) can be obtained from the circuits of Fig. 9.7.

At standstill

$$I_2 = \frac{E_2}{Z_2} = \frac{nE_1}{(R_2^2 + X_2^2)^{1/2}} \hspace{2cm} (9.8)$$

When running

$$I_r = \frac{E_r}{Z_r} = \frac{nsE_1}{[R_2^2 + (sX_2)^2]^{1/2}} \hspace{2cm} (9.9)$$

9.7 Rotor copper loss

Torque is given by

$$T = \frac{60 \times P \text{ (watts)}}{2\pi N} \text{ newton metres}$$

If P_2 is the power input to the rotor from the rotating field and P_m is the mechanical power output (including friction losses) then the torque can be expressed in terms of either the input or the output.

Thus

$$T = \frac{60P_2}{2\pi N_s} = \frac{60P_m}{2\pi N}$$

from which

$$\frac{P_2}{N_s} = \frac{P_m}{N}$$

or

$$\frac{P_m}{P_2} = \frac{N}{N_s}$$

$$\therefore \ 1 - \frac{P_m}{P_2} = 1 - \frac{N}{N_s}$$

$$\therefore \ \frac{P_2 - P_m}{P_2} = \frac{N_s - N}{N_s}$$

but

$$\frac{N_s - N}{N_s} = \text{slip } s$$

$$\therefore \ P_2 - P_m = sP_2$$

160

but $P_2 - P_m$ must be the electrical or copper loss in the rotor,

i.e.,
$$P_2 - P_m = I_r^2 R_2$$

$$\therefore \text{ Slip } s = \frac{\text{rotor copper loss}}{\text{rotor input power}} = \frac{I_r^2 R_2}{P_2} \tag{9.10}$$

9.8 Torque equation

$$\text{Torque } T = \frac{60 P_2}{2\pi N_s} \text{ newton metres} \tag{9.11}$$

From Eq. (9.10) we have
$$P_2 = \frac{I_r^2 R_2}{s}$$

So Eq. (9.11) becomes
$$T = \frac{60}{2\pi N_s} \times \frac{I_r^2 R_2}{s}$$

From Eq. (9.9) we get
$$I_r^2 = \frac{n^2 s^2 E_1^2}{R_2^2 + (sX_2)^2}$$

$$\therefore T = \frac{60}{2\pi N_s} \times \frac{n^2 s^2 E_1^2}{R_2^2 + (sX_2)^2} \times \frac{R_2}{s} = \frac{60}{2\pi N_s} \times \frac{n^2 s E_1^2 R_2}{R_2^2 + (sX_2)^2}$$

This gives the torque per phase since all values in the equation are phase values, so if there are m phases

$$\text{Torque } T = \frac{60 m n^2}{2\pi N_s} \times \frac{s E_1^2 R_2}{R_2^2 + (sX_2)^2} \text{ newton metres}$$

$$= \frac{9.55 m n^2}{N_s} \times \frac{s E_1^2 R_2}{R_2^2 + (sX_2)^2} \text{ newton metres} \tag{9.12}$$

The left-hand term in the equation will be constant for a particular machine

$$\therefore T = k \times \frac{s E_1^2 R_2}{R_2^2 + (sX_2)^2} \tag{9.13}$$

or
$$T \propto \frac{s E_1^2 R_2}{R_2^2 + (sX_2)^2} \tag{9.14}$$

9.9 Maximum torque

Under normal conditions, the supply voltage is usually constant so that Eq. (9.14) can be modified.

$$T \propto \frac{sR_2}{R_2^2 + (sX_2)^2}$$

$$\propto \frac{R_2}{R_2^2/s + sX_2^2}$$

Thus torque will be a maximum when the denominator of the above equation is a minimum and it can be shown that this occurs when

$$R_2^2/s = sX_2^2$$

i.e., when $\qquad s = \dfrac{R_2}{X_2} \qquad$ or $\qquad R_2 = sX_2 = X_r \qquad$ (9.15)

Thus, maximum torque occurs when the rotor resistance and rotor reactance are equal.

9.10 Induction motor calculations

EXAMPLE

A 415 V, three-phase, 50 Hz, four-pole, star-connected induction motor operates at 1425 rev/min on full load. The rotor resistance and reactance per phase are 0.4 Ω and 4 Ω, respectively, and the effective rotor–stator turns ratio is 0.8 : 1. Calculate (1) the full-load torque, (2) the power output if the mechanical losses amount to 480 W, (3) the maximum torque, (4) the speed at which maximum torque occurs, and (5) the torque at start.

1. Synchronous speed $N_s = \dfrac{60f}{p} = \dfrac{60 \times 50}{2} = 1500$ rev/min

$$\text{Slip } s = \frac{N_s - N}{N_s} = \frac{1500 - 1425}{1500} = 0.05$$

$$E_1 \text{ (phase value)} = \frac{415}{1.73} = 240 \text{ V}$$

Three-phase motor, $\therefore m = 3$
Using Eq. (9.12):

$$\text{Full-load torque } T = \frac{9.55 \, mn^2}{N_s} \times \frac{sE_1^2 R_2}{R_2^2 + (sX_2)^2}$$

$$= \frac{9.55 \times 3 \times 0.8 \times 0.8}{1500} \times \frac{0.05 \times 240 \times 240 \times 0.4}{(0.4)^2 + (0.05 \times 4)^2}$$

$$= 0.0122 \times \frac{1152}{0.2} = 70.27 \text{ newton metres}$$

Note: 0.0122 is the constant k for the machine.

2. Output (incl. friction losses) $P_m = \dfrac{2\pi}{60} \times TN$

$$= \dfrac{2\pi}{60} \times 70.27 \times 1425 = 10\ 480\ \text{W}$$

$\therefore$ Power output $= P_m -$ mechanical losses

$$= 10\ 480 - 480 = 10\ 000\ \text{W} = 10\ \text{kW}$$

$\left(\text{bhp would be } \dfrac{10}{0.746} = 13.4\ \text{hp} \right)$

3. Max. torque occurs when $X_r = R_2 = 0.4\ \Omega$.

$$s = \frac{R_2}{X_2} = \frac{0.4}{4} = 0.1$$

$\therefore$ By using these values in the torque Eq. (9.13), the maximum value is obtained.

$$\therefore T_{max} = k \times \frac{0.1 \times 240 \times 240 \times 0.4}{(0.4)^2 + (0.4)^2}$$

$$= 0.0122 \times \frac{2304}{0.32} = 87.9\ \text{newton metres}$$

4. For max. torque $s = 0.1$.

$\therefore$ Slip speed $= 0.1\ N_s = 150\ \text{rev/min}$

$\therefore$ Speed for max. torque $= 1500 - 150 = 1350\ \text{rev/min}$

5. At start $s = 1$, i.e., standstill condition.

$\therefore$ Starting torque $= k \times \dfrac{E_1^2 R_2}{R_2^2 + X_2^2}$

$$= 0.0122 \times \frac{240 \times 240 \times 0.4}{(0.4)^2 + (4)^2}$$

$$= 0.0122 \times \frac{23\ 040}{16.16} = 17.4\ \text{newton metres}$$

Note: The torque at start is very much less than full-load torque.

EXAMPLE

Find the rotor current and rotor copper loss at full load for the machine in the previous example, and also find the starting current.

163

Rotor current $I_r = \dfrac{nsE_1}{[R_2^2 + (sX_2)^2]^{1/2}}$ (9.9)

$$= \frac{0.8 \times 0.05 \times 240}{[(0.4)^2 + (0.05 \times 4)^2]^{1/2}} = \frac{9.6}{0.4472} = 21.45 \text{ A}$$

Rotor copper loss $= I_r^2 R_2 = 21.45^2 \times 0.4 = 184$ W/ph

$\therefore$ Total rotor copper loss $= 3 \times 184 = 552$ W

Starting current $I_2 = \dfrac{nE_1}{(R_2^2 + X_2^2)^{1/2}}$ (9.8)

$$= \frac{0.8 \times 240}{[(0.4)^2 + (4)^2]^{1/2}} = \frac{192}{4.02} = 47.8 \text{ A}$$

Note: The starting current is considerably higher than the full-load current.

EXAMPLE

Using the same motor as in the previous examples, find the input power and the efficiency of the machine at full load if the stator losses amount to 0.6 kW. What will be the current taken from the supply at full-load if the motor runs at a power factor of 0.89 lagging?

From the previous examples, gross output $P_m = 10.48$ kW

rotor copper loss $= 0.552$ kW

$\therefore$ Stator input $= P_m +$ rotor loss $+$ stator loss

$= 10.48 + 0.552 + 0.6 = 11.632$ kW

Net output from previous example $= 10$ kW.

$\therefore$ Motor efficiency $= \dfrac{\text{output}}{\text{input}} = \dfrac{10}{11.632} = 0.86$ p.u.

Power input $P_1 = 1.73\,VI \cos \phi$.

$$\therefore I = \frac{P_1}{1.73\,V \cos \phi} = \frac{11.632 \times 1000}{1.73 \times 415 \times 0.89} = 18.2 \text{ A}$$

EXAMPLE

What would be the resistance of the rotor winding of the above machine if maximum torque were required at start?

At start $\qquad s = 1 \qquad$ so $\qquad sX_2 = X_2$

So, for maximum torque at start

$$R_2 = X_2 = 4\,\Omega$$

164

Thus, if this is a wound-rotor machine with slip-rings then an external star-connected resistance of 3.6 Ω per phase can be added to the rotor resistance of 0.4 Ω per phase to give maximum torque at start. It will be seen later that this is used as a method of starting.

9.11 The torque–slip characteristic

There are two factors which mainly influence the characteristic of the induction motor. These are the inductive reactance and the resistance of the rotor winding. The e.m.f. generated in the rotor and its frequency depend upon the slip. At start the slip is 100% and the rotor frequency f_r will be the same as the supply frequency and the inductive reactance ($X_r = 2\pi f_r L$) will be high. As the motor increases speed the slip gets smaller and rotor frequency f_r becomes less. The reactance becomes less, being reduced to zero if the machine could run at synchronous speed (i.e., zero slip). The rotor resistance is independent of frequency and remains con-

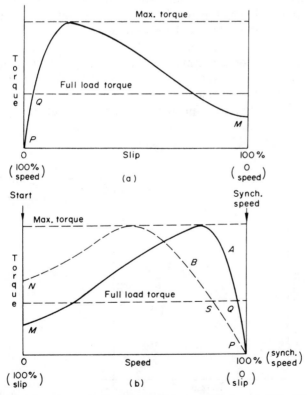

Fig. 9.8 **Cage induction motor characteristics: (a) torque–slip characteristic, (b) torque–speed characteristic**

165

stant. The maximum torque occurs when the inductive reactance is equal to the resistance (i.e., $X_r = R_2$) and since the resistance is very small, especially with a cage rotor, this point occurs when the motor is only about 15–20% below synchronous speed. From this point the characteristic will drop to zero torque at synchronous speed, since an induction motor cannot produce torque unless there is some slip. At start, that is 100% slip, the reactance is high compared with the resistance, so torque will be small and starting on load may prove difficult. Figure 9.8(a) shows a typical torque–slip characteristic for a three-phase cage induction motor.

9.12 The torque–speed characteristic

The practical engineer usually thinks in terms of speed rather than slip and Fig. 9.8(b) shows a typical torque–speed characteristic which is really a mirror image of the torque–slip curve. It can be seen that at start the curve is at point M, which gives a starting torque less than full-load torque and the motor will start only on light load or no-load. The normal full-load torque is at point Q, which is only about 5% less than synchronous speed, and this gives a motor which is highly efficient when running at full load. Full-load torque is usually about one-half to one-third of the maximum torque. Curve A is for a normal cage motor. If a high starting torque is required, that is, starting on full-load, the rotor will be made with high-resistance conductors, which give maximum torque at a lower speed, resulting in a characteristic similar to curve B. This gives a good starting

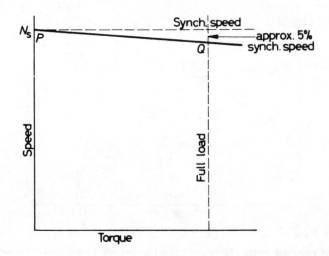

Fig. 9.9 Speed–torque characteristic over the normal working range

torque at point N but a lower full-load running speed at point S with a lower efficiency.

With a wound-rotor machine resistance can be added externally for starting, giving it the advantages of both types of characteristic.

That part of the curve which covers the normal working range of an induction motor is that between points P and Q in Fig. 9.8(b). This has been redrawn in Fig. 9.9 with the vertical and horizontal scales reversed to give the speed–torque characteristic which will probably be more familiar to the student. Figure 9.9 shows that for normal running there is a slight drop (about 5%) in speed between no-load and full load. This is almost identical with the speed–torque characteristic of a d.c. shunt motor and, in fact, it is often called a *shunt characteristic*. Although the curve shows a slight reduction in speed as load is increased, the induction motor can be said to be essentially a constant-speed machine.

9.13 Three-phase induction motor performance

It is seen that the cage induction motor generally has a small starting torque and must be started light. Also, at start the motor acts like a transformer with a short-circuited secondary, so that the starting current may be anything up to five times normal full-load current. These difficulties are overcome with the wound-rotor machine by the ability to add resistance externally to the rotor circuit.

The torque equation (9.14) shows that torque depends upon the square of the supply voltage. Thus voltage variations can have a serious effect upon the motor performance.

The power factor and full-load efficiency of the three-phase induction motor are usually in the range of 0.8 to 0.9 power factor lagging with efficiencies of 80–92%. In general, the larger the motor the higher are the values for both power factor and efficiency. Motors below two or three kilowatts may have figures somewhat less than those above. Full-load slip may range from about 5% for small motors to 1.25% for large machines.

9.14 Starting of induction motors

There are three items to consider when starting an induction motor.
1. Torque is determined by the resistance of the rotor circuit. This resistance is usually small, giving good running conditions, but it gives a small torque at start. Thus, unless it is specially designed with a high-resistance rotor, the cage induction motor can be started only on no-load or very light load. With a wound-rotor machine resistance can be added externally for starting purposes.
2. At the moment of start the rotor is stationary and there is a transformer

effect between stator and rotor windings. Since the rotor windings of a cage motor are short-circuited this can cause excessive current at the moment the supply is switched on.

3. To reduce the large starting current indicated above, the voltage applied to the stator may be reduced. It can be shown that torque depends upon (voltage)^2 in an induction motor, so by reducing the voltage there will be a serious reduction in torque which, in a cage motor, is already quite small at start.

Thus to provide methods of starting for a cage induction motor, a balance must be sought between reducing the starting current and maintaining the starting torque.

9.15 Starting methods for the cage motor

The following three methods of starting cage induction motors are used. Starting is on no-load or very light load.

Direct-on-line Starting. As the name implies, the supply is directly switched on to the motor through a suitable contactor-type starter as shown in Fig. 9.10. The starting current is high and may cause interference with supplies to other consumers on the same system. The supply authority

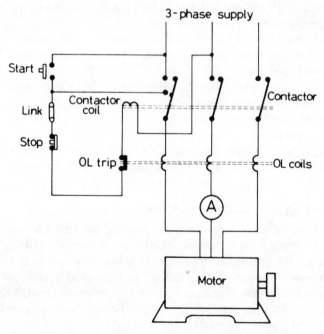

Fig. 9.10 Contactor starter for direct-on-line starting

generally restricts the use of this method of starting to motors below about 2 kW (about $2\frac{1}{2}$–3 hp). If the supply is isolated, as may be the case when a factory has its own generators, there is no such limit and motors of several hundred kilowatts are started by the direct-on-line method.

Auto-transformer Starting. For this method a three-phase auto-transformer is used to reduce the stator voltage, thereby reducing the starting current, as shown in Fig. 9.11. This method seriously reduces the starting torque, so

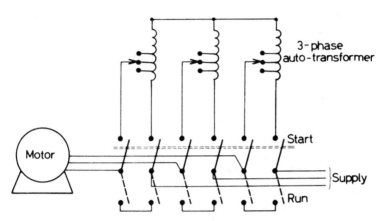

Fig. 9.11   Auto-transformer starting

the voltage is reduced only sufficiently to give the required reduction of the starting current. The auto-transformer usually has tappings which reduce the line voltage to 50%, 65%, and 80% of the normal value, giving torque reduction to 25%, 42.2%, and 64% of normal, respectively.

These figures show the disadvantage of too great a reduction of the stator voltage. Only one set of tappings is used in a starter which will be connected permanently to the tapping found most suitable for the particular situation. A double-throw switch connects the auto-transformer in circuit for starting, and after the motor has run up to speed the switch is moved into the run position, which connects the supply directly into the motor. Some form of interlocking mechanism is used to safeguard against the switch being closed in the run position while the motor is stopped.

Star–delta Starting. With this method, the six connections to the three stator phase windings of the motor are brought out to the starter (Fig. 9.12). For normal running the windings are connected in delta, but for starting they are star-connected so that the voltage across each phase winding will be 1/1.73 times the line voltage at start. Thus the starting voltage per phase is reduced to 57.7% of the running voltage. This reduces the starting current but also reduces the starting torque to 33.3% of normal. The

169

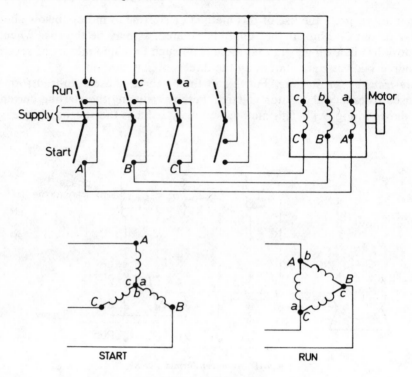

Fig. 9.12 Star–delta starting

changeover from star starting to delta running is made by a double-throw switch, with interlocks to prevent starting with the switch in the run position.

9.16 Starting a wound-rotor motor

Rotor Resistance Starting. The wound-rotor machine must generally be used if on-load starting is required. The rotor windings are brought out to slip-rings, which enables resistance to be added to the rotor circuit externally so that maximum torque is obtained at start. The star-connected rotor starter resistance is usually of the face-plate type, the starter arms forming the star point. Figure 9.13 shows a number of torque–speed characteristics. Curve *A* is for the motor operating normally with the slip-rings short-circuited. Curve *B* is the characteristic for a high-resistance rotor, that is when all the starter resistance is in the rotor circuit. Curves *C* and *D* are two intermediate characteristics as resistance is reduced. The motor is started with all the starter resistance in circuit (curve *B*), giving maximum starting torque. As the motor increases speed, the resistance is reduced and

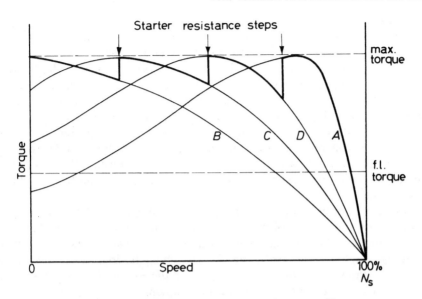

Fig. 9.13   Starting characteristic of a wound-rotor machine

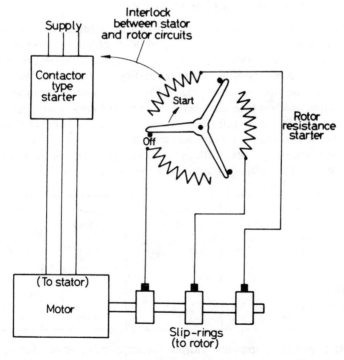

Fig. 9.14   Rotor resistance starter for a wound-rotor machine

171

the motor operates on curve C, then on to curve D, and finally runs normally as curve A with the rotor short-circuited. The characteristic during start follows the top of each of the characteristic curves, as shown in Fig. 9.13. When running normally, the starter arm forms the short circuit across the slip-rings but with some machines the short-circuiting may be achieved by a device at the slip-rings themselves and the brushes raised to minimize wear. Figure 9.14 is a circuit diagram for a rotor resistance starter. The stator circuit will include a contactor-type starter with overload and no-volt release similar to that of Fig. 9.10, but with electrical or mechanical interlock with the rotor resistance to ensure that the stator contactor cannot be closed with the motor stopped until all rotor resistance is in circuit.

For very large motors, the starting resistance may be of the liquid type, giving very gradual and smooth starting. There are also motors having a small number of resistance steps where these resistances are actually mounted on the rotor shaft and the switching is done by a centrifugal switch on the shaft. This method eliminates the use of slip-rings, but it can produce excessive heat if starts are too frequent.

9.17 Induction motor load test

A load can be applied to an induction motor by a brake test, as described for the d.c. machine in Sec. 5.11, using a mechanical dynamometer or eddy-current type of brake. The torque in newton metres may be calculated or it may be given as a direct reading on the brake balance. The circuit for this test is shown in Fig. 9.15. The power is measured by the two-wattmeter method (see Chapter 15). The load can be applied in stages up to about 30–50% over full load. At each stage the voltmeter, ammeter, and wattmeter readings are recorded together with the torque (T newton metres) and speed (N rev/min). The readings may be tabulated with columns for the following calculations to be made:

Input power	Apparent power	Power factor	Power output	Efficiency
$P_1 = W_1 + W_2$	$S = 1.73\,VI$	$P_1/S = \dfrac{W_1 + W_2}{1.73\,VI}$	$P_2 = \dfrac{2\pi}{60}NT$	P_2/P_1
(sum of wattmeter readings) watts	volt amperes		watts	p.u.

From the results, graphs are plotted for efficiency, power factor, speed, torque, and current against output power.

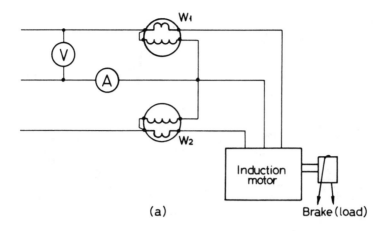

(a)

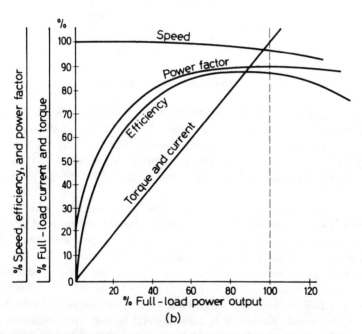

(b)

Fig. 9.15 Induction motor load test: (a) circuit, (b) typical test results

9.18 The synchronous induction motor

The synchronous induction motor combines the features of both the synchronous motor and the induction motor. It has been seen that the wound induction motor has a three-phase distributed winding on the rotor

173

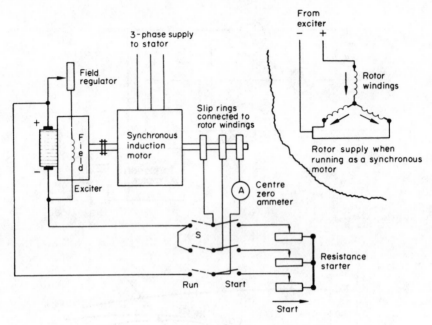

Fig. 9.16   Synchronous induction motor circuit

which is brought out to slip-rings and that the motor has the ability to start on load but that owing to *slip* it runs at a little less than synchronous speed and also at a lagging power factor. The synchronous induction motor also has a wound rotor brought out to slip-rings and it is started as an induction motor with a resistance starter. The circuit is shown in Fig. 9.16.

The motor is started with switch S in the 'start' position which puts the resistance starter in the rotor circuit. It can be started on load and as the machine increases speed the starting resistance is gradually cut out until the motor is running normally as an induction motor with the starter resistance short-circuited. The rotor winding for this type of machine has large cross-section conductors to reduce the rotor resistance, which makes the slip as small as possible so as to give a speed as near as possible to synchronous speed. Switch S is now moved to the 'run' position, which switches the rotor to the d.c. supply from the exciter. The small diagram in Fig. 9.16 shows the rotor connection at this stage. The d.c. supply to the rotor circuit causes fixed rotor poles to be formed and the motor pulls into synchronism and then runs as a synchronous motor at synchronous speed. Care must be taken to close the switch at the right instant, otherwise the motor may stall, especially if it is on load. The correct moment to switch in the exciter supply is found by having a centre-zero ammeter in the circuit of one phase as shown. When the motor is running as an induction motor, the ammeter will swing slowly, owing to the slip. The switch is operated when the ammeter is zero and starting to increase in the same direction as the exciter current will flow. The power factor at which the motor operates can be adjusted by variation of the regulator in the exciter field circuit.

10. Small a.c. motors

10.1 The single-phase induction motor–principle

In Chapter 9 it was seen that a three-phase stator winding will produce a rotating field. By applying the same principle to a two-phase winding where the phase difference is 90°, again a rotating field is produced. Consider coil AA' only of Fig. 9.3 being connected to a single-phase supply. An alternating field will be produced, but this field will always be in the same plane (I). It will be pulsating but not rotating. Any rotor conductor in this field will have an alternating e.m.f. induced in it, but the direction will be such that the torque produced will alternate in direction between clockwise and anticlockwise, so that the resultant torque will be zero. Thus a single-phase induction motor with a simple single-phase winding will not start because no overall torque is produced.

Now, if the rotor is made to rotate in either direction, then the conductors will cut across the magnetic flux and the induced e.m.f. will now produce a resultant torque in the direction of rotation and the motor will pick up speed. If synchronous speed were to be reached, the conductors would rotate at the same rate at which the field is alternating and again the resultant torque would be zero. Actually, zero torque occurs at a little below synchronous speed. Thus, an induction motor with one single-phase winding will continue running once it has been started, but at a speed somewhat less than synchronous speed. That is, slip is as necessary for the single-phase induction motor as for the three-phase machine.

The torque–speed characteristic of the single-phase motor is similar to that of the three-phase induction motor, except that the torque is zero at start and the slip when running at full load is somewhat greater, with zero torque occurring at a little below synchronous speed instead of at synchronous speed. Figure 10.1(a) shows the characteristic. This means that the single-phase motor has a lower efficiency and power factor than the three-phase machine; also, once started, the torque to accelerate the motor up to its final running speed is not as good. Since the torque is produced by a pulsating field instead of a rotating field, the single-phase induction motor is not as smooth-running as the polyphase machine and is apt to be noisier and more subject to vibration.

The problem of starting the single-phase induction motor is overcome by artificially introducing a second phase, so that a rotating field is produced

176

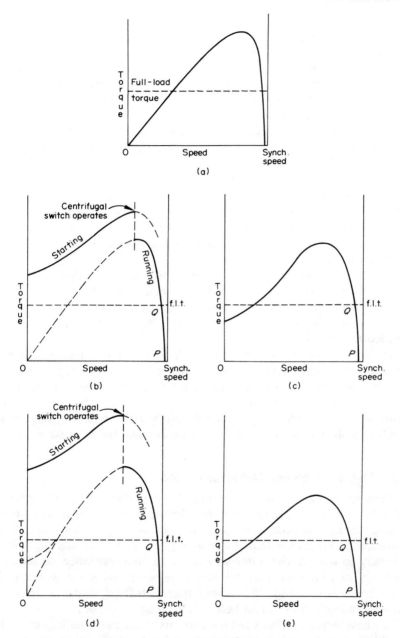

Fig. 10.1   Torque–speed characteristics of single-phase induction motors: (a) basic characteristic (running winding only), (b) split-phase, (c) capacitor start and run, (d) capacitor start motor and two-capacitor motor, (e) shaded-pole

177

for starting purposes. This is usually achieved by the motor having two stator windings and in order to produce a phase difference between the currents in the two windings an inductance or a capacitor is introduced into the starting winding circuit. Generally, the starting winding is switched out of circuit when the motor has almost reached its normal speed and the motor continues running with only one stator winding energized. As the starting winding is only used for a short time, it is usually made of fine wire and is short-time rated. It is essential, therefore, to ensure that the winding is switched out of circuit once it has served its purpose in order to safeguard against a burnout.

The usual method of switching the starting winding circuit is by a centrifugal switch mounted on the motor shaft. This allows the starting winding to be switched out of circuit a little before the motor reaches its normal speed. Also, the switch will close automatically when the motor stops, thus ensuring the starting winding being in circuit when the motor is switched on again.

Sometimes, a special starting switch is used in which there is a double toggle. When the motor has reached its normal speed, the hand is removed from the switch and one toggle which is spring-loaded causes the starting winding switch to open. In some cases, the starting winding may be switched by a relay.

The single-phase induction motor will continue running in whichever direction it is started and this is determined by the relative phase difference between the winding currents. Thus, reversing the leads to one of the windings will reverse the motor.

The above principles are applied to the various types of single-phase induction motors that follow. A cage rotor is usual for all these motors.

10.2   The split-phase induction motor

The term *split-phase* is usually applied to one particular type of very small motor in which the phase difference between the running and starting winding currents is produced by having the starting winding of a higher resistance or reactance than the running winding. The starting winding itself may be wound with a fine wire having a high resistance, or additional resistance or reactance may be placed in series with the winding. The circuit is shown in Fig. 10.2 where the centrifugal switch will cut the starting winding out of circuit before full speed is reached.

The phase difference between the currents in the two windings caused by the additional resistance is quite small, and not much better if reactance is used. It follows that the starting torque for the split-phase motor is very small. Its use generally is for very light duty with no-load or very light load starting, e.g., light office machines and domestic applications. The motor

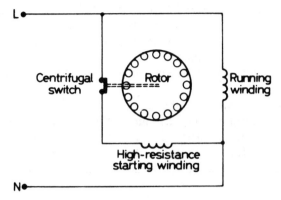

Fig. 10.2 Split-phase (resistance start) induction motor

takes four to six times full-load current at start and operates at efficiencies around 60% with a power factor of about 0.7 lagging. The torque–speed characteristic is shown in Fig. 10.1(b); the point at which the centrifugal switch operates is shown and at this point the characteristic takes up the curve due to the running winding only. Over the normal working range, that is between points P and Q on the graph, the motor has a shunt-type characteristic which means that it is essentially a constant-speed motor.

10.3 Capacitor-start induction motor

The running winding of the single-phase motor is embedded in iron and, therefore, is highly inductive. By using a capacitor of suitable size in the starting winding circuit, a considerable phase difference between the cur-

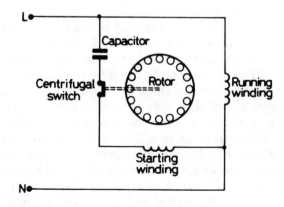

Fig. 10.3 Capacitor-start induction motor

179

rents in the two windings can be achieved. This gives the motor a high starting torque and makes the capacitor-start motor the most common small single-phase motor for general use. It is used for light industrial work and office and domestic applications were a better starting torque is required than that offered by the split-phase motor. The circuit is shown in Fig. 10.3.

The capacitor-start motor runs efficiently with a fairly good power factor. Its starting torque can be as high as three times its full-load torque, with a starting current about three-and-a-half times full-load current. The characteristic curve for this motor is shown in Fig. 10.1(d). When running normally (points P to Q) the speed is essentially constant, as this is a shunt-type curve.

10.4 Capacitor motor

This is sometimes known as the *capacitor start and run* or the *capacitor start–capacitor run* motor since the starting winding is left in circuit during running and is now called the *auxiliary winding*. There are two types of motor. One type has a circuit similar to Fig. 10.3 but with the centrifugal switch omitted. This means that the motor continues running like a two-phase machine. This gives smoother running with a good power factor, but the capacitor and auxiliary winding must now be continuously rated. To give a high starting torque the value of the capacitor must be high but this leads to inefficient running conditions where a much smaller capacitor would be best. This type of motor is generally used where a high starting torque is not required so that a capacitor of lower value, more suitable for the running conditions, can be used to give more efficient running. It is used for ventilating fans, small pumps, circulation pumps in central heating systems, etc. The characteristic curve for the permanent capacitor start and run motor is shown in Fig. 10.1(c).

A far more efficient motor, one that can be used for heavier loads and also for on-load starting, is shown in Fig. 10.4. This uses two capacitors, the larger one being switched out by the centrifugal switch before the motor reaches full speed, and therefore can be short-time rated. This is a smooth-running machine with an efficiency of 80–85% and a power factor of about 0.8 lagging at full load. Although this is a more expensive motor initially, there is a saving in the long run due to its higher running efficiency. The characteristic curve is Fig. 10.1(d), which shows that over the normal working range P to Q the speed is virtually constant. The motor has a good starting torque and is quiet-running, which is most useful for light industrial purposes and office machines. The size of the capacitors varies with the rating of the motor, but for a 1 kW machine the starting capacitor would·be about 120 µF and the running capacitor 15–20 µF.

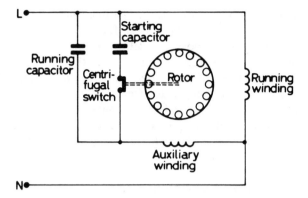

Fig. 10.4 Capacitor motor with separate capacitor for starting

10.5 The shaded-pole motor

The *shaded-pole* motor has salient poles, each of which is split into two sections, as shown in Fig. 10.5. The smaller portion of each pole face is wound with a short-circuited ring of heavy copper known as a *shading ring*. When the supply is switched on there is a transformer effect with the shading ring as a short-circuited secondary. This causes the flux under the shaded portion of the pole to lag behind the unshaded pole flux and so produce a two-phase rotating field in the direction unshaded to shaded pole. This is sufficient to start the rotor rotating but as the field is weak the starting torque will be poor, as shown by the characteristic curve of Fig. 10.1(e). One form of construction of the shaded-pole motor is shown in Fig. 10.5.

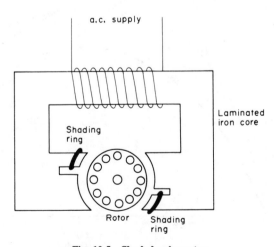

Fig. 10.5 Shaded-pole motor

ELECTRICAL POWER EQUIPMENT AND MEASUREMENTS

There are continuous heat losses in the shading ring and the efficiency of this type of motor is low and the power factor poor. The direction of rotation is determined by the position of the shading ring on the split pole so, once constructed, the motor cannot be reversed. Owing to its inefficiency, this motor is manufactured only in small sizes, but as its construction is simple and cheap it is often used instead of the resistance split-phase motor for desk fans and small domestic fan heaters. It is also used for record players and tape recorder drives. Under normal running conditions it has a shunt-type characteristic, which means that it is essentially a constant-speed motor.

10.6 The single-phase series motor

This is a commutator motor which is basically like the d.c. series motor and has similar characteristics, including a high starting torque and consider-

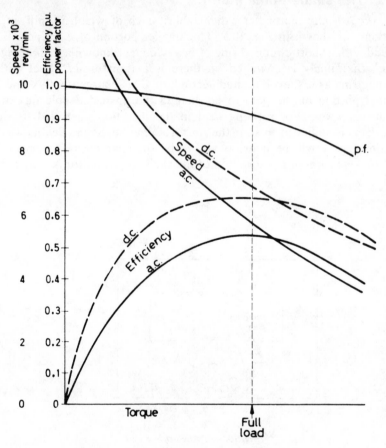

Fig. 10.6 Characteristics of universal series motor

able speed variation with load. Reversing the polarity at the terminals of a d.c. machine does not reverse rotation, since both armature and field are reversed together. Thus the machine will also work on a.c., although for successful operation certain modifications must be made. With an a.c. supply the torque will be pulsating, so the machine will not run as smoothly on a.c. as on d.c. The solid poles of a d.c. machine would cause very large eddy currents to flow if it were connected to an a.c. supply, thus producing excessive heat and large losses. For a.c. working, the field must be laminated. The poles can project in a similar manner to the d.c. machine but it is more usual for the winding to be distributed in stator slots like an induction motor winding. Such a motor can be used on both a.c. and d.c., and is often called a *universal motor*. As a fractional horsepower motor it is fitted into many domestic and small-power industrial appliances. As in the case of the d.c. series motor, the a.c. motor must be directly connected to the load.

Another complication when using a series motor on a.c. is that there is also a transformer effect between the stator and rotor windings, which causes an e.m.f. to be induced in the rotor. The windings being short-circuited by the brushes during commutation, although in the neutral plane of the main field, will still have an e.m.f. induced in them by this trans-former effect. This leads to a greater amount of sparking at the brushes when the motor operates on a.c. The sparking is minimized by keeping the number of turns per rotor slot small, but even so this drawback limits the size of universal motors to the fractional horsepower ratings. Figure 10.6 shows typical universal series motor characteristics, with d.c. speed and efficiency curves shown for comparison for the same a.c. and d.c. voltages.

For higher output ratings, the single-phase a.c. series motor must be specially designed by the introduction of compensating windings to counter-act the bad commutation due to the transformer effect. Such motors are used for traction purposes.

11.   Industrial drives

11.1   Choice of an electric motor

Before considering the characteristics of different types of motors, and the tasks for which they are most suited, it is as well to look at the conditions in general that may limit the choice of a motor.

1. Supply Available. Most industrial supplies today are three-phase a.c. The voltage, frequency, and number of phases of the motor must suit the supply. If d.c. is required, it may be necessary to install costly rectifying and control equipment. Variations of voltage may be caused by long cable runs and this could affect the speed and torque of some motors. If a new motor is to be installed, it must be ascertained that there is sufficient spare capacity at the supply intake point to cater for the additional load. The power factor of the load must also be considered, as this may affect the tariff charges.

2. Starting and Control. The type of motor or the type of starter may depend upon a limit set to the starting current; for example, the supply authority may not allow the direct-on-line starting of a cage induction motor above a certain rating. The frequency of starting will influence the type of starter. Where a motor is continually being started and stopped, or where there is a long acceleration time during starting, the equipment may have to have a continuous rating. The type of motor can be limited if on-load starting is necessary, and if reversals are required it must be suitable for such operation. If speed control is required, the choice of motor will be limited to a special costly type of a.c. motor or a d.c. machine with electronic control.

3. Enclosures. The enclosure will depend upon the atmosphere in which the motor is working. Clean air, a moist atmosphere, the presence of dust, chemical vapours, or explosive gas, or a variety of other conditions, will determine the type of motor enclosure. In hot atmospheres additional ventilation may be necessary, and at high altitudes or low temperatures precautions must be taken to avoid lubrication and condensation trouble.

4. Rating. Most motors have a *continuous rating*. This is the load they can drive continuously without overheating. If the ambient temperature is high, this load may have to be reduced to avoid overheating. If a motor is run intermittently with enough standing time for cooling it can be *short-time rated.*

5. Motor Mountings. The type of motor bearings will be determined by the position of the motor. It may drive the load with its shaft horizontal or vertical, or excessive thrust may occur due to the type of drive or coupling. If there is excessive vibration, resilient mountings and special terminals will be necessary. Motors must not be placed in such a position that surrounding structures obstruct the flow of ventilating air.

6. Special Conditions. There may be other conditions to consider, such as noise. Motors specially designed for quiet running are often required in hospitals, hotels, for lifts, air-conditioning, office machines, drives for some musical instruments, etc.

11.2 Motors for industrial drives

When motors for machine drives are installed, the layout of the factory must be considered, together with the availability of circuits, the position of control equipment, the standardization of equipment, etc.

There are two types of drives—group drive and individual drive.

With group drive, one large motor drives all the machines on the workshop floor, generally through overhead shafting. Each machine is belt-driven and starting and stopping is by a fast-and-loose pulley system on the line shaft. The main advantage of this system is the relatively lower initial cost. One large motor of, say, 100 kW output will cost less than ten 10 kW motors driving individual machines. It is also very unlikely that all machines will be in use at the same time, so ten 10 kW machines could probably be driven by a 75 kW group drive motor, thereby giving a further saving. The electrical installation and maintenance costs will be less as there will be only one circuit and one set of control equipment. The disadvantages of this drive, however, far outweigh the advantages in most cases, with the result that it is seldom used today. The overhead shafting and belt drives are always a potential source of danger and they cause dust and dirt and also obstruct the light and ventilation. A motor breakdown is costly, as it shuts down every machine in the workshop and stops production. The only exception would be where the shutting down of one machine in a continuous process would necessitate all other machines being stopped in any case. The cost of keeping a spare motor of this size in store in case of breakdown would be high. Running costs are also high, as the motor will often be running at light loads when its efficiency is low, and there will be additional losses in the line shaft.

With individual drive, each machine is coupled direct to its own motor. There will have to be separate circuits and control equipment for each machine, and the initial costs will be greater than for a group drive. Maintenance costs also will be somewhat higher. However, the greater flexibility of this type of drive makes it preferable to group drive in almost every case. The running costs are less, as each motor is stopped when the machine it is driving is not in use, and this leads to more efficient running and smaller losses. In case of breakdown, only one machine will be affected, which in most cases will not upset production. Also, if the individual motors have been standardized as far as possible, the cost of keeping a spare in the store will not be great. Line shafting will not be required; this will result in greater safety, a lighter and cleaner workshop, and a more efficient spacing of the machines, hence a better use of the floor area and greater flexibility.

A motor normally runs at its highest efficiency at about full load. Thus, motors should be matched to the machines they are driving. However, there are certain preferred sizes which help both manufacturers and users to standardize their equipment. It is to the user's advantage to specify a manufacturer's standard-size motor. The cost is kept to a minimum. If the motor is not immediately available delivery is generally quick, and replacements and spares are readily available.

Preferred speeds are as follows:

3000 rev/min for squirrel-cage induction motors only.

1500, 1000, and 750 rev/min for a.c. and d.c. motors up to 100 hp.

Also, 600 rev/min for a.c. and d.c. motors between 50 and 100 hp.

The above speeds are synchronous speeds on a.c.; the actual speed of an induction motor is subject to slip and will be slightly less than these values.

11.3 Characteristics of motors

A review of the characteristics of different types of motors in general use is given below. The reference numbering in each case is as follows:

1. Speed characteristic.
2. Speed control.
3. Starting method.
4. Starting torque.
5. Applications and remarks.

D.C. Shunt Motor

1. Almost constant speed–slight drop with load.
2. Field regulator for speeds above normal.
   Armature controller for speeds below normal—wasteful of energy.
   Armature voltage control by controlled rectifier (a.c. supply) giving wide range of speed variation.

3. Armature resistance starter.

4. About 1.5 times full-load torque.

5. Light or medium duty at constant speed or slightly variable.
Automatic control at precision speeds using electronic control.
Used for lathes, conveyors, fans. Not suitable for heavy and fluctuating loads.

D.C. Series Motor

1. Large drop in speed as load is applied. Dangerous high speed possible if run at no-load.

2. Field diverter speed control, or series controller (wasteful).

3. Resistance starter.

4. High starting torque—about $2\frac{1}{2}$ to 3 times full-load torque.

5. Heavy duty with intermittent starting, e.g., traction, cranes, hoists. Always directly coupled to load so that no-load working is not possible.

D.C. Compound Motor

1. Reduction in speed with increase of load. Safe no-load speed.

2. Field regulator.

3. Armature resistance starting.

4. About twice full-load torque.

5. Suitable for on-load starting, for fluctuating loads, and the sudden application of heavy loads; e.g., metal shears, machine-shop punches and presses, etc.

A.C. Squirrel-cage Induction Motor

1. Almost constant speed—slightly under synchronous speed.

2. No speed control.

3. (i) Direct-on-line where starting surge is permitted.
   (ii) Star–delta starting for motors up to about 20 kW.
   (iii) Auto-transformer starting for motors between 20 and 250 kW.

4. Starting torque generally poor, especially with reduced voltage starting. No-load or very-light-load starting except for a double-cage rotor machine.

5. A cheap and efficient general-purpose motor where almost constant speed is required and load can be applied after starting. Starting current high and power factor lagging.

A.C. Wound-rotor (Slip-ring) Induction Motor

1. Almost constant speed—slightly under synchronous speed.
2. Generally no speed control. The use of a rotor resistance controller is wasteful, lowers the efficiency, and adds to the cost.
3. Rotor resistance starter.
4. Good starting torque—2 to 3 times full-load torque.
5. Used for general drives requiring almost constant speed and on-load-starting. Used to drive large lathes, pumps, sawmill machines, air compressors, etc.

A.C. Induction Motors—Special Types

1. Speed almost constant for each of several speed settings.
2. (i) Pole-changing. Usually gives a choice of two speeds.
   (ii) Cascade control. Two coupled motors are required. A range of four speeds can be obtained by using motors with different numbers of poles.
3. Rotor resistance starting.
4. Usually good starting—on-load starting.
5. Suitable for drives requiring a limited choice of almost constant speeds; e.g., drives for cranes requiring high speed for light loads and low speed for heavy loads, rolling mills, colliery winders, etc.

A.C. Synchronous Motors

1. Always runs at synchronous speed.
2. No speed control.
3. Has to be run up to speed, usually by pony motor, and then synchronized with the supply.
4. Motor itself has no starting torque.
5. Suitable for continuous service to avoid unnecessary starting. Used for driving large ventilating fans, compressors, pumps, motor-generator sets, etc. Its ability to run at a leading power factor makes it useful for power factor improvement.

A.C. Synchronous Induction Motor

1. Runs at synchronous speed but slight reduction may occur on overload.
2. No speed control.
3. Starts as an induction motor and is pulled into synchronism by excitation and runs as a synchronous motor.
4. Good—2 to 3 times full-load torque.

188

5. Same service as a synchronous motor, including power factor improvement, but with easier starting.

Single-phase a.c. Motors

These are generally in the fractional horsepower range. For drives over 1 to 2 kW, a single-phase motor would be used, as a rule, only if a three-phase supply is not available. The capacitor-start–capacitor-run motor runs at almost constant speed and can be started on load, although the starting current is high and may have to be restricted. Details of single-phase motors are given in Chapter 10.

11.4 Motor enclosures

The type of casing or enclosure of a motor depends upon the conditions under which it has to function. The types of enclosure are given below under six general headings, although modifications to the general type can give several subdivisions. With the exception of the open machine, all types of enclosures must give protection to safeguard against accidental or inadvertent contact with the internal moving or live parts. The open machine will be used in generator or motor rooms in which only authorized persons are permitted.

Open Machine (Fig. 11.1). The ends of this machine are completely open, allowing free ventilation over and through the windings. Air is drawn

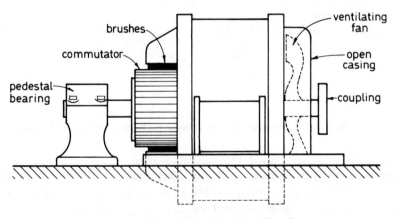

Fig. 11.1 Open machine with pedestal bearing

through the motor by a fan attached to the shaft. This type of enclosure is only suitable in a perfectly clean and dry atmosphere. The bearing may be supported by an open end-bracket, but pedestal bearings with independent supports are often used for large machines.

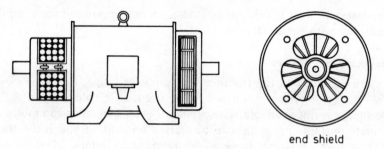

end shield

Fig. 11.2 Screen protection

Protected Type (Fig. 11.2). With this enclosure, the internal and live parts of the machine are protected mechanically, but without seriously affecting the flow of ventilating air, which is drawn through the machine by a fan on the machine shaft. The motor end shields may be provided with suitable openings, or ventilating openings may be provided at the sides and covered with screens of wire mesh, expanded metal, perforated metal, or similar covers. These are known as *screen-protected types.*

Drip-proof Machine (Fig. 11.3). This is, basically, a protected type of machine in which the ventilating openings are so constructed, or further

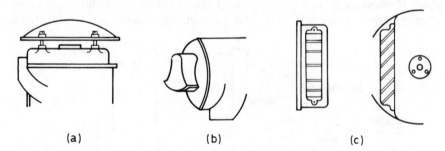

(a)   (b)   (c)

Fig. 11.3 Drip-proof protection: (a) vertical drive, (b) horizontal drive, (c) louvre type

protected by a hood or cowl, that moisture or dirt falling vertically cannot enter the machine. Modifications of this type exclude moisture from entering the motor from other angles or under pressure as from a hose. These are known as *splash-proof type* and *hose-proof type.*

Pipe or Duct-ventilated Type (Fig. 11.4). If the air in the room in which the motor is situated is not suitable for passing through the machine for ventilating purposes (e.g., too hot, or the atmosphere is damp or dirty, or there are chemical fumes or vapour, etc.) then cool, clean air must be drawn in from outside. This is done by means of a pipe or duct connected to the ventilation inlet of the motor. The outlet may be of the screen-

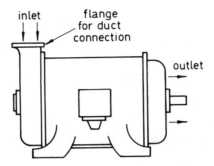

Fig. 11.4   Duct ventilation (duct inlet, outlet to room)

protected type so that the air passes into the room, but if there is a possibility of damaging fumes, vapour, or dirt settling in the machine while it is stopped then a pipe or duct outlet is also fitted. If the motor's own fan is not sufficient then additional fans may be placed in the inlet or outlet ducts or in both.

Totally Enclosed Machine (Fig. 11.5). This is a machine in which the air inside the casing has no connection with the air outside but it is not necessarily airtight. A fan on the shaft inside the motor circulates the air

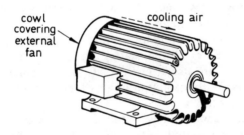

Fig. 11.5   Totally enclosed machine

through the windings and cooling is by conduction through the casing. Cooling is much slower than with the free-ventilated type and requires a large cooling surface. The surface area is generally increased by means of fins, but even so a totally enclosed motor is usually physically larger than a protected type of the same rating. An additional fan is sometimes fitted to the shaft outside the casing to give a greater cooling effect. A shaped hood or cowl over this fan directs the air across the casing.

In some special machines there is a separate cooling system in which air, a gas, or a cooling liquid is circulated through special ducts inside the machine.

Modifications to this type of enclosure enable motors to be used under

191

various conditions; e.g. *weatherproof machine, watertight machine, submersible machine.*

Flameproof Machine. This is a special type of machine which is constructed to enable it to be used in conditions where there is a possibility of flammable dust, gas, or vapour being present. It is totally enclosed with special bearings, packing, and glands, so that flammable gases cannot get into the machine and also, in case of fault, sparking or flashovers in the machine cannot affect the outer atmosphere. The machine must comply with the stringent regulations for flameproof enclosures.

11.5 Motor rating—intermittent duty

When a motor is running, there are always electrical losses in the field and armature, and these losses produce heat. This heat increases with increase of load and must be dispersed to save the machine from overheating. Thus, the load is limited by the balance between the rate of cooling and the rate at which heat is produced. The *rating of a motor* can be stated as being the output of the motor under specified working conditions, without the temperature rise exceeding a specified value.

Many standard motors have Class 'A' insulation, consisting of synthetic resin insulation for wires, micanite, and insulating board, for which the temperature rise is limited to about 55°C.

Where the ambient temperature is high, or there is a moist or acid atmosphere, Class 'E' or 'B' insulating materials, which will withstand higher temperatures, are used. These consist of enamels, terylene, mica, and glass products. With insulation of this type temperature rises ranging up to 75°C are permitted.

Most motors are 'continuously' rated, or given a *continuous maximum rating* (c.m.r.), which is stated on the nameplate of the machine. This is the load at which the motor may be operated continuously under its specified conditions without overheating. There is no overload rating, but momentary overloads that do not affect the temperature may be permitted, though not sustained overloads.

Motors on intermittent duty, as used for lifts, hoists, etc., may be given a *short-time rating.* With this rating, allowance is made for cooling between the periods of working, thereby enabling a rating somewhat higher than the c.m.r. value to be given. The short-time rating is stated as a *one-hour* or *half-hour rating,* as appropriate. The motor may be run at the rated load for the time stated when started at ambient temperature. The standing time is not stated, but this must be sufficient to allow for cooling.

There is a third type of rating for intermittent running where a motor is on a definite working cycle which is repeated. This is a *'duty cycle rating'.*

The motor manufacturer will allocate this rating when given details of the required duty cycle, but the following method of calculation will give a rough guide to the size of motor required. Generally, a more precise calculation is not necessary, as the result will usually be rounded off to the next highest rating of a commercially available motor.

In a given circuit:

Heat produced is proportional to (current)$^2 \times$ (time current flows)

Output power P is almost proportional to current, therefore it may be said that

Heat produced is proportional to $(P)^2 \times$ (time motor is loaded)

If P = theoretical continuous rating (kW or hp or current)

P_1 = actual loading for time t_1

t = time for the complete duty cycle,

then, in order to run the motor within its specified temperature limits,

Heat produced by continuous running =

heat produced by duty-cycle running

i.e.,
$$P^2 \times t = P_1^2 \times t_1$$

$$\therefore P^2 = P_1^2 \times \frac{t_1}{t}$$

$$\therefore \text{Theoretical continuous rating} = P_1\left(\frac{t_1}{t}\right)^{1/2}$$

EXAMPLE

A motor runs on a five-minute duty cycle, having a 30 kW load for three minutes and no load for two minutes. What will be the theoretical continuous rating for a motor suitable for this duty?

$$P = P_1\left(\frac{t_1}{t}\right)^{1/2} = 30\left(\frac{3}{5}\right)^{1/2} = 23.2 \text{ kW}$$

This figure would be rounded off to the next higher standard rating.

Another type of duty cycle is one in which the load varies during the cycle, as in the following example.

A motor loading is P_1 kW for t_1 minutes

P_2 kW for t_2 minutes

no-load for t_3 minutes

193

$$\therefore \text{ Heat produced} \propto (P_1^2 \times t_1) + (P_2^2 \times t_2)$$

$$\text{Time for cycle} = \text{running time} = t_1 + t_2 + t_3$$

$$\therefore \text{ Theoretical power rating } P = \left[\frac{(P_1^2 \times t_1) + (P_2^2 \times t_2)}{t_1 + t_2 + t_3}\right]^{1/2}$$

$$= \left[\frac{\text{sum of } (P^2 \times \text{time})}{\text{running time}}\right]^{1/2}$$

If the motor is stopped during part of the cycle instead of running on no-load then cooling will be slower owing to lack of fan ventilation. To allow for this, the standstill time should be divided by a factor of 3 or 4, so that the equation becomes (using factor 3):

$$\text{Theoretical power rating } P = \left[\frac{\text{sum of } (P^2 \times \text{time})}{\text{running time} + \frac{1}{3}\text{ standstill time}}\right]^{1/2}$$

EXAMPLE

What will be the theoretical continuous rating of a motor which has a duty cycle of 20 kW for two minutes, 5 kW for two minutes, 10 kW for three minutes, and stopped for three minutes?

$$\text{Heat} \propto (P_1^2 \times t_1) + (P_2^2 \times t_2) + (P_3^2 \times t_3)$$

$$\propto (20^2 \times 2) + (5^2 \times 2) + (10^2 \times 3) \propto 1150$$

Running time = 7 min

Standstill time = 3 min

So, assuming a factor of 3,

$$\text{Equivalent cooling time} = 1 \text{ min}$$

$$\therefore \text{ Theoretical rating} = \left(\frac{1150}{7+1}\right)^{1/2} = 12 \text{ kW}$$

12. Three-phase rectifiers

12.1 Summary of single-phase rectifiers

So that a comparison can be made between single-phase and three-phase rectification, the basic single-phase circuits and wave forms are shown in Fig. 12.1.

It will be seen from the wave forms of Fig. 12.1(a) that for the half-wave rectifier only one-half of each cycle is utilized. Figure 12.1(b) gives full-wave rectification in which both half-cycles are rectified. There are two basic circuits for full-wave rectification. The bi-phase circuit utilizes only half the transformer winding for each half-cycle, whereas the bridge circuit makes far better use of the transformer secondary, and the whole of the secondary voltage is used for rectification during both half-cycles.

In both types of single-phase circuits the current varies from a maximum to zero, which means that unless effective smoothing circuits are added, there will be a considerable amount of ripple in the output.

12.2 Three-phase half-wave rectifier

As the name implies, only one half-cycle is rectified in each phase, but since the phases overlap there is always at least one phase which is positive with respect to the others, so the rectifier current never reduces to zero. The circuit and wave form are shown in Fig. 12.2.

In Fig. 12.2 the three-phase voltage wave form is shown as a broken line. The rectified wave is shown as a full line. When phase R is positive with respect to the other phases, rectifier r will conduct, giving the rectified wave as shown for r. As phase Y becomes more positive then rectifier y conducts giving the rectified wave shown as y. Next, rectifier b conducts giving wave b, and so on. Thus the three-phase rectified wave never becomes zero, so a smoother wave is obtained than by single-phase rectification, although some ripple remains. Note that with a single-phase half-wave rectifier there is only one peak per cycle in the rectified current, two peaks with single-phase full-wave, but three peaks with three-phase half-wave. Thus, the ripple frequency is increased to three times the supply frequency when using a three-phase half-wave rectifier.

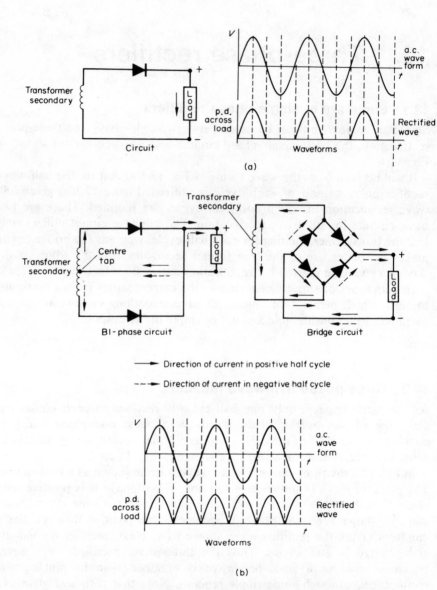

Fig. 12.1 Single-phase rectifiers: (a) half-wave rectifier, (b) full-wave rectifier

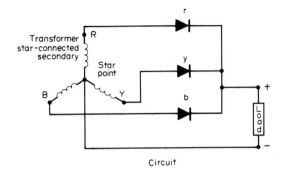

Circuit

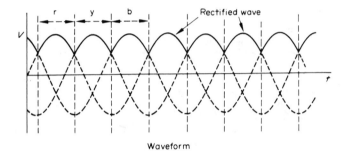

Waveform

Fig. 12.2 Three-phase half-wave rectifier

12.3 Three-phase full-wave centre-tap rectifier

For this type of rectifier the transformer secondary windings are centre-tapped to provide the star point. Note that the circuit for any one phase is similar to the bi-phase circuit of Fig. 12.1(b). Thus, by having the centre tapping, each phase winding provides a bi-phase supply and this type of rectifier is known also as a *six-phase half-wave rectifier*. The circuit and wave form are shown in Fig. 12.3.

There is full-wave rectification in each phase. With phase R, rectifier r_1 operates when its e.m.f. has a higher positive potential than the other phases. Rectifier r_2, in effect, reverses the negative half-cycle of phase R and it too will operate when its potential is the highest. Thus the positive and reversed negative peaks will be rectified by the various rectifier elements as indicated on the rectified wave form. This gives a much smoother output, that is, a much reduced ripple. The ripple frequency will now be six times the a.c. supply frequency.

197

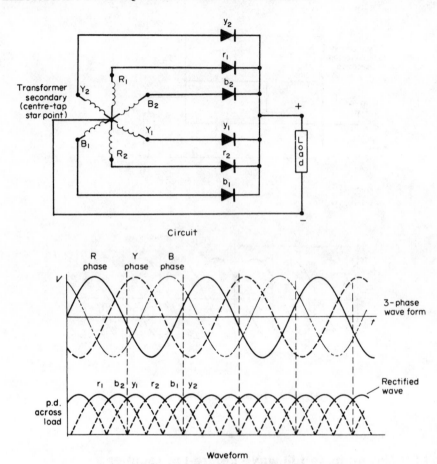

Fig. 12.3   Three-phase full-wave centre-tap rectifier

12.4   Three-phase bridge rectifier

The three-phase bridge rectifier does not require a centre-tapped transformer secondary and the whole of the voltage across each phase winding is utilized, unlike the setup in Fig. 12.3 in which only half of each phase winding is used at any instant. The bridge rectifier gives a higher output voltage than the other three-phase types if the supply transformers have similar turns ratios. The circuit is given in Fig. 12.4. If a three-wire d.c. supply is required, the star point of the supply transformer secondary can be brought out as the neutral.

When phase R is positive with respect to phases Y and B, rectifier r_1 will conduct, and current will flow through the load and will return through

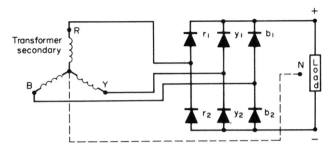

Fig. 12.4 Three-phase bridge rectifier

rectifiers y_2 and b_2. Similarly, y_1 will conduct when phase Y is positive with respect to B and R and current will return via r_2 and b_2, and so on.

12.5 Smoothing

All rectifiers allow current to flow in one direction only, but, as the wave forms show, although the current is unidirectional, it varies considerably in magnitude with a pronounced ripple. This ripple can be reduced in magnitude if the number of phases supplying the rectifier is increased. In order to supply large amounts of power and to reduce the ripple in the output, six-, twelve-, and even twenty-four phase rectifiers are used.

For some purposes, such as battery charging or supplying d.c. motors, some ripple is not a serious drawback. If the d.c. is used to supply radio and amplifier circuits the ripple can cause an intolerable hum. Also, there are circuits which may be adversely affected by the harmonic content of an unsmoothed rectifier current. Thus there are many cases where some form of smoothing circuit must be added to the rectifier output. For this purpose there are several forms of filters which can be employed.

12.6 The capacitor filter

This is a simple form of filter in which a capacitor is connected across the rectifier output in parallel with the load, as shown in Fig. 12.5(a).

In Fig. 12.5(b) the rectifier output wave is shown as a broken line. This causes the capacitor to be charged to about the maximum p.d. of the rectified wave as at point A. The rectifier output voltage now drops, leaving the capacitor charged. The capacitor potential is now greater than the rectifier output potential and the capacitor discharges through the load, enabling the load potential to be maintained at a high value. The potential of the capacitor drops slightly as it is discharging, but at point B the next wave from the rectifier builds up the capacitor p.d. again to point C where the process is repeated. This gives a considerable reduction in the mag-

199

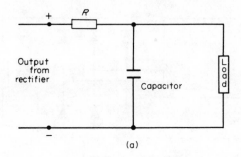

(a)

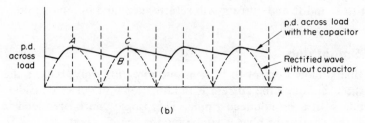

(b)

Fig. 12.5   The capacitor filter

nitude of the ripple. The value of the capacitor must be such that its reactance at the ripple frequency is small compared with the load resistance. To safeguard the rectifier circuit from excessive charging currents, a current-limiting resistor R is often included in the circuit.

12.7   The inductor filter

The *inductor* or *choke* consists of a coil wound on an iron core. The resistance of the coil is low so it has little effect upon the d.c. component of the rectified output current. However, the coil is highly inductive and offers a large reactance to any a.c. components, that is, to the ripple. Since the reactance is proportional to the frequency, it follows that the inductor is capable also of subdueing any higher harmonic frequencies which may be present in the ripple.

The inductor filter is used generally in full-wave rectifiers and is suitable for giving a steady output voltage when there are large load variations and it tends to subdue current impulses which could otherwise damage the rectifier elements. The main disadvantage is that the greater the inductance the more effective is the smoothing but this means a great increase in

200

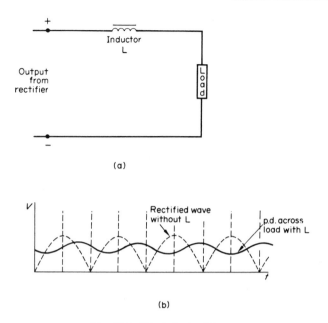

Fig. 12.6 The inductor filter

weight and cost of the inductor. Figure 12.6 shows the inductor circuit and the wave forms.

12.8 The choke input filter

Figure 12.6(b) shows that with the inductor filter there is still some ripple left in the output wave, especially if the inductor weight and cost are kept to reasonable values. To smooth these remaining ripples, a capacitor C can be placed in parallel with the load, as shown in Fig. 12.7(a).

Capacitor C operates like a capacitor filter of Sec. 12.6. One drawback is that for light loads the choke has little effect, and this results in a high no-load voltage, owing to the charge on the capacitor. As the load current increases there is a rapid drop in voltage up to point A of the load characteristic (Fig. 12.7b). After point A the p.d. across the load remains constant except for the normal voltage drops which occur in the various circuit elements. To avoid this initial rapid volt drop a resistor R, known as a *bleeder resistor*, is sometimes placed in parallel with the load. R takes a current equivalent to that of point A on the characteristic and thereby stabilizes the voltage at this point even on no-load.

201

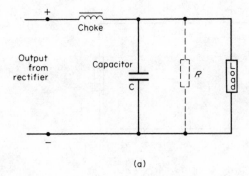

(a)

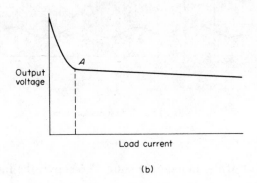

(b)

Fig. 12.7   The choke input filter

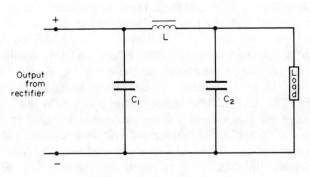

Fig. 12.8   The Π-filter

12.9 The Π-filter

This filter is similar to the choke input filter but with the addition of another capacitor C_1 at the input. C_1 is charged by the rectifier output in the same way as a capacitor filter and its p.d. is maintained at around peak value. C_1 is sometimes called a *reservoir* capacitor. The output of C_1 passes into the choke input filter composed of choke L and capacitor C_2. The addition of C_1 provides a higher voltage for the output and eliminates the initial voltage drop which occurs with the choke input filter of Sec. 12.8. This filter provides an almost pure d.c. output. The circuit is shown in Fig. 12.8.

13   Control systems

13.1 Control systems

For the efficient operation of an industrial undertaking or process, each item or element in that undertaking must work at a predetermined level. That is, motors must be run at their correct speed, heaters must be maintained at their correct temperature, liquids must flow at the correct rate, etc. In other words there must be some form of control. The simplest form of control is an on–off switch but in this case the control offers two extremes only. A better form of control is one where the process or output can be controlled or kept within very fine limits. Take the example of a motor which has to be kept running at a given fixed speed shown on an indicator. A man watching the indicator will make the necessary adjustment on a speed controller to bring the motor back to its normal speed whenever the indicator shows any change from normal. The motor, the indicator, the controller, and the man together form a simple control system. The man may be subject to human errors due to tiredness, distractions, etc., so he may be replaced by some form of automatic control. There is also the safety aspect to consider. In many modern industrial plants where a high degree of precision is required it would be impossible to operate them safely by manual control and automatic control becomes essential. Thus, any interconnected arrangement of elements or units which keeps a system, a process, or a machine operating in a predetermined manner is known as a *control system.*

For a comprehensive range of definitions of terms used in control systems the student should refer to BS 1523.

13.2 Open-loop system

The open-loop control system is one where the output is not monitored or fed back to the controller so that errors can be corrected. A simple example is where a d.c. motor speed is set on a speed controller at a fixed graduated marking and is left running at this particular speed. If the motor load changes or the supply voltage varies, there is likely to be a change in the motor speed but without some form of monitoring a rise or fall in speed cannot be corrected. The layout of this form of control is shown in Fig. 13.1.

204

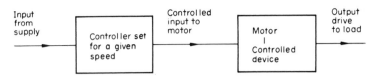

Fig. 13.1   Simple open-loop control system

An open-loop system similar to the one shown is quite adequate for a large number of applications, not just for motor control, but for heating, the flow of liquids in pipes, etc., where precision is not required. The system is stable but it is not self-correcting and it lacks precision.

13.3   Closed-loop system

Figure 13.2 shows how the above open-loop system can become a simple closed-loop system by adding a means of measuring the output speed and having a human operator to correct any change observed by adjusting the controller.

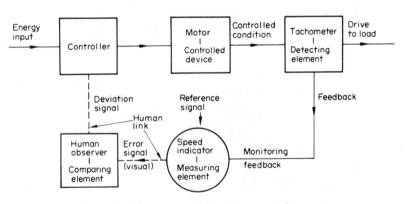

Fig. 13.2   Simple manual closed-loop control system

In this case the speed of the motor is measured by a tachometer connected to the motor shaft. This is known as the *detecting element*. The tachometer output is fed to some form of speed indicator known as the *measuring element* and this can be seen by the human operator, that is, the speed is monitored and gives a feedback of information to the operator. The indicator shows if there is any difference from the required or reference speed. Any error is seen by the operator who becomes a *comparing element* in the loop. The loop is completed when the observer

205

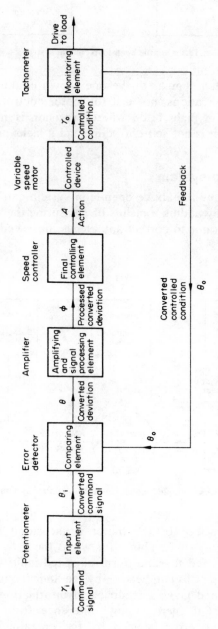

Fig. 13.3 Simple automatic closed-loop control system

operates the controller in such a way that the error is eliminated. This type of system with a human operator has its uses but it is subject to human frailty, so it is not as efficient as a system which replaces the human operator by a means of automatic control.

Figure 3.3 shows a typical automatic closed-loop type of control system. There are many applications of this system, but for simplicity its operation is explained below in terms of motor speed control, and typical elements for this particular application are indicated above each block in the diagram.

The speed at which it is required to run the motor is set by the operator at the *input element*. In this case it is shown as a potentiometer, which will probably have a speed scale marked on it. The setting will be the *command signal* γ_i. The output from the potentiometer will be a potential proportional to the command signal, which is fed into the error detector or *comparing element*. Here the *converted command signal* θ_i is compared with the feedback as indicated below and the difference or *deviation* is passed to an amplifier which amplifies the signal and, if necessary, changes its character so that it is of a type suitable to operate the speed controller or the *final controlling element*. This controller passes the necessary energy to the motor, that is, the *controlled device*, to bring it to the set speed or the *controlled condition* γ_o. The tachometer becomes the *monitoring element* and detects this speed and converts it into a signal known as the *converted controlled condition* θ_o. This is fed back to the comparing element, which detects any difference between the set speed represented by θ_i and the actual speed represented by θ_o. This difference, called the error signal or *converted deviation* $(\theta = \theta_i - \theta_o)$, is fed to the speed controller via the amplifier, so that the motor speed is varied in such a way that the deviation is reduced to its minimum value. In terms of the command signal γ_i, the error or deviation is given by $\gamma = \gamma_i - \gamma_o$.

The diagram is typical of a simple closed-loop system but any particular system does not necessarily include all the elements shown. For example, in some cases the command signal is suitable to pass directly into the comparing element, thus eliminating the input element. There are cases also where the amplifier is not necessary.

To summarize, there are three essential elements in a closed-loop control system:

1. A monitoring or measuring element to give a feedback.
2. A comparing element which compares the feedback from the output with the set signal for a desired output and produces an error signal or deviation.
3. A controlling element, actuated by the deviation, which reduces the deviation to a minimum.

207

A high degree of accuracy and precision is obtained by the automatic closed-loop system. Human error is eliminated and the system is self-correcting, which enables the output to be consistent. However, a closed-loop system must be carefully designed and adjusted, since a disturbance or excessive gain can cause instability. All systems can be subject to disturbances such as variations in voltage, temperature, or steam pressure, sudden changes of load, etc. The automatic closed-loop system must be capable of correcting the effects of such disturbances.

13.4 Regulator systems

The closed-loop control can be applied to a number of different types of systems. A *regulating system* is one where the controlled condition is held at a constant value or is varied in a predetermined manner. The above speed control system is of this type. Figure 13.4 shows another form of closed-loop speed control or regulator system.

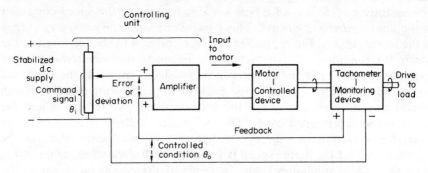

Fig. 13.4   Regulator system for the speed control of a motor

In this case the amplifier applies a constant voltage to the motor, so that it runs at a constant speed determined by the potentiometer setting, which gives the command signal θ_i. The speed of rotation of the motor shaft is monitored by the tachometer, which gives a voltage feedback θ_o. The deviation voltage θ fed into the amplifier is the difference between the applied and the feedback signals, i.e., $\theta = \theta_i - \theta_o$. If $\theta_i = \theta_o$ then there would be no deviation signal to amplify to drive the motor. Thus in this type of system there must always be a deviation under normal operating conditions.

Figure 13.5 shows another type of regulator system. In a steam plant the speed of the steam engine can be controlled by a mechanical device known as a governor. If the steam engine or turbine is driving a d.c. generator, or if there is a tachometer on the driven shaft, then the generator output can

208

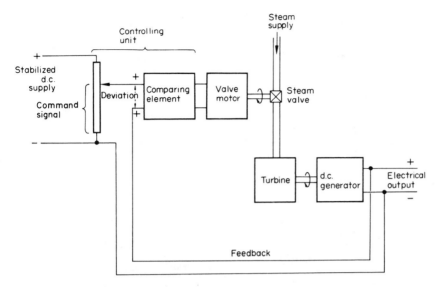

Fig. 13.5 Closed-loop control of a steam plant

be fed back to a controlling unit, as shown in the diagram. In this case the deviation or error signal, amplified if necessary, drives the valve-operating motor in the correct direction to reduce the deviation, thus keeping the electrical output at the correct potential set by the potentiometer in the controlling unit.

13.5 Servomechanism or position control

A *servomechanism* is defined as an automatic kinetic control system which includes a power amplifier in the main forward path. In a servomechanism the controlled device or element is displaced or moved such that it follows the changes of the input element, that is, it can be used as a means of remote position control. It has many uses. A directional aerial or a radio telescope can be rotated, if necessary continually, through 360° horizontally or to any angle vertically, or directed to one particular point. This method can be used to train guns on to a target, instrument pen recorders can be operated by self-balancing potentiometers or bridges, machine tools can be controlled, and many other similar operations can be carried out.

Servomechanisms have as their basis some form of transducer to obtain a deviation signal. A potentiometer may be used but for a high degree of accuracy a synchro element connected in an a.c. circuit is generally used. The principle of the synchro element is illustrated in Fig. 13.6.

The transmitter and receiver synchro elements are similar in con-

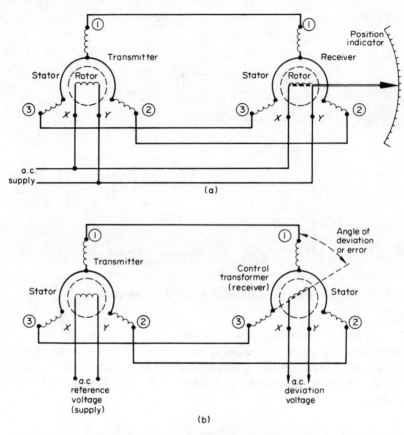

Fig. 13.6 Principle of the synchro: (a) open-loop for data transmission, (b) arrangement for error detection to feed into a closed-loop system

struction except that the receiver has special low-friction bearings and a form of damping to subdue oscillation. There are three stator (fixed) coils wound in slots to give a distributed winding similar to that of a miniature three-phase motor. The rotor consists of a single coil which rotates within the stator and is connected to the external circuit via slip-rings X and Y. There is a transformer effect between the rotor winding as primary and the stator windings as secondary. The e.m.f. induced in each of the stator windings and its phase when a current is flowing in the rotor will depend upon the relative position of the rotor with reference to each stator winding. When both transmitter and receiver rotors are connected to the same supply as in Fig. 13.6(a) and the rotors are in alignment then the e.m.f.s will be the same in the equivalent stator windings. If the stator windings are connected together as shown then the net e.m.f.s in the stator circuit will be zero and there will be no stator current. If the transmitter rotor is rotated through an angle α then there will be a difference in e.m.f. and phase between the transmitter and receiver induced e.m.f.s in the stator windings and a stator current will flow. This will produce a torque on the receiver rotor which will cause it also to move through the same angle α until the two rotors are in alignment again and the stator current has been reduced to zero. The torque produced is very small so this method is suitable only as an indicator with a lightweight pointer attached to the rotor, or in similar applications.

When more torque is required a driving motor, known as a servomotor, must be used and in this case the synchros produce a deviation signal in a closed-loop system. In Fig. 13.6(b) only the rotor of the transmitter is supplied from an a.c. source. The receiver now becomes known as a control transformer and its rotor is connected into the feedback of the closed-loop system. The transmitter rotor, which is shown horizontal in the

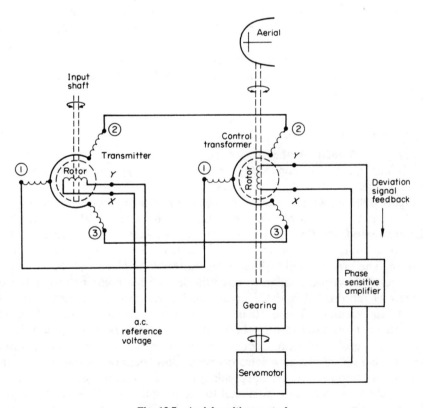

Fig. 13.7   Aerial position control

diagram, induces e.m.f. in its stator windings and, since the receiver rotor is not connected to the a.c. supply, the receiver will set up a similar field in its stator windings and induce an e.m.f. in its rotor. This e.m.f. will be a maximum when the rotor winding is parallel to the field, that is, when it is horizontal. When the receiver rotor is at right angles to its stator field then the induced e.m.f. will be zero. In the diagram this would be when the rotor is vertical. Thus all deviations of the rotor from the vertical will produce an e.m.f. in the rotor circuit and this e.m.f. can be used as a deviation signal in a closed-loop control system.

Figure 13.7 is a diagram of a simple servomechanism to give position control of, for example, an aerial. The desired position of the aerial is set by the position of the input shaft by rotating the transmitter rotor. Unless the aerial is already correctly positioned, the control transformer rotor will not be at right angles to the field set up by the stator windings and an e.m.f. will be induced in it. This will be the deviation signal, which is fed back to a phase-sensitive amplifier which amplifies the signal and also detects the direction of the deviation and so determines the direction in which the *servomotor* will turn the aerial. The amplified signal drives the motor in the correct direction, which also rotates the control transformer rotor until it lies at 90° to the stator field. It is then 'aligned' with the input signal and the deviation is reduced to zero. The servomotor stops and the aerial is in its desired position. If a d.c. motor is used a rectifier will also be incorporated in the amplifier circuitry.

13.6 Process control

Process is defined as the act of physically or chemically changing or combining matter or converting energy. A *process control system* is a system which controls such a process.

Figure 13.8 shows the basic closed-loop system for process control.

The input is some physical quantity, such as a liquid, a fuel, or a chemical, and its flow into the processing plant is controlled by the regulating unit, which may be in the form of a valve or a hopper feed control. The process will be such that changes take place and the pressure, the rate of flow, the temperature, or the level, or a combination of these, has to be controlled and this controlled condition is measured by the monitoring element. These quantities are non-electrical, so some form of transducer is required to turn these physical quantities into a proportional electrical signal. The transducers may be in the form of strain gauges, potentiometers, bridges, electromagnetic flow meters, variable core inductances, thermostats, etc., depending upon the quantity being measured. The electrical signal θ_o proportional to the output quantity is fed back into the comparing element where the desired output θ_i has been set. The

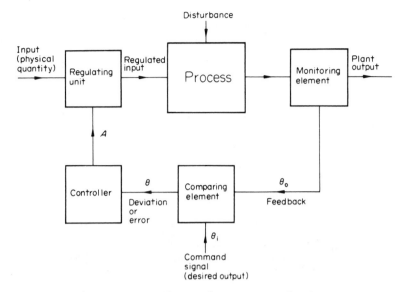

Fig. 13.8 Block diagram of a process control system

deviation or error $(\theta = \theta_i - \theta_o)$, amplified if necessary, is fed into the controller, where it is converted into an output A, which is fed into the regulating unit, where the input into the system is adjusted to give the desired output, so reducing the deviation to a minimum. The regulating unit may be operated electrically or pneumatically by the output of the controller, depending upon the system used.

In many cases in industry today the control system is almost completely pneumatic. Although this requires a system of compressed-air pipes throughout the plant, the pneumatic elements are mechanically simple and considerably reduce fire hazard which, in many cases, gives it a definite advantage over an electrical system.

The correcting action in a process control system is usually slower than with other types of control, as there is generally a delay between a change in the input and its effect being observed at the output.

13.7 A temperature control system

One type of process control is the control of temperature and a block diagram of this is shown in Fig. 13.9. The heating process is carried out by means of a burner, which has its fuel supply controlled by a motor-operated valve. The temperature of the process is detected, in this case by a thermocouple, and measured by a potentiometer. The electrical signal θ_o, which is proportional to the temperature, is fed back to the comparing

213

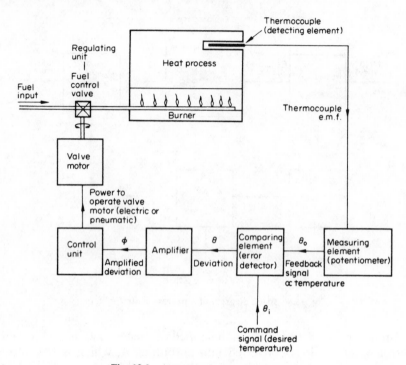

Fig. 13.9 A temperature control system

element in which the desired temperature θ_i is set. Any difference between these two signals is detected and the deviation or error θ is amplified and passed to the control unit which converts the deviation into a suitable form of energy to drive the fuel control valve motor in the required direction to correct the deviation. The valve motor may be electrical or pneumatic. The control may be affected some distance from the actual process and the four elements—measuring element, comparing element, amplifier and control element—may be constructed as one unit known as an *automatic controller.*

13.8 Feedback and stability

It was seen in Sec. 13.3 that greater precision can be obtained by employing feedback. In a control system the input and output may be different physical quantities, although they may be represented in parts of the loop by voltages. For simplicity, the control system may be represented by a voltage amplifier with a forward gain m. Figure 13.10 is a block diagram

214

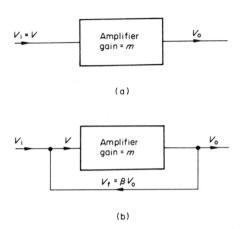

(a)

(b)

Fig. 13.10 Feedback in an amplifier: (a) open-loop, (b) closed-loop
V_i = input voltage; V_f = feedback voltage
V_0 = output voltage; β = fraction of V_0 used as feedback
V = amplifier input voltage;

showing the amplifier as an open-loop (a) and as a closed-loop (b) arrangement.

Amplifier gain $m = \dfrac{V_o}{V_i} = \dfrac{V_o}{V}$ in the open-loop system

In the closed loop, feedback voltage $V_f = \beta V_o$

Input to amplifier $= V = V_i + \beta V_o$

$$\therefore V_i = V - \beta V_o$$

$$\therefore \text{Closed-loop gain } m' = \frac{V_o}{V_i} = \frac{V_o}{V - \beta V_o} = \frac{V_o/V}{1 - \beta V_o/V} = \frac{m}{1 - \beta m} \quad (13.1)$$

where m = forward gain and βm = loop gain.

In the above case the feedback is added to the input V_i, giving the input to the amplifier as $V = V_i + \beta V_o$. This means that the feedback signal is in phase with the input and this is called *positive feedback*.

If the feedback is subtracted from, that is in phase opposition to, the input then this is known as *negative feedback* and

$$V = V_i - \beta V_o$$

$$\therefore V_i = V + \beta V_o$$

215

Thus for negative feedback

$$\text{Closed-loop gain } m' = \frac{V_o}{V_i} = \frac{V_o}{V + \beta V_o} = \frac{V_o/V}{1 + \beta V_o/V}$$

$$= \frac{m}{1 + \beta m} \qquad (13.2)$$

Consider the following example:

1. An amplifier has a forward gain of 20 and the proportion of the output fed back is 0.04. Calculate the closed-loop gain if positive feedback is used.
2. If for some reason the forward gain becomes reduced by (a) 25% and (b) 50%, calculate the closed-loop gain under these conditions.
3. With the forward gain of 20 what will be the closed-loop gain if the proportion of feedback is increased to 0.05?

1. $m = 20$, $\beta = 0.04$.

$$\therefore \text{ Loop gain } m\beta = 20 \times 0.04 = 0.8$$

$$\therefore \text{ Closed-loop gain } m' = \frac{m}{1 - \beta m} = \frac{20}{0.2} = 100$$

2. (a) If m is reduced by 25% its new value will be 15

$$\therefore \text{ Loop gain } m\beta = 15 \times 0.04 = 0.6$$

$$\therefore \text{ Closed-loop gain } m' = \frac{m}{1 - \beta m} = \frac{15}{0.4} = 37.5$$

(b) If m is reduced by 50% its new value will be 10.

$$\therefore \text{ Loop gain } = m\beta = 10 \times 0.04 = 0.4$$

$$\therefore \text{ Closed-loop gain } m' = \frac{m}{1 - \beta m} = \frac{10}{0.6} = 16.66$$

3. If $\beta = 0.05$ then $m\beta = 20 \times 0.05 = 1$.

$$\therefore \text{ Closed-loop gain } m' = \frac{m}{1 - \beta m} = \frac{20}{1 - 1} = \frac{20}{0} = \infty$$

Note: The same result would be obtained if m was increased by 25% and β remained at 0.04.

The above example shows that positive feedback gives a large increase in the overall gain which, at first sight, appears to be a great advantage. However, items of equipment within the amplifier can deteriorate and cause the forward gain to change. The same applies to items or elements in a control system. The example shows that a reduction of forward gain of 25% causes an overall reduction of 62.5%, and a reduction of forward gain of 50% causes an overall reduction of 83.3%. So one big disadvantage of using positive feedback in a system is that disturbances in or to the system can cause very large variations in the overall gain.

A further disadvantage is shown in the final calculation where β is increased so that $m\beta = 1$. Alternatively, m may be increased, again making $m\beta = 1$. This is the condition that occurs when $\beta = 1/m$ or $m = 1/\beta$. The overall gain is seen to be infinity, which means that, in effect, an output will be maintained when there is no input and the system becomes unstable and oscillation occurs.

Thus, if the loop gain is unity or greater than unity then the system becomes unstable which, in a control system, is not only undesirable but can be dangerous.

It must be pointed out, however, that there are special applications of positive feedback, as in the design of oscillators and also in magnetic amplifier circuits.

EXAMPLE

The application of negative feedback can be seen in the following example.

An amplifier has a forward gain of 1000 and the proportion of the output in the negative feedback loop is 0.05. Calculate the closed-loop gain with the amplifier (1) operating normally, (2) with a forward gain reduction of 5%, and (3) with a forward gain reduction of 50%.

1. $m = 1000$, $\beta = 0.05$.

$\therefore$ Loop gain $= m\beta = 1000 \times 0.05 = 50$
$\therefore$ Closed-loop gain for negative feedback

$$= m' = \frac{m}{1 + m\beta} = \frac{1000}{51} = 19.6$$

2. $m = 950$, $\beta = 0.05$.
$\therefore$ Loop gain $= m\beta = 950 \times 0.05 = 47.5$

$$\therefore m' = \frac{m}{1 + m\beta} = \frac{950}{48.5} = 19.59$$

3. $m = 500$, $\beta = 0.05$.

$$\therefore \text{Loop gain} = m\beta = 500 \times 0.05 = 25$$

$$\therefore m' = \frac{m}{1 + m\beta} = \frac{500}{26} = 19.23$$

It can be seen that, although there is a very great reduction in the overall gain, it then remains almost constant even when there are significant changes in the forward gain of the amplifier. A reduction of 50% in forward gain only causes a 1.89% reduction in the overall gain. For a small reduction, which could easily occur when there are disturbances, the overall gain changes by only 0.05% which is negligible.

So for negative feedback it can be said that gain $\simeq 1/\beta$.

Thus negative feedback gives a much higher degree of accuracy and normally it is stable except under certain conditions of phase shift occurring in the feedback signal, as explained in Sec. 13.9. The reduction in gain can be overcome by adding further stages to the amplifier.

13.9 Transfer function in a control system

The feedback principle outlined in Sec. 13.8 can be applied to the closed-loop control system so it can be said that:

1. Positive feedback is a disadvantage for, although it increases gain, disturbances in the system will produce large variations of gain and the system can easily become unstable.

2. Negative feedback gives an overall reduction in gain but this gain remains essentially constant, even when large disturbances occur. Basically the system is stable also, subject to certain conditions of phase shift in the feedback loop.

Section 13.8 is based upon one item of equipment, an amplifier. In a control system there are several items, both electrical and mechanical, that can affect the feedback. On the mechanical side, the inertia of a moving part or the inclusion of gearing can cause a lag in the system. Electrical components containing inductance can also cause a current phase lag. This results in the output signal being out of phase with the input signal. If the input signal for a negative-feedback system is shown in terms of an alternating voltage $e_i = E_{im} \sin \omega t$ then the output signal will be $e_o = E_{om} \sin (\omega t + \phi)$. It can be seen from these two equations that if there is a phase shift in the system of 180° then the polarity of e_o with respect to e_i will be reversed. In effect the feedback becomes positive with its inherent instability.

With mechanical components the inertia of a controlled device whose output is being corrected can cause it to overshoot the desired value and so introduce another correcting signal in the reverse direction. Unless there is some suitable damping further overshooting may occur and the unstable condition known as *hunting* can take place.

So it can be seen that the stability of a control system depends upon the characteristics of each element whether the element is electrical or mechanical.

218

In order to assess the performance of a particular control system the relationship between the input and output of each element must be known. This relationship is called the *transfer function*. The *transfer function* can be defined as the complex ratio of output to input for different types of input signal. Thus the transfer function indicates not only the magnitude of the output to input, that is the gain, but also the phase shift within the element. The importance of the transfer function is that items of mechanical equipment have equations similar to those of particular electrical circuits. This means that a control system, in the design stage, can be simulated by electrical circuitry in, say, a computer and its performance assessed.

A simple closed-loop system was shown in Fig. 13.3. If there is no feedback circuit then it will operate as an open loop with an output of θ_0 when the input is θ.

Thus the open-loop transfer function will be:

$$T_o = \frac{\theta_o}{\theta} \qquad (13.3)$$

The amplifier, speed controller, motor, and tachometer will each have its own transfer function T_1, T_2, T_3, T_4, respectively.

$$\therefore \ \phi = \theta T_1, \quad A = \phi T_2 = \theta T_1 T_2, \quad \gamma_o = A T_3 = \theta T_1 T_2 T_3,$$

and
$$\theta_o = \gamma_o T_4 = \theta T_1 T_2 T_3 T_4.$$

$\therefore$ the open-loop transfer function

$$T_o = \frac{\theta_o}{\theta} = T_1 T_2 T_3 T_4 \qquad (13.4)$$

Thus the open-loop transfer function is the product of the transfer functions of the individual elements. This can be quite a complicated mathematical formula since each item will have gain and may also produce a phase shift.

If the loop is now closed with feedback θ_o, (see Fig. 13.3)

then
$$\theta = \theta_i - \theta_o$$

or
$$\theta_i = \theta + \theta_o$$

$\therefore$ the closed-loop transfer function is

$$T_c = \frac{\theta_o}{\theta_i} = \frac{\theta_o}{\theta + \theta_o} = \frac{\theta_o/\theta}{1 + \theta_o/\theta}$$

but
$$\frac{\theta_o}{\theta} = T_o \quad \text{i.e., the open-loop transfer function} \qquad (13.3)$$

219

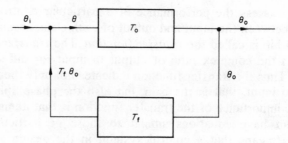

Fig. 13.11 Closed-loop transfer function

$\therefore$ the closed-loop transfer function is

$$T_c = \frac{\theta_o}{\theta_i} = \frac{\text{(open-loop transfer function)}}{1 + \text{(open-loop transfer function)}}$$

$$= \frac{T_o}{1 + T_o} \qquad (13.5)$$

In many closed-loop systems the whole of the output θ_o is not fed back so that there will be a further element in the feedback loop which also has a transfer function T_f. If the transfer function of the forward path is T_o then the block diagram of the system will be as Fig. 13.11.

From Fig. 13.11 the feedback $= T_f\theta_o$

$$\therefore \theta_i = \theta + T_f\theta_o = \frac{\theta_o}{T_o} + T_f\theta_o = \theta_o\left(\frac{1}{T_o} + T_f\right)$$

$$= \theta_o\frac{1 + (T_o \times T_f)}{T_o}$$

$$\therefore \text{Overall transfer function} = \frac{\theta_o}{\theta_i} = \frac{T_o}{1 + (T_o \times T_f)} \qquad (13.6)$$

T_o and T_f are complex terms giving both gain and phase shift. However, in terms of the gain only T_o is similar to the amplifier gain m and T_f is similar to the proportion of feedback β in Eq. (13.2) where closed-loop gain $m' = m/(1 + \beta m)$ for negative feedback and therefore the same conclusions can be drawn regarding stability. This can be stated as follows:

$(T_o \times T_f)$, being a complex term, will have both real and imaginary components which will depend upon the signal frequency. The system will be stable as long as the real component does not exceed -1. This would represent a phase shift of $180°$ for this component, which would give a condition similar to positive feedback in an amplifier, as in Sec. 13.8.

14. Measuring instruments and testing

14.1 Sources of error when using indicating instruments

The accuracy of an indicating instrument depends to a great extent upon the care and attention which goes into its construction. An instrument is subject to a number of errors but, by using special materials, the artificial ageing of some materials, and a very high degree of precision during manufacture, most of these errors can become negligible and some can even be eliminated. To produce an instrument with precision accuracy can be very costly. For most workshop and general switchboard use a high degree of accuracy is not usually required and cheaper instruments are manufactured in which expensive means of reducing errors are not used.

Sources of instrument errors are as follows:

1. Friction at the bearings of moving parts. This can be minimized by using high-class jewelled bearings. There are also pivotless instruments in which the moving part is suspended by means of a fine ribbon thus eliminating friction.

2. Temperature errors, i.e., when the resistance of the instrument changes with change of temperature. Considerable errors can occur in ammeters using a shunt and in voltmeters. In high-class instruments, materials having very small temperature coefficients are used. Copper is used only where it is absolutely necessary.

3. Changes occurring in the tension of the control spring.

4. Changes occurring in the properties of magnets.

In the above two cases (3) and (4) these errors are made negligible in high-class instruments during manufacture by the use of special materials and by careful ageing of these materials.

5. Stray external magnetic fields. In general these errors can be overcome by the careful screening of the instrument by enclosing it in a cast-iron or pressed-steel case.

6. Circuit disturbance—surges. Sudden excessive loads beyond the normal range of an instrument can cause a change in its characteristics,

221

leading to calibration errors. Where this is likely to occur, as in the case of starting an induction motor, special ammeters are used where the upper end of the scale is compressed to allow for such excess currents.

7. Circuit disturbance—harmonics. Some instruments are calibrated at one particular frequency and are only correct for a sine wave. Harmonics produce a distorted wave form and this can seriously affect the accuracy of the instrument.

8. Parallax error. This is a human error which occurs when the instrument is viewed from an angle instead of perpendicular to the scale. Many instruments have a mirror under the pointer so that the reading is taken only when the pointer and its mirror image coincide, thus avoiding parallax error.

9. Human error—external fields. Instruments are normally protected (see item 5) from stray external fields, but very strong fields can still cause serious errors. In carrying out workshop and laboratory tests care should be taken to avoid placing instruments, particularly portable types, on or near equipment with strong magnetic fields, e.g., iron-cored chokes, machine field coils, etc.

10. Human error—portable instruments. Instruments are usually calibrated in one position and errors may be introduced if used in any other position. Portable instruments are generally calibrated when horizontal.

14.2 Classification of instruments

Nine classifications are given for measuring instruments in BS 89:1970, which should be referred to for details of indicating instruments. The class index number for an instrument depends upon its limits of error. Thus an instrument with a class index of 0.2 has limits of error of $\pm 0.2\%$. The nine classes are 0.05, 0.1, 0.2, 0.3, 0.5, 1.0, 1.5, 2.5, and 5.0. These numbers represent the *calibration accuracy* of an instrument, that is, they give the limits of error or variation over the normal range of use.

The highest grades are 0.05 and 0.1. These will be expensive precision instruments used mainly for laboratory testing and as reference standards.

For general laboratory work, where a fairly high degree of accuracy is required, instruments of classes 0.2, 0.3, and 0.5 are used. Some portable instruments may be in this group, but usually they would not be very robust.

Most instruments for general workshop and switchboard use, and portable test sets, are in the remaining classes 1.0, 1.5, 2.5, and 5.0. For many practical applications only a rough indication of the quantity being measured is required and for this a cheap, low-grade instrument is sufficient.

14.3 Instrument calibration

A simple way of checking an instrument is to calibrate it against another instrument. This reference instrument should be a precision type in the 0.05 or 0.1 class. Circuits for this type of test are shown in Fig. 14.1. The reference instrument could be of the digital type, which will give a direct numerical reading and avoid the human error which can occur when reading a pointer over a scale.

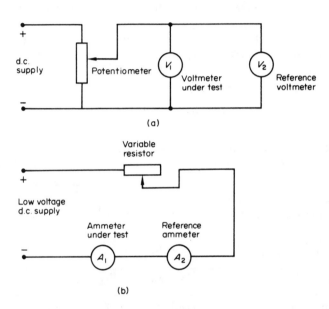

Fig. 14.1   Circuits for instrument calibration: (a) voltmeter test, (b) ammeter test

Before starting the test and zero of each instrument is checked. The circuit is adjusted to give a *definite marked value* on the *instrument being tested*. This is because the reference instrument can be read with a greater degree of accuracy. For each marked value of the instrument under test, the true value is read on the reference instrument. From these readings the error and correction can be found.

If the measured value on the instrument being tested = S (amps or volts) and the true value given by the reference = T (amps or volts) then

$$\text{Absolute error} = S - T \qquad (14.1)$$

A negative error indicates a low reading and a positive error a high reading. The correction to be made will be the same value but of the opposite polarity.

223

Thus if the measured value is 10 A and the true value is 10.05 A, then

$$\text{Error} = S - T = 10 - 10.05 = -0.05 \text{ A}$$

Correction required at *this* marked value = +0.05 A

The error is more usually expressed as a percentage of the *fiducial value.* Thus

$$\% \text{ error} = \frac{\text{measured value} - \text{true value}}{\text{fiducial value}} \times 100 \qquad (14.2)$$

The *fiducial value* (see BS 89) is the effective range of an instrument used for reference when specifying the accuracy of that instrument. In many cases this will be the full-scale reading, but it may not be the case when part of the scale is specially compressed or when the instrument has a displaced zero.

The following is an example of a calibration test:

TYPE . Moving-coil ammeter .... *SERIAL NO.* ....
RANGE ... 0–5 A ....

In this case, fiducial value = full-scale reading = 5 A.

Typical test results are given below using the circuit of Fig. 14.1(b).

Instrument under test: marked scale reading	S amps	1	2	3	4	5
True value on reference ammeter	T amps	1.1	2	2.95	4.05	5.02
Error = $S - T$	amps	−0.1	0	+0.05	−0.05	−0.02
Correction	amps	+0.1	0	−0.05	+0.05	+0.02
$\% \text{ error} = \dfrac{S-T}{5} \times 100$	%	−2%	0	+1%	−1%	−0.4%

These typical results show that the accuracy of an instrument can vary over the scale length. Also, in this particular case, the tests have been made at only five definite points on the scale and there is no indication of the error at intermediate points. For example, the error at the 2.5 A marking could be positive, negative, or zero and is not necessarily midway between that of 2 A and 3 A. So an instrument calibration can only be assessed at the points where the tests were made. Graphs can be drawn showing the errors and the corrections required at the specific test points. As intermediate errors are not known, these calibration graphs are always made by drawing *straight lines* joining the points of known error. Figure 14.2 shows the calibration graphs for the above example.

224

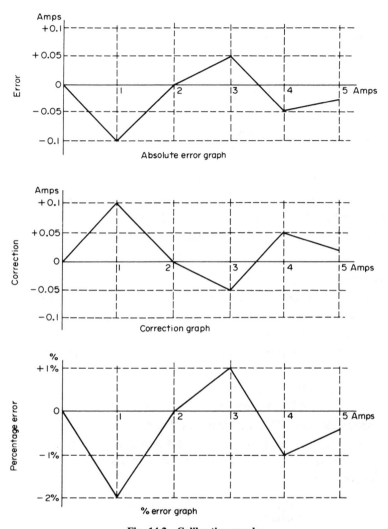

Fig. 14.2 Calibration graphs

14.4 Instrument characteristics and selection

To enable the correct instrument to be selected for a particular circuit, the characteristics, limits of use, advantages, and disadvantages of various types of indicating instruments are given below. The student should be familiar already with the construction details and principle of operation of these instruments.

225

Moving-coil

Accuracy: Can be made to any classification including the highest accuracy.

Limits: D.C. only.

Scale: Gives a mean value reading on a linear scale.

Ranges: 0–5 μA, 0–30 mA, 0–1 mV (instrument alone),

0–200 A (internal shunts),
0–750 V (internal resistors),
0–5000 A (external shunts),
0–30 000 V (external resistors).

Advantages: High sensitivity. Uniform scale. Low power consumption. Affect of stray fields negligible. No hysteresis errors.

Disadvantages: D.C. only. Not as cheap as moving-iron type.

Moving-iron

Accuracy: Can be made for classes 0.3 to 5.0 in a.c. circuits. Less accurate in d.c. circuits.

Limits: D.C. and low-frequency a.c. (up to about 400 Hz).

Scale: Reads r.m.s value on an uneven scale which is cramped at the lower end.

Range: 0–20 mA, 0–800 A without CT
0–1 V, 0–800 V without PT

Advantages: Robust. Cheap. Measures d.c. and a.c.

Disadvantages: Affected by stray fields. Hysteresis error on d.c. Errors caused by change of frequency and by distorted wave form. Not suitable at high frequencies.

Thermal (Vacuo-junction)

Accuracy: Generally classes 1.0 to 5.0 but precision types can be made.

Limits: D.C. and a.c. with a large frequency range.

Scale: Reads r.m.s. values on a square-law scale.

Range: 0–1 A, 0–600 V and frequencies up to 20 MHz.

Advantages: Accurate on both d.c. and a.c. and at all frequencies. Can be calibrated on d.c. for a.c. use. Indicates r.m.s. value and is not affected by wave form distortion. Used for radio frequency measurements.

Disadvantages: Fragile—may be damaged if overloaded more than 5%. Cramped lower scale. Response sluggish.

Rectifier Moving-coil

Accuracy: Classes 1.0 to 5.0.

Limits: A.C. over a wide frequency range.

Scale: Indicates average value but calibrated in terms of r.m.s. value assuming a sine wave. Linear scale.

Range: 0–100 μA, 0–100 mA, 0–5 V, 0–250 V, frequency range 25 Hz to 20 kHz.

Advantages: High sensitivity—up to 20 000 ohm/volt (better than most other a.c. instruments). Low power consumption. Wide frequency range. Linear scale.

Disadvantages: Errors introduced by distorted wave form. For low voltage measurements rectifier resistance can cause errors.

Electrostatic

Accuracy: Classes 1.0 to 5.0.

Limits: High voltage d.c. and a.c. with frequencies up to 10 kHz.

Scale: Reads r.m.s. values on a square law scale.

Range: Quadrant type, 30–150 V, but generally high voltage up to 20 kV. Attracted-disk type, over 15 kV.

Advantages: Negligible power consumption. Can be connected direct into e.h.v. circuits. Measures true r.m.s. value. Not affected by frequency variations or distorted wave form.

Disadvantages: Very small operating torque, so zero readings and low voltage readings are not practicable. Expensive compared with other types of instruments for medium voltages, so it is generally restricted to high voltage use. Cramped lower end of scale.

Induction-type

Accuracy: Classes 1.0 to 5.0.

Limits: A.C. only and at one marked frequency only.

Scale: As a wattmeter it reads active power on a linear scale.

Range: As a wattmeter up to 50 A/750 V.

Advantages: Large scale (300° or more). Robust. Very good damping.

Disadvantages: A.C. only. Expensive. High power consumption. Errors with variation of frequency. Must be used only at the frequency it was calibrated at.

Note: This type of instrument is seldom constructed as an ammeter or voltmeter as its accuracy is not high, it is costly and has a square law scale for these measurements.

227

Electrodynamic Ammeter or Voltmeter

Accuracy: Classes 0.2 to 0.5.

Limits: D.C. and a.c. at power frequencies (25–500 Hz).

Scale: Reads r.m.s. value on a square-law scale.

Range: 0–1 A, 0–5 A, 0–75 V, 0–750 V.

Advantages: Measures d.c. or a.c. High degree of accuracy and can be used for precision work.

Disadvantages: Expensive, therefore limited to precision work. Frequency range limited. Cramped lower end of scale.

Electrodynamic Wattmeter

Accuracy: Generally classes 1.0 to 5.0 but classes 0.2 to 0.5 with a limited range are available.

Limits: D.C. and a.c. at power frequencies (25–500 Hz).

Scale: Reads active power on a linear scale.

Range: Self-contained up to 20 A/300 V. Multi-range up to 100 A/750 V.

Advantages: Measures d.c. or a.c. and equally accurate on both. Useful for comparing d.c. and a.c. measurements. Can be calibrated on d.c. for use in a.c. circuits. Wave form and frequency variations have little effect. Accurate at all but very low power factors.

Disadvantages: For accurate low power factor measurement the instrument must be specially designed. Corrections must be made for volt drop in the coils when measuring low values of power.

14.5 Digital instruments

The digital instrument is an electronic device in which the measured value is shown as a numerical readout instead of an analogue display, that is, a pointer over a calibrated scale. This leads to a high degree of accuracy and eliminates the human errors associated with the reading of a pointer over a scale. The digital instrument is useful where accuracy is essential, or where the instrument has to be read at a distance or by a group of people at the same time, or where readings have to be made by an unskilled person. For general use, the digital instrument is usually more expensive than the analogue types, which will still be used where a high degree of accuracy is not required.

The block diagram of Fig. 14.3 shows the principle of one type of digital voltmeter.

The voltage to be measured is fed into a comparator. The signal from a saw-tooth oscillator having a linear increase of voltage with time is also fed

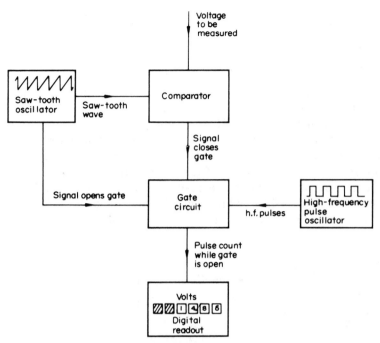

Fig. 14.3   Principle of a digital instrument

into the comparator. Signals from the comparator and from the saw-tooth oscillator are fed into a gate circuit, which also receives signals from a high-frequency pulse oscillator. The instant the saw-tooth oscillator voltage starts to increase a signal opens the gate circuit. This allows the high-frequency pulses to pass to the digital counter which records the number of pulses. The instant the saw-tooth voltage in the comparator reaches the same value as the voltage to be measured, a signal from the comparator closes the gate circuit. This stops the pulses flowing to the digital counter. So the number of pulses registered on the counter is determined by the time it takes for the saw-tooth voltage to reach the value of the voltage to be measured. Thus the readout becomes a measure of the input voltage. The frequencies of the saw-tooth oscillator and the pulse oscillator are so chosen that the readout becomes a direct reading of the voltage being measured.

For example, if the voltage to be measured is, say, 14.86 V and the saw-tooth oscillator voltage increases at a uniform rate of 1 V/ms then the gate circuit will be opened for 14.86 ms. During this time the high-frequency pulses from the pulse oscillator will be registered on the digital readout. If the pulse frequency is 100 kHz then in 14.86 ms there will be 1486 pulses recorded on the readout. The decimal point will appear in the

229

correct place depending upon the voltage range set on the instrument, in this case it will read 14.86 V.

14.6 Effect of instruments in a circuit

The following examples of the measurement of a resistance will give a simple illustration of how the instruments themselves may affect the accuracy of the measurement. The relevant circuits are shown in Fig. 14.4.

In Fig. 14.4(a) the voltage is being measured first by a voltmeter having a comparatively low resistance of $100\,\Omega$ (1). This means that quite a large proportion of the 2 A will be diverted through the voltmeter and, in fact, the actual current i_1 through the resistor will be 1.818 A, not 2 A. The voltmeter will read 18.18 V, which will give an error of 9.1%.

If a voltmeter (2) having a high resistance of $10\,000\,\Omega$ is used then the

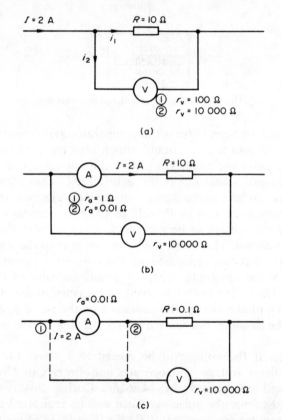

(a)

(b)

(c)

Fig. 14.4 Effect of instrument upon accuracy: (a) effect of voltmeter resistance, (b) effect of ammeter resistance, (c) effect when measuring low resistance

current diverted from the main circuit will be very small. Current i_1 will be 1.998 A and the voltmeter will read 19.98 V, which gives an error of only 0.1%. In any case this will probably be better than the accuracy range of the instrument itself.

Now consider the ammeter in Fig. 14.4(b). The first ammeter (1) has a resistance of 1 ohm so when a current of 2 A is flowing there will be a volt drop across the ammeter of 2 V. The voltmeter will read 22 V. The resistance R will be calculated as $V/I = 22/2 = 11 \, \Omega$, which is an error of 10%.

If an ammeter (2) having a low resistance of 0.01 Ω is used then the volt drop across the ammeter will be only 0.02 V and the voltmeter reading will be 20.02 V. This gives a calculated value for R of 10.01 Ω, which is an error of only 0.1%. In both cases a correction can be made by subtracting the resistance of the ammeter, although in the case of the low-resistance ammeter the error in the instrument reading itself may be greater than the 0.1%.

From the two circuits of Fig. 14.4(a) and (b) it can be stated that for a high degree of accuracy a voltmeter should have a high resistance and an ammeter a low resistance compared with the resistance of the main circuit. Figure 14.4(b) shows the circuit for the measurement of resistances of more than 1 Ω. For resistances less than one ohm, that is, where the circuit resistance becomes comparable with the ammeter resistance, the voltmeter connection can make a considerable difference to the accuracy, as illustrated in Fig. 14.4(c).

With the voltmeter connected at (1) its reading would be 0.22 V giving a calculated resistance of $V/I = 0.22/2 = 0.11 \, \Omega$, that is an error of 10%. At connection (2) the voltmeter would read 0.199 V, giving a calculated resistance of 0.0999 Ω, an error of only 0.01%.

So, for the measurement of low resistances, the voltmeter should be connected at point (2), directly across the resistor. The error then is insignificant and, in fact, the errors in the instrument readings themselves will probably be greater than the 0.01%.

The errors introduced in using a wattmeter to measure power in a circuit can be minimized by the connection used. The normal connection for most measurements is shown in Fig. 14.5(a), in which current terminal M and potential terminal V_1 are made a common connection. Although the current coil is of low resistance, the load current flowing through it will cause a volt drop, and the pressure-coil voltage will be the load voltage plus this volt drop, and the wattmeter will give a high reading. In Fig. 14.5(a) the wattmeter reading will be $(V + v)I$, whereas the power of the load circuit is VI. Since $v = IR$, the wattmeter loss I^2R can be calculated and subtracted from the wattmeter reading to give the correct power for the load.

In Fig. 14.5(b), terminals L and V_1 are linked so that the wattmeter

231

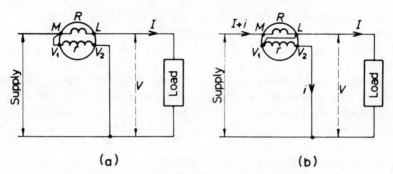

Fig. 14.5 **Alternative wattmeter connections**

potential is the same as the load potential V but the voltmeter current i flows through the current coil in addition to the load current I and the wattmeter again indicates a high reading, which will be $V(I + i)$. Since $i = V/r$, the wattmeter loss will be V^2/r and this is subtracted from the wattmeter reading to give the correct power for the load.

The resistance of both wattmeter coils is usually indicated on the instrument, and an ammeter and a voltmeter are normally used in conjunction with a wattmeter so the above corrections can easily be made. In both cases, the errors are quite small and can usually be neglected except when the power being measured is small.

The errors can be minimized by using connection (a) for low-current circuits and connection (b) when the potential is low. These alternative connections are shown for the open-circuit and short-circuit tests of a transformer (Figs 6.13 and 6.14).

14.7 The CRO as a voltmeter

Most oscilloscopes are provided with a transparent graticule divided into centimetre squares, and the oscilloscope deflection is calibrated in volts per centimetre. The deflection caused by a signal on the Y-plates can thus be measured in volts. If there is no scale, a marked strip of perspex can easily be made.

To calibrate the oscilloscope the circuit of Fig. 14.6(a) can be used. First, with terminals $Y_{d.c.}$ and E short-circuited, Y-shift control is adjusted to centre the spot. The circuit is then connected as shown, V being an accurate high-resistance d.c. voltmeter. The input voltage is adjusted to deflect the spot to a definite scale reading. The voltage is read on the voltmeter and the oscilloscope scale is calibrated:

$$\text{Calibration} = \frac{\text{voltmeter reading}}{\text{deflection of spot in centimetres}} \text{ volts/centimetre}$$

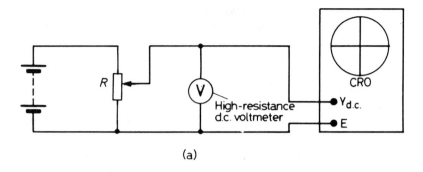

(a)

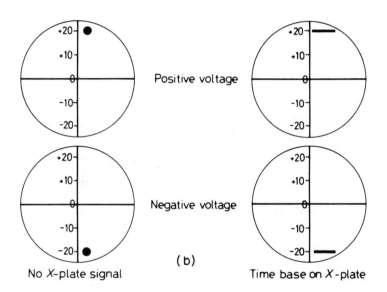

(b)

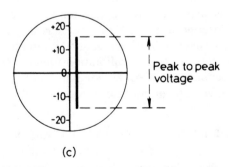

(c)

Fig. 14.6   The oscilloscope as a voltmeter: (a) calibration circuit, (b) measurement of a direct voltage, (c) measurement of an alternating voltage

233

Reversing the polarity should give an equal opposite deflection. The spot may be zeroed near the bottom of the scale to give a larger voltage range. To increase the range, it may be necessary to use an attenuator. Figure 14.6(b) shows the measurement of a d.c. potential of ±20 V. In the right-hand diagrams, the time base has been used to give a sweep along the X-axis. This produces a line which is often more convenient than a single spot for an accurate reading of the scale.

If an alternating voltage is applied to the same terminals, $Y_{d.c.}$ and E, with no sweep signal on the X-plates, the spot will be deflected between the positive and negative peaks and will be seen as a vertical line as in Fig. 14.6(c). The same calibration is used, the line in this case indicating a *peak-to-peak* voltage of 30 V. If the waveform is a sine wave, the maximum voltage will be 15 V and the r.m.s. value $0.707 \times 15 = 10.6$ V.

The oscilloscope may be calibrated by an alternating voltage, using the circuit of Fig. 14.7. (Sometimes a calibration circuit is included in the

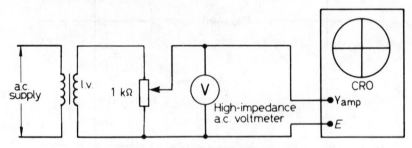

Fig. 14.7 Alternating voltage calibration

oscilloscope itself.) The CRO indicates the *peak-to-peak* value, but the a.c. voltmeter indicates *r.m.s.* value and this must be taken into consideration. The calibration, however, could be in terms of r.m.s. values, if it is known that all the voltages to be measured are sine waves. In this case the terminals Y_{amp} and E are used. The amplifier gain control can be used to adjust the vertical sweep for calibration purposes.

The oscilloscope used as a voltmeter is a very high impedance instrument, and has negligible effect upon the circuit to which it is connected. For a.c. measurements, the calibration remains constant over a very wide range of frequencies and, as long as only peak-to-peak voltages are required, the waveform does not affect the calibration.

14.8 Measurement of current using a CRO

Figure 14.8 shows the circuit by which the CRO can be used to determine current by measuring the volt drop V across an accurate known non-inductive resistance R through which the current flows. The CRO is

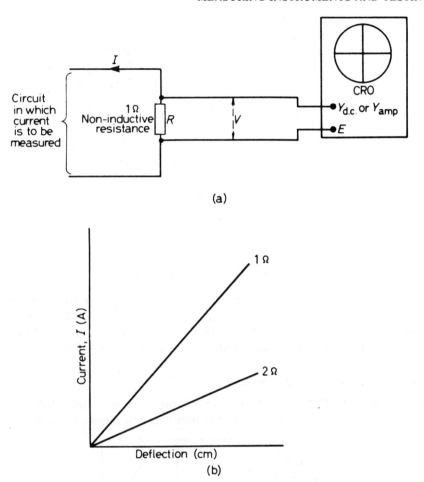

Fig. 14.8   Measurement of current by CRO: (a) circuit, (b) calibration graph

calibrated to read volts as in Sec. 14.7, but if a 1 ohm resistance is used the current will be numerically the same as the p.d., giving a direct reading in amperes. Alternatively, a calibration graph can be drawn for various values of resistance from which the current can be read off after noting the deflection (Fig. 14.8b). Terminals $Y_{d.c.}$ and E can be used for both d.c. and a.c. or Y_{amp} and E for a.c. For a.c. measurement, it must be remembered that it is the peak-to-peak value that is indicated.

14.9   The CRO as a null indicator

If the CRO is calibrated with a centre zero, it can be used as a null indicator, as for example for bridge measurements as indicated in Fig. 14.9. If there is an amplifier in the circuit, then it becomes very sensitive and

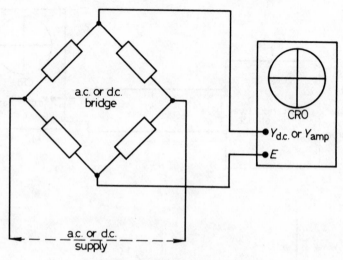

Fig. 14.9   The CRO as a null indicator

precision measurements can be made. For a d.c. bridge, the spot (or line if there is a time-base sweep) will be brought to the scale centre when the bridge is balanced. For an a.c. bridge, the Y_{amp} terminal is used and balance is obtained when the vertical line is reduced to a spot or to its minimum length.

14.10   Display of a waveform

It has been seen (Sec. 14.7) that an alternating voltage is indicated by the electron beam sweeping out a vertical line between positive and negative

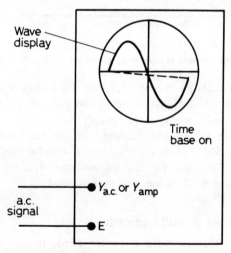

Fig. 14.10   Displays of alternating wave

peaks. If the time-base voltage is applied to the X-plates, the beam will at the same time move steadily to the right and the voltage wave will be displayed on the screen (Fig. 14.10). The sweep of the time base can be adjusted so that just one cycle of the incoming wave can be seen, or several cycles, as required. The X- and Y-signals are synchronized, so that the wave repeats in the same position each time, giving a steady display.

14.11 Measurement of phase difference

If two sinusoidal signals of the same frequency and amplitude are applied, one to the X-plates (X_{amp} and E terminals) and the other to the Y-plates (Y_{amp} and E terminals), they will give a pattern on the screen which will

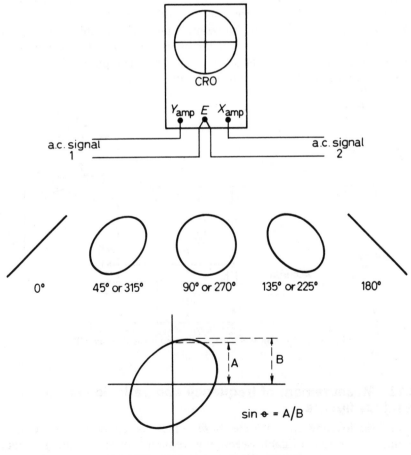

Fig. 14.11   Measurement of phase difference

depend upon the difference in phase between the two signals. The X and Y amplifier gains can be adjusted to obtain equal signal amplitudes, but the amplifiers should be identical to make internal phase shift negligible. Terminals $X_{a.c.}$ and $Y_{a.c.}$ could be used if the signals are large enough. The patterns formed are called *Lissajous figures*, and are shown for various angles in Fig. 14.11. Although some figures represent two angles, one lagging and the other leading, actually the spot is travelling in opposite directions. The correct angle can be determined by introducing a known phase shift into one of the inputs and observing the direction in which the figure changes. Any angle can be determined by centring the figure on the scale and measuring the distances A and B, as shown in Fig. 14.11. The phase angle can be found from the equation $\sin \theta = A/B$.

Some oscilloscopes have three Y-plates, the centre plate splitting the electron beam and the two outer plates, Y_1 and Y_2, deflecting each half of the beam separately. This is known as a *double-beam* CRO. The same time base deflects both beams in the horizontal plane. This enables two separate traces to be seen on the screen, and can be used to show waves due to both voltage and current in a circuit at the same time. The phase difference can be seen and measured. The circuit is shown in Fig. 14.12.

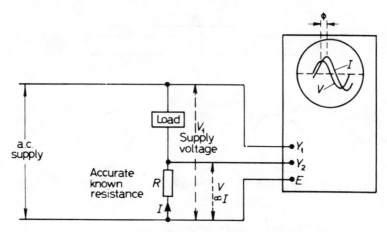

Fig. 14.12 **Current and voltage waves on a double-beam CRO**

14.12 Measurement of frequency and periodic time— Lissajous figures

If the oscilloscope has a time base which is calibrated in terms of frequency or in time of each sweep, the frequency of an incoming signal on the Y-plates can be found. The number of cycles n traced on the screen for a time-base frequency f_x will give the Y-signal frequency as

$$f_y = nf_x \text{ hertz}$$

If the calibration is in seconds per sweep along the X-axis then the periodic time γ of one cycle of the Y-signal can be ascertained by comparing it with the X-sweep. The Y-signal frequency is $f_y = 1/\gamma$ hertz.

If f_x is the time base frequency and only one wave is displayed then the periodic time will be given by

$$\gamma = \frac{1}{f_x} \text{ seconds} \tag{14.3}$$

Another method of measuring frequency is to supply the X-plate externally with a sine wave of known frequency from a calibrated signal generator. The gain controls should be adjusted to give the same amplitude

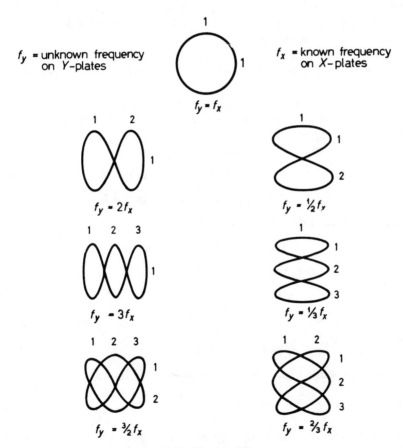

Fig. 14.13   Lissajous figures

for both X and Y-signals. The signal generator frequency is adjusted until the pattern on the screen forms a steady figure of the type shown in Fig. 14.13. These are called *Lissajous figures*, and by counting the loops the relationship between the unknown frequency f_y and the known signal generator frequency f_x can be found. The frequency relationships are shown with each figure. There is a limit to the number of loops which can be counted accurately, especially if the CRO display is unsteady or the screen small. Three or four loops are usually about the limit.

14.13   The Wheatstone bridge

The Wheatstone bridge is a method to determine the value of an unknown resistance. It is a null method. This means that adjustments are made until no current flows through the detecting device. This enables a very sensitive instrument—usually a galvanometer—to be used, which leads to a very high degree of accuracy when it is employed in conjunction with other precision elements in the bridge.

Basically, the bridge consists of four resistors P, Q, R, and S, connected as shown in Fig. 14.14(a) with a galvanometer connected between points B and D.

Suppose S is the unknown resistance, P and Q are known values, and R is a known variable resistor. R is varied until no current flows through the galvanometer, that is, balance is obtained.

At balance no current flows between B and D.

Thus   Current in P = current in $Q = i_1$

and   Current in R = current in $S = i_2$

B and D will be at the same potential.

$$\therefore \text{ Volt drop } i_1 P = \text{volt drop } i_2 R$$

and   Volt drop $i_1 Q$ = volt drop $i_2 S$

$$\therefore \frac{i_1 P}{i_1 Q} = \frac{i_2 R}{i_2 S}$$

$$\therefore \frac{P}{Q} = \frac{R}{S}$$

From this the value of the unknown resistance is found:

$$S = R\frac{Q}{P} \tag{14.4}$$

A simple Wheatstone bridge giving fair results can be made using a slide-wire one metre long and of uniform cross-section. This is AC in **Fig.**

240

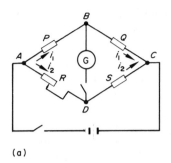

(a)

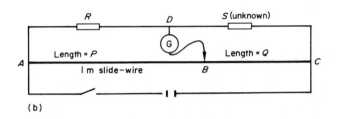

(b)

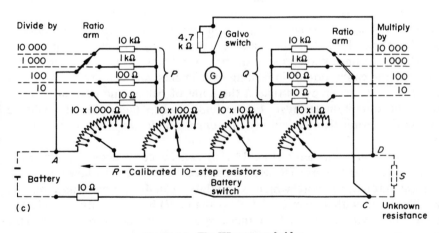

Fig. 14.14   The Wheatstone bridge

14.14(b). In this case R is a fixed resistor of known value. By moving the contact B along the slide wire until balance is obtained, the ratio P/Q is varied. Since the wire is of uniform resistance, the ratio of the lengths BC/AB will be the same as the resistance ratio Q/P and the value of S can be calculated using Eq. (14.4).

There are commercial types of Wheatstone bridge which are precision made using standard resistors. These bridges can often measure resistances

241

over a very wide range, from fractions of an ohm to several megohms, with an accuracy of ±0.01%. A typical commercial bridge circuit is shown in Fig. 14.14(c). The variable resistor R consists of a four-stage stepped-decade resistor which can be set to any value from 1 Ω to 11 110 Ω in steps of 1 Ω. Resistors P and Q, known as the ratio arms, consist of standard resistors in steps of multiples of ten. Thus the value of the unknown resistor S will be given at balance by the total value of R multiplied by the ratio Q/P where Q/P can be adjusted to give ratios of $\frac{1}{1000}$, $\frac{1}{100}$, $\frac{1}{10}$, 1, 10, 100, and 1000. Note that Q/P is a ratio and the ohmic values of Q and P need not be known. During rough balance the galvanometer is safeguarded by a high resistance in series which is shorted out to give maximum sensitivity when the final balance is obtained.

14.14   The potentiometer

As the name implies, the potentiometer is an instrument for the measurement of potential or voltage although with certain modifications to the input circuit the measured value can be interpreted in terms of current or resistance. This also is a null method of measurement which, in a precision made commercial instrument, leads to an extremely high degree of accuracy. Voltages as small as 1 μV can be measured. The upper limit is usually about 1.5 V but this can be extended by means of a precision resistance dropper known as a volt box (see below). The potentiometer is used for the calibration of indicating instruments, and one great advantage, apart from its accuracy, is that at the point of balance no current is taken from the circuit under test. For example, when measuring the voltage across the terminals of a cell it is the *open-circuit e.m.f.* that is measured, not the p.d.

A simple potentiometer (Fig. 14.15a) can be constructed by placing a uniform resistance wire AB along a marked scale. A 2 V battery supplies a current through the wire which will exhibit a uniform volt drop along its length. A cell with an e.m.f. of E (less than 2 V) has its positive connected to A. There will be a point C on the wire where the volt drop $AC = E$. This point can be found by connecting a slide to the negative of the cell through a galvanometer G. Point C is found by moving the slide until the galvanometer shows a zero reading.

At balance

$$\text{Unknown e.m.f. } E = \text{volt drop } AC$$

$$\therefore E \propto \text{length of wire } A \text{ to } C$$

If the volt drop per centimetre of wire is known then the value of E can be found.

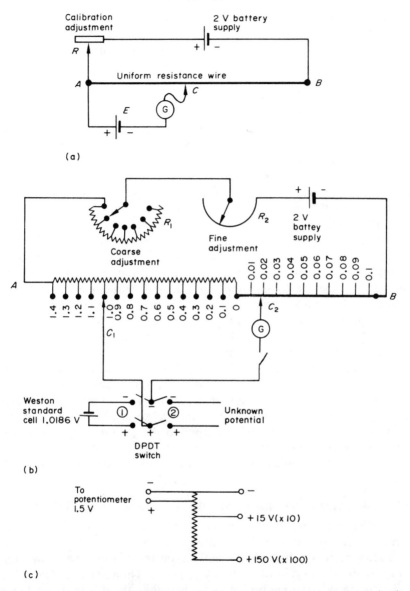

Fig. 14.15 The potentiometer: (a) basic circuit, (b) commercial type potentiometer circuit, (c) volt-box

If E is a standard cell whose e.m.f. is known then this can be used to calibrate the wire and from this other e.m.f.s can be measured.

The scale under the wire can be calibrated in terms of voltage. For a Weston standard cell with a known e.m.f. of 1.0186 V the point C will be at

243

the marking 1.0186 on the scale. In this case the potentiometer is balanced or *standardized* by means of the variable resistor *R*. With *R* remaining fixed at this setting other voltages can then be measured direct from the scale reading by finding the balance *C* in each case.

Figure 14.15(b) shows the circuit of a typical commercial type potentiometer. The potentiometer 'wire' consists of two sections of precision resistors. One section is in resistance steps representing voltage steps of 0.1 V from 0 to 1.4 V. The other section is a slide-wire calibrated from 0 to 0.1 V with a finely divided scale, enabling voltages to be read to a high degree of accuracy to the nearest millivolt. These two resistor sections are usually in a circular formation with contacts C_1 and C_2 on rotating arms. At balance the measured value is the sum of the two scale readings. A double-pole double-throw switch in position (1) connects a Weston standard cell of e.m.f. 1.0186 V to the potentiometer. With contact C_1 on the 1 V stud and C_2 at 0.0186 V on the scale, the coarse and fine adjustments are made to give zero galvanometer reading. The potentiometer is now standardized. With many commercial types of potentiometer the standard cell can be connected to permanent connections corresponding to 1.0186 V by means of a push-button switch. With the double-pole double-throw switch in position (2) an unknown e.m.f. can be applied to the potentiometer. C_1 and C_2 are adjusted to obtain balance and the unknown e.m.f. can be read directly on the scales below C_1 and C_2.

To measure voltages greater than 1.5 V the voltage must be reduced by using a *volt-box*. This is merely a ratio box, a simple form being illustrated in Fig. 14.15(c). It is a precision tapped resistor and in the case illustrated it has tappings for inputs up to 15 V and up to 150 V. As no current is transferred at balance, the 1.5 V output to the potentiometer is an exact proportion of the input, so when the 15 V tapping is used the potentiometer reading must be multiplied by 10. For the 150 V tapping the factor is 100.

14.15   A bridge measurement of inductance and Q-factor

For precise measurements of inductance or capacitance an a.c. bridge method is usually preferred. There are quite a number of different types of a.c. bridge, selection depending mainly upon the property being measured, its range, and the degree of accuracy required. The circuit configuration is similar to the Wheatstone bridge, but whereas in the d.c. bridge balance is obtained when the volt drops across the first two arms are equal, in the a.c. bridge there must be balance of both voltage and phase to give zero reading. The supply is usually low-voltage at commercial frequency, supplied through a transformer, and the detector will be a vibration galvanometer. Oscillators are used with audio or cathode ray type detectors for high-frequency measurements.

One type of a.c. bridge for the measurement of self-inductance in terms

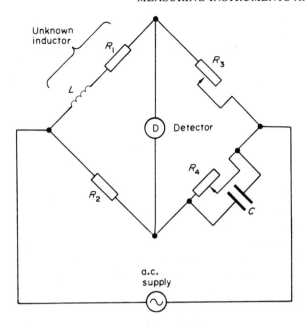

Fig. 14.16 Maxwell bridge

of a capacitance is the *Maxwell bridge*, one form of which is shown in Fig. 14.16. The circuit is the basis of a number of commercial bridges.

In the bridge circuit

L = self-inductance to be measured,
R_1 = unknown resistance of the inductor,
R_2 = known non-inductive resistance,
R_3, R_4 = known variable non-inductive resistances, and
C = standard capacitor.
(In some cases C is a known variable instead of R_3.)

Balance is obtained by adjusting R_3 and R_4 (or C and R_4 if C is the variable). In the a.c. bridge balance is given in terms of both resistance and reactance and in the above case at balance:

$$R_1 = \frac{R_2 R_3}{R_4} \tag{14.5}$$

and
$$L = C R_2 R_3 \tag{14.6}$$

Thus the values of the inductance L and the inductor resistance R_1 can be found. If C and R_2 are both fixed values then the variable resistor R_3 can be calibrated directly to read inductance values.

The Maxwell bridge can also be used to measure the *magnification*

245

factor or *Q-factor* of a coil, although for high-frequency work a Q-meter is generally preferred.

The Q-factor of an inductor is given by $\omega L/R_1$. At balance

$$Q = \frac{\omega L}{R_1} = \frac{\omega L R_4}{R_2 R_3} = \frac{\omega C R_2 R_3 R_4}{R_2 R_3} = \omega C R_4 \qquad (14.7)$$

Thus if the frequency and C are fixed the Q-factor can be found by varying R_4, which can be calibrated in Q-values.

14.16   The 'MEGGER'

The 'MEGGER' is basically an ohmmeter arranged to test insulation. (*The name is the trademark of Evershed and Vignoles Ltd, Dover, England, the manufacturer of 'MEGGER' Testers, who have kindly given permission for details and circuits to be given.*) There are several models. The most commonly used types are the Model WM4 (the 'WEE MEGGER'), which has a hand generator, and the battery-operated tester. Both types are used for testing insulation and continuity.

The simplified circuits for the WM4 'MEGGER' are shown in Fig. 14.17. Diagram (a) is the circuit for the insulation test and diagram (b) that for the continuity test. For simplicity, the changeover from one circuit to the other by means of a switch is not shown.

The generator consists of a permanent magnet rotated by hand through suitable gearing. This induces alternating current in the stator winding, which is fed to the ohmmeter circuit via a voltage doubler circuit consisting of two diodes and two capacitors. The test voltage is 250 V or 500 V.

The ohmmeter movement consists of two coils fixed at an angle to each other. The *control* or *pressure* coil is connected across the generator output in series with resistor D. This coil replaces the control spring in other types of instruments and when the generator handle is turned it causes the pointer to move towards infinity. For insulation tests (Fig. 14.17a) the *deflecting* or *current* coil is connected to the generator output in series with the insulation resistance under test and the deflecting circuit resistance C. This coil causes the pointer to move towards zero. The instrument measures the ratio of the currents in the two coils which will depend only on the resistance of the insulation being tested. Thus the instrument is an ohmmeter and it is calibrated in megohms and thousands of ohms.

For continuity tests (Fig. 14.17(b)) the changeover switch connects the deflecting coil in parallel with the resistance under test, so that for very low resistances the deflecting coil current is small and the pointer will move anticlockwise, that is, the scale reads in the opposite sense from that used for insulation tests. For the continuity test a reduced voltage is applied by using only part of the stator winding. The scale is calibrated in ohms.

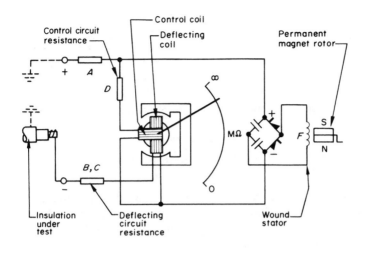

(a)

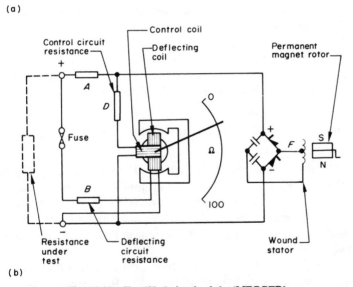

(b)

Fig. 14.17 Simplified circuit of the 'MEGGER'

14.17 Tests of an installation and equipment and the location of faults

Most simple tests can be carried out using a 'MEGGER' continuity and insulation tester. Before any tests are made the circuit or equipment must be isolated from the supply by opening the circuit switch or circuit breaker or removing the circuit fuses. Further precautions are generally necessary,

247

especially in large installations and where the tests are being carried out at a point remote from the control switchgear. The person making the test must ensure that the circuit is safely isolated and must take possession of any fuses removed. Switchgear must be locked in the open position and the key handed to the person making the tests. In addition danger notices should be placed on the switchgear. With high-voltage equipment, very strict regulations must be observed and written authority obtained before circuits and equipment can be worked on.

When a circuit has been isolated the following insulation tests can be made using a 'MEGGER'. All fuse links are left in the circuit except those which had to be removed in order to isolate the circuit.

1. All conductors are connected together electrically and the test made between these conductors and the earth connector. All fuse links must be in place and all switches closed. The insulation resistance should not be less than 1 MΩ.

2. If possible, all appliances and equipment, including lamps and motors, should be removed or disconnected from the circuit and all switches closed. If this is not possible, switches controlling equipment left connected should be opened. The test is now made between each conductor in turn and the other conductors in the circuit. Again, the insulation resistance should not be less than 1 MΩ.

3. A test between the terminals and the casing or framework of each piece of equipment should give an insulation resistance of not less than 0.5 MΩ.

If lower values than these are obtained, then the circuit should be investigated to find if a fault exists or is developing. Faults may develop owing to the presence of moisture, deterioration of insulation due to heat or chemical vapours, or mechanical damage to the cable or equipment. It may be necessary to sectionalize the system in order to locate the position of the fault.

When testing equipment, such as motors, for a fault it may be necessary to separate armature from field windings, rotor from stator windings, or, in a.c. motors and equipment, to separate the phase windings where this is possible. Starters should also be tested as separate items. With transformers, each phase winding should be tested separately if possible, in order to isolate a fault, and the insulation test should be made between primary and secondary windings.

It is possible, where long lengths of cable are concerned, either in series or in parallel, for a low insulation resistance to be obtained. This is due to the fact that all insulation resistances are in parallel. This is illustrated by Fig. 14.18 and the following example. If such a system is sectionalized and

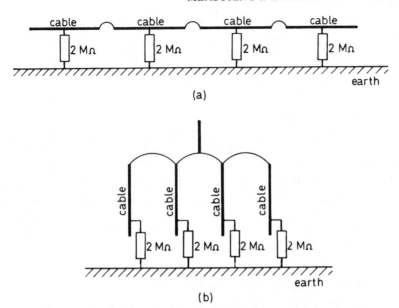

Fig. 14.18 Insulation resistance: (a) cables in series, (b) cables in parallel

each section gives a satisfactory test result, then the whole system can be assumed to be healthy.

EXAMPLE

Four cables each have an insulation resistance to earth of 2 MΩ. Find the total insulation resistance when the cables are connected (a) in series, (b) in parallel.

It can be seen from the diagrams that the insulation resistances are in parallel, whether the cables are in series or in parallel.

In both cases,

$$\frac{1}{\text{Resultant resistance}} = \tfrac{1}{2}+\tfrac{1}{2}+\tfrac{1}{2}+\tfrac{1}{2} = \frac{4}{2} = \frac{2}{1}$$

∴ Resultant insulation resistance $= \tfrac{1}{2}$ MΩ

The example shows that, although the insulation of each cable is satisfactory, when they are connected together the test result will be less than the minimum requirement. Such a system, however, is quite satisfactory.

With the 'MEGGER' switched to continuity test the resistance of the earth-continuity conductor can be found. The test is made from the earth connector at the distribution board for the circuit to the farthest point of the earth-continuity conductor, the supply to the circuit being tested having been disconnected. A long lead of known resistance may be required, its value being subtracted from the measured value. One of the leads in the final subcircuit under test can be used for this purpose if its resistance is known. If pipe or steel conduit forms part of the earth-continuity conductor circuit then the measured resistance must not exceed 0.5 Ω, but if the conductor is composed entirely of copper, copper alloy, or aluminium then the resistance can be up to but not exceeding 1 Ω.

With the supply still disconnected, the continuity of the circuit conductors can be checked in a way similar to the earth-continuity conductor test described above. Care must be taken to ensure that all switches are closed. Another circuit conductor can be used as the return conductor for this test, after first making sure that both conductors are insulated from each other by means of an insulation test. If the test shows no continuity then the cable must be sectionalized at suitable points and each section tested separately to locate the fault.

14.18 Tests to locate cable faults

Within a factory, cable lengths are generally comparatively short and cable runs readily accessible so that faults are not usually difficult to trace by sectionalizing the circuits. In many cases the fault will be obvious when the cable run is examined. However, with some circuits, and especially where underground cables are used, a loop test may be necessary to locate a short circuit or an earth fault. The *Murray loop test* is one simple method based upon the Wheatstone bridge principle. For this test, it is essential to have one good conductor as a return lead. Instruments are made to enable loop tests to be carried out, and Fig. 14.19 shows the arrangement for the Murray loop test.

The good and the faulty conductors are connected together at one end and the test made from the other end. In the case of the fault to earth (Fig. 14.19a), the battery is in the earth circuit. When the fault is between two cores (Fig. 14.19b) one faulty core is connected to the good core, and the other faulty core is used as the return and is in the battery circuit. In both cases the resistance of the fault, being in the battery circuit, will not affect the accuracy of the measurement, although it may affect the sensitivity. Balance is obtained by adjusting the variable known resistances P and Q. The resistance of the good conductor plus the resistance from the far end to the fault is R and the resistance from the test end to the fault is X. The total resistance of the good and faulty cores (lead and return) is $L = R + X$. This resistance, if not known, can easily be calculated or measured.

From the Wheatstone bridge principle (Fig. 14.19c),

at balance $$\frac{P}{Q} = \frac{R}{X}$$

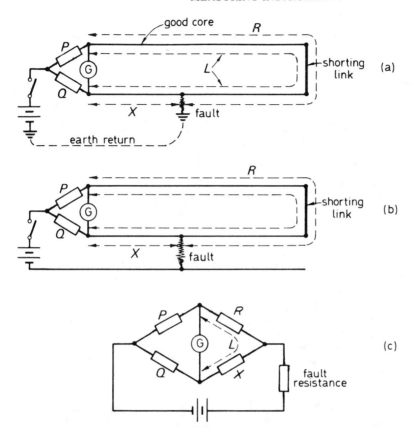

Fig. 14.19 Murray loop test: (a) fault to earth, (b) fault between cores, (c) equivalent Wheatstone bridge circuit

$$\therefore \quad \frac{P+Q}{Q} = \frac{R+X}{X}$$

from which
$$X = \frac{(R+X)Q}{P+Q} = \frac{LQ}{P+Q} \text{ ohms}$$

When the resistance X is found in ohms, this can be converted to metres for the particular size of conductor being tested and the position of the fault found.

Another test for finding a cable fault is the *Varley loop test*. This is also based upon the Wheatstone bridge principle. The circuit is shown in Fig. 14.20(a). As with the Murray loop test, the loop is formed by connecting together a good core and the faulty core of the cable at the end remote from the test equipment. Balance is obtained by adjusting a standard variable resistor S while the ratio arms P and Q remain at a definite fixed

251

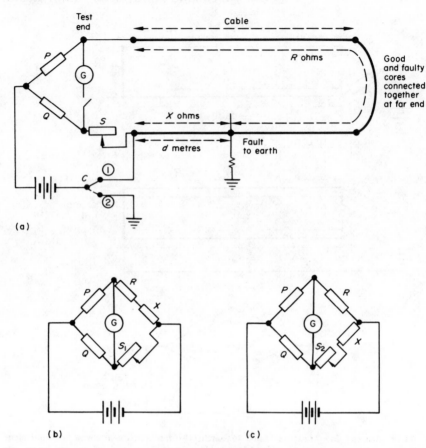

Fig. 14.20   The Varley loop test: (a) Varley loop circuit; (b), (c) equivalent Wheatstone bridge circuits: (b) test 1, switch position (i), (c) test 2, switch position (ii)

value. The test is in two parts, the first part enabling the resistance of the whole loop consisting of both good and faulty cores to be found.

Figure 14.20(b) and (c) show the equivalent Wheatstone bridge diagrams for both parts of the test which are carried out as follows.

Test 1. Switch C on position (1). S is adjusted for balance, the value being S_1. This measures the total cable resistance of the lead and return.

$$R + X = S_1 \times \frac{P}{Q} = L \text{ ohms} \tag{14.8}$$

Test 2. Switch C on to position (2). S is adjusted for balance, the value now being S_2. Note that in this part of the test R and X have been transferred into different arms of the bridge. The fault resistance is in the battery circuit and will only affect the sensitivity of the test but not the accuracy.

Thus at balance
$$\frac{P}{Q} = \frac{R}{X + S_2} \qquad (14.9)$$

$$\therefore \frac{P}{Q} + 1 = \frac{R}{X + S_2} + 1$$

$$\therefore \frac{P + Q}{Q} = \frac{R + X + S_2}{X + S_2}$$

from which
$$X + S_2 = \frac{Q(R + X + S_2)}{P + Q}$$

$$\therefore X = \frac{Q(R + X + S_2)}{P + Q} - S_2$$

$$= \frac{Q(R + X + S_2) - S_2(P + Q)}{P + Q}$$

$$= \frac{Q(R + X) - S_2 P}{P + Q}$$

$$= \frac{R + X - (P/Q)S_2}{P/Q + 1}$$

But $R + X = L$ ohms from Test 1 (Eq. 14.8) and $P/Q = $ ratio arm multiplier $= M$.

$$\therefore X = \frac{L - MS_2}{M + 1} \text{ ohms} \qquad (14.10)$$

This equation enables the position of the fault to be found in terms of the cable resistance. This can then be converted into metres from the test point, as the total length of cable or its size is generally known.

15. The measurement of power

15.1 The dynamometer wattmeter

This wattmeter is essentially a moving-coil instrument in which the main magnetic field is produced by two fixed coils. The moving coil rotates within the fixed coils, being pivoted centrally between them, and is controlled by a spring. The main field is produced by the current in the fixed coils and is proportional to it. The force rotating the moving coil is proportional to its current and the field strength, which is proportional to the fixed-coil current. Thus the deflection is proportional to the product of the two currents and if the current in the moving coil depends upon the p.d. of the circuit the deflection will be proportional to $V \times I =$ power in watts.

Any change of direction of current in the circuit affects both coils, and the direction of deflection remains unaltered. Thus, the instrument can be used on both a.c. and d.c. circuits. On a.c., the deflection will be the average value of the product of instantaneous values of current and voltage. This means that the wattmeter measures the true or active power in the circuit, that is, the deflection is proportional to $VI \cos \phi$. Figure 15.1 shows the coil arrangement when using the instrument as a wattmeter. The moving coil becomes the voltage or potential coil and is connected across the supply. A high-resistance R is connected in series with the coil in the same way as the high resistance in a voltmeter.

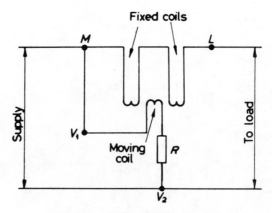

Fig. 15.1 Dynamometer wattmeter

15.2 Measurement of power in a single-phase circuit

In a d.c. circuit, power is the product of the ammeter and voltmeter readings, and a wattmeter is not absolutely necessary. In an a.c. circuit, the product of ammeter and voltmeter readings gives the apparent power or volt amperes but does not take power factor into account. The wattmeter is necessary to indicate active power in watts. The normal circuit connections are shown in Fig. 15.2. (For alternative connections see Chapter 14, Fig. 14.5).

Wattmeter reading   = active power $P = VI \cos \phi$ watts

Product of V and A = apparent power $S = VI$ volt amperes

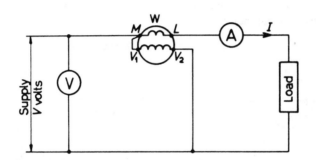

Fig. 15.2   Measurement of single-phase power

From these instrument readings the power factor of the load can be calculated.

$$\text{Power factor } (\cos \phi) = \frac{VI \cos \phi}{VI} = \frac{P}{S} \qquad (15.1)$$

From this, sine ϕ can be found and the reactive power, in reactive volt amperes (VA r), can be calculated.

Reactive power $= Q = VI \sin \phi$ reactive volt amperes   (15.2)

If the reactance is X ohms

then $\qquad\qquad Q = \dfrac{V^2}{X} \quad \text{or} \quad X = \dfrac{V^2}{Q} \qquad (15.3)$

This equation enables the reactance to be found from which the inductance ($L = X/2\pi f$ henry) or the capacitance ($C = 10^6/2\pi fX$ microfarad), as the case may be, can be calculated.

255

15.3 Extension of wattmeter range

The range of a wattmeter can be extended on a.c. circuits by the use of instrument transformers. A potential transformer (PT) is connected to the moving-coil circuit and a current transformer (CT) to the fixed coils of the wattmeter, making sure that the CT is never open-circuited. Both the PT and CT multiplying factors must be applied to the wattmeter reading. Full details of instrument transformers and how they are used are given in Chapter 6 and connections to a wattmeter are shown in Fig. 6.24.

15.4 Measurement of power in a three-phase circuit

1. One-wattmeter Method. This method of measuring power in a three-phase circuit can only be used if the load is balanced.

In Fig. 15.3(a) the wattmeter indicates the power in one phase only and since the load is balanced

$$\text{Total power} = 3 \times \text{wattmeter reading}$$

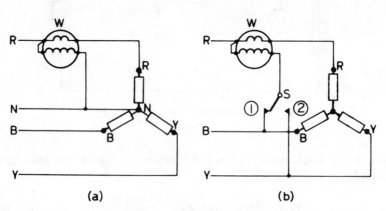

(a)   **(b)**

Fig. 15.3   One-wattmeter method (balanced loads): (a) four-wire system, (b) three-wire system

In Fig. 15.3(b) there is no neutral, so the potential coil of the wattmeter is connected between lines with a switch S in circuit so that connection can be made to both lines in turn. The potential across the wattmeter coil will be 1.73 times the phase voltage and will have a 30° phase-shift. Two readings are taken, first with S on position (1) then with S on position (2). The total three-phase power is the sum of these two readings.

$$\text{Total power} = P_1 + P_2$$

2. Two-wattmeter Method. This is the most commonly used method for measuring power in a three-wire system, since it can be used for both

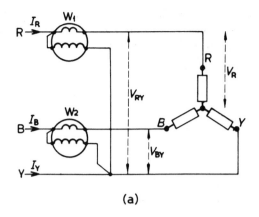

(a)

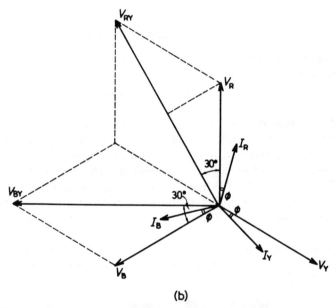

(b)

Fig. 15.4 Two-wattmeter method for three-wire system: (a) circuit, (b) phasor diagram for balanced load

balanced and unbalanced, star or delta loads. The current coils of the wattmeters carry the current in two lines and the potential coils are connected across to the third line, as in Fig. 15.4. The phasor diagram for a balanced load is also shown.

The current in wattmeter W_1 is I_R and the potential is V_{RY}. In W_2 the current is I_B and the potential is V_{BY}. The phasor diagram shows that the

257

phasor V_{RY} leads V_R by 30° and V_{BY} lags 30° behind V_B. If the load power factor is cos ϕ lagging, then the phase angle between the current and voltage in W_1 is $30° + \phi$, and in W_2 is $30° - \phi$.

$$\therefore \quad W_1 \text{ measures } V_{RY}I_R \cos(30 + \phi) = P_1$$

$$W_2 \text{ measures } V_{BY}I_B \cos(30 - \phi) = P_2$$

For balanced conditions

$$V_{RY} = V_{BY} = V$$

$$I_R = I_B = I$$

$$\therefore \quad W_1 + W_2 = VI \cos(30 + \phi) + VI \cos(30 - \phi)$$
$$= VI(\cos 30 \cos \phi - \sin 30 \sin \phi + \cos 30 \cos \phi + \sin 30 \sin \phi)$$
$$= VI \times 2 \cos 30 \cos \phi$$

But $\quad 2 \cos 30 = 1.73$

$$\therefore \quad W_1 + W_2 = 1.73 \; VI \cos \phi = \text{total power } P \text{ watts}$$

This is the equation for power in a three-phase circuit.

∴ Total power is given by the sum of the wattmeter readings.

This is also true if the load is unbalanced and there is no fourth wire in the system.

If the phase angle ϕ is 60° then the angle between V_{RY} and I_R will be 90°. This is similar to a pure inductive circuit and wattmeter W_1 will read zero. In this case, W_2 will indicate all the power in the circuit. If ϕ is greater than 60° wattmeter W_1 will give negative readings which must be subtracted from the reading of W_2. When W_1 gives this negative reading, it is necessary to reverse the potential coil connections to bring the indication on the scale. In some instruments a changeover switch is included for this purpose.

For an unbalanced load, the phase angle may be different for each phase, but when the load is balanced the power factor can be found.

From the above equation:

$$W_2 + W_1 = 1.73 \; VI \cos \phi$$

$$W_2 - W_1 = VI(2 \sin 30 \sin \phi) = VI \sin \phi$$

$$\therefore \quad \frac{W_2 - W_1}{W_2 + W_1} = \frac{VI \sin \phi}{1.73 \; VI \cos \phi} = \frac{1}{1.73} \tan \phi$$

$$\therefore \quad \tan \phi = \frac{1.73(W_2 - W_1)}{W_2 + W_1} \tag{15.4}$$

From Eq. (15.4) the power factor cos ϕ can be found.

The following points regarding the two-wattmeter method when measur-

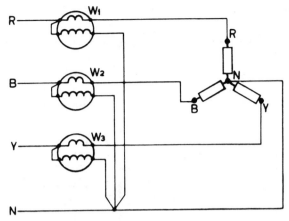

Fig. 15.5   Three-wattmeter method for four-wire system

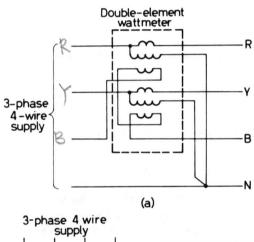

(a)

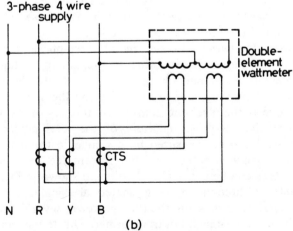

(b)

Fig. 15.6   Double-element wattmeter connections: (a) divided current coil connection, (b) current coils supplied from current transformers

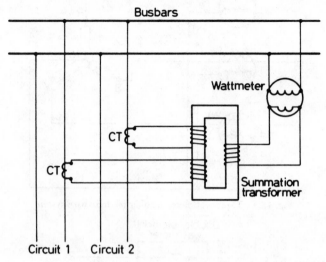

Fig. 15.7   Measurement of total power in two circuits

ing power in a balanced system may be noted:

1. If $W_2 = W_1$, $\phi = 0$,   p.f. $= 1$.
2. If $W_2 = 2W_1$, $\phi = 30°$, p.f. $= 0.866$.
3. If $W_1 =$ zero, $\phi = 60°$, p.f. $= 0.5$.
4. If W_1 is negative, $\phi > 60°$, p.f. < 0.5.

3. Three-wattmeter Method. If the system is four-wire and the load is unbalanced, three wattmeters are necessary. These are connected as in Fig. 15.5. Each wattmeter measures the power in one phase. The total power will be the sum of the three wattmeter readings.

4. Three-phase Wattmeters. Power in a three-phase circuit is often measured by a single instrument which contains two wattmeter elements. The two elements are connected in a similar way to the two-wattmeter method. The two moving coils are mounted on the same spindle and the resultant torque is the algebraic sum of the torques of the two elements, and therefore gives a direct measure of the total power. Power in a four-wire system can be measured by a similar instrument if the current coil of each element is halved and the current fed from each phase, or alternatively CTs can be used. The circuits are shown in Fig. 15.6.

The circuits for three-phase energy meters are similar.

It is also possible to measure the total power in several circuits with one wattmeter by using a summation transformer. This transformer has several primaries, each fed by a CT in one of the circuits. The secondary will carry a current proportional to the phasor sum of the separate circuit currents, which is fed into the wattmeter. Figure 15.7 shows the basic principle.

260

16. Complex waves

16.1 Fundamental and harmonic components

In a.c. theory, the alternating wave is generally assumed to be sinusoidal. This simplifies calculations, and in practice generators for power supplies are designed to produce this ideal wave as near as possible. In general, any distortion from the sine wave is so small that errors in calculations based upon the sine wave can be ignored. Distortion does occur, however, in circuits containing certain devices such as rectifiers, thermionic valves, discharge lamps, saturated iron cores, etc. Although efforts are made to minimize distortion it does occur in synchronous generators and rotating

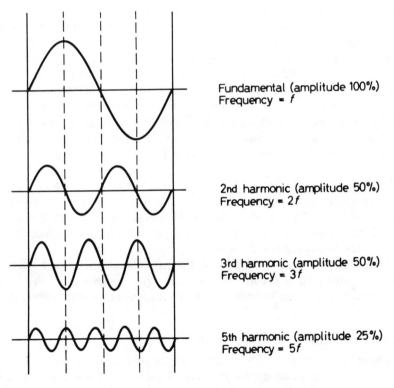

Fundamental (amplitude 100%)
Frequency = f

2nd harmonic (amplitude 50%)
Frequency = $2f$

3rd harmonic (amplitude 50%)
Frequency = $3f$

5th harmonic (amplitude 25%)
Frequency = $5f$

Fig. 16.1 Fundamental and harmonic waveforms

machines. A distorted wave, made up of a *fundamental* sine wave and one or more *harmonics* which are sine waves, is called a *complex* wave. Complex waves can be analysed and are found to consist of several pure sine waves of different frequencies and amplitudes. The main sine wave has the same frequency as the complex wave and is called the *fundamental*. Other component sine waves have frequencies that are exact multiples of the fundamental frequency and are called *harmonics*. The second harmonic has twice the frequency of the fundamental, the third harmonic has three times the fundamental frequency, and so on. These harmonics vary from each other in frequency, and can also vary in amplitude and phase. Figure 16.1 shows a fundamental wave with second, third, and fifth harmonic waves. The amplitude of a harmonic is usually quoted as a percentage of the amplitude of the fundamental.

16.2 Synthesis of waveforms

In Fig. 16.2, complex waves have been produced by a fundamental and one harmonic. In diagrams (a) and (b), the second harmonic has been added to the fundamental, in (b) the harmonic lagging by 45° of the fundamental wave. In both cases, the positive and negative halves of the complex wave are different. In (a), the positive half-wave starts steeply and finishes in a gradual curve, whereas the negative half-wave starts in a curve and finishes steeply. In (b), the difference between the two halves is more obvious.

In (c) and (d), a third harmonic is added to the fundamental, in (d) the harmonic being displaced along the axis by 30° of the fundamental wave. It will be seen that in both cases the positive and negative halves of the complex wave are the same. In diagram (e), the fundamental and fifth harmonics are added and again the two halves of the complex wave are identical.

Only six examples are given here, but the student may wish to produce a complex wave by adding other harmonics or a combination of harmonics to the fundamental. In Fig. 16.3, the fundamental, third, and fifth harmonics are added, again giving a complex wave with both halves identical. This leads to the following conclusion.

If the complex wave consists of the fundamental and odd harmonics only, the positive and negative half-waves will be identical. If the complex wave contains an even harmonic, the two half-waves will be different.

16.3 Production of harmonics

Synchronous generators are designed to produce a sine wave, but even so the fact that the windings are in slots in the iron of the magnetic circuit means that there is bound to be some distortion of the magnetic flux and

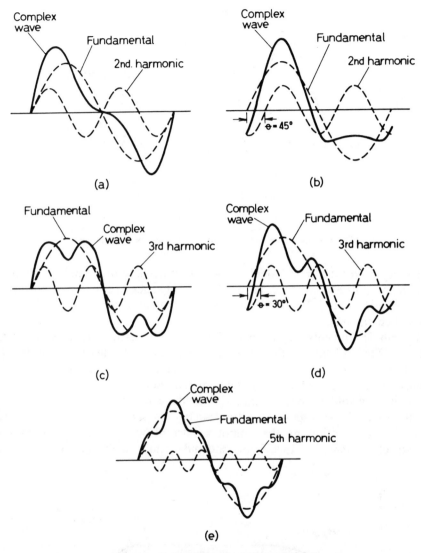

Fig. 16.2 **Composition of complex waveforms**

harmonic e.m.f.s are produced. Since the machine is rotating, the same coils have e.m.f.s induced in them alternately by a north pole then a south pole, and any distortion affects both half-cycles equally. In general, a rotating machine produces half-cycles which are identical, and therefore the complex wave contains only odd harmonics. The more important of these in a supply system are the third, fifth, and seventh, but in general these are so small compared with the fundamental that they can be

263

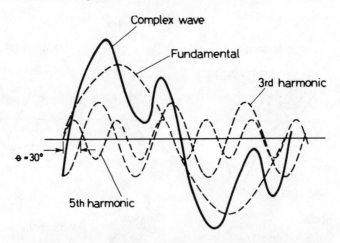

Fig. 16.3 Complex wave containing third and fifth harmonics

neglected in most circuit calculations. The third harmonic, and harmonics which are multiples of three, have special properties in connection with the three-phase system. These harmonics, i.e., the third, ninth, fifteenth, etc., are called *triplens*.

Harmonic currents occur in iron-cored coils, especially if saturation occurs. This is due to the *B–H* curve and the hysteresis loop being non-linear. If an iron-cored choke of negligible resistance is supplied with a sinusoidal e.m.f., then the resultant current must produce an equal and opposite sinusoidal induced e.m.f. To produce this sine wave the current must increase more rapidly as saturation occurs and the *B–H* curve levels out. The production of the complex current wave can be shown by construction, as in Fig. 16.4. For a sinusoidal e.m.f., the magnetic flux wave

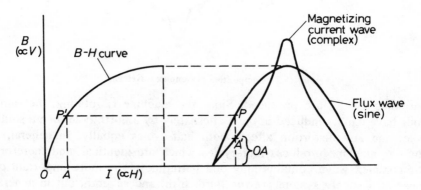

Fig. 16.4 Effect of *B–H* curve on the current waveform

must be a sine wave as shown. To produce the flux at point P, the necessary magnetizing current OA is obtained by projecting across to P' on the B–H curve. OA to scale gives the point A' on the current wave corresponding to P on the flux wave. Other points are found in a similar way, which results in a peaked current wave which contains a pronounced third harmonic, the negative half-cycle being similar. The magnetizing current of a transformer has a waveform of this type.

If the circuit impedance is non-linear, harmonic currents are again produced. This occurs in circuits containing rectifiers, arcs, discharge lamps, thermionic valves. A non-linear impedance causes the positive and negative half-waves to be different. For example, a rectifier passes current during the positive half-wave only, the negative wave being zero. Since the two halves are different, there must be even harmonic currents produced. With a rectifier, the current wave has a d.c. component and a pronounced second harmonic.

16.4 Effect of reactance in a circuit

If a circuit is supplied with a sinusoidal e.m.f., the current wave will also be sinusoidal if the circuit elements, whether resistance or reactance, are linear.

Inductive reactance $(X_L = 2\pi f L)$ is proportional to frequency, so an inductance will offer higher reactances to the harmonics than to the fundamental of a complex current. This tends to subdue the harmonic currents, producing a current wave that is closer to the ideal sine wave. Thus inductive reactance smooths out a distorted current wave.

Capacitive reactance $(X_c = 1/2\pi f C)$ is inversely proportional to frequency, so a capacitance will offer lower reactances to the harmonics than to the fundamental when supplied by a complex e.m.f. Capacitance in a circuit, if supplied with a complex e.m.f., tends to magnify the distortion in the current wave, leading to higher harmonic current losses. This shows one reason why it is desirable to have a sinusoidal e.m.f. as near as possible.

16.5 R.M.S. value of a complex wave

As fundamental and harmonics are all sine waves, the r.m.s. value of each can be found $(I = 0.707 I_m)$.

It can be shown that the r.m.s. value of the complex wave is given by the equation:
$$V = (V_1^2 + V_2^2 + V_3^2 + \cdots)^{1/2}$$
where V_1 is the r.m.s. voltage of the fundamental,
V_2 is the r.m.s. voltage of the second harmonic etc.

265

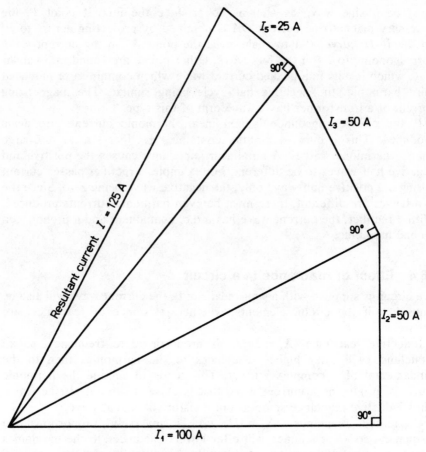

Fig. 16.5 Graphical method to find r.m.s. value of a complex wave

The r.m.s. value of the complex current wave is similar

$$I = (I_1^2 + I_2^2 + I_3^2 + \cdots)^{1/2}$$

A graphical method of finding the r.m.s. value of a complex wave is shown in Fig. 16.5. This is an extension of Pythagoras's theorem and adds the fundamental and harmonics drawn to scale in a series of right-angled triangles. Note that this is merely a geometric construction and not a phasor diagram.

Take the relative amplitudes of the fundamental, second, third, and fifth harmonics as being the same as the waves of Fig. 16.1. If the r.m.s. value of the fundamental current is 100 A, that is I_1, then $I_2 = 50$ A, $I_3 = 50$ A and

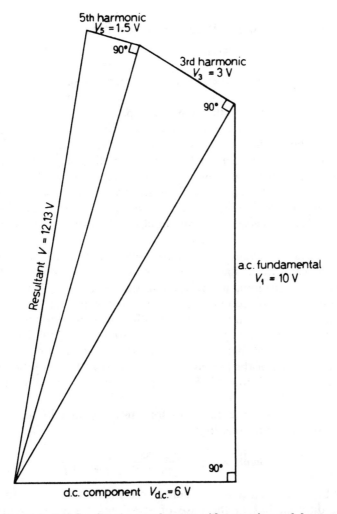

Fig. 16.6 R.M.S. value of a complex wave with a superimposed d.c. e.m.f.

$I_5 = 25$ A. The construction is shown in Fig. 16.5, giving the resultant, that is, the r.m.s, current of the complex wave as 125 A.

A d.c. component can be added in a similar way, as shown in Fig. 16.6, where a d.c. e.m.f. of 6 V is superimposed on an a.c. e.m.f. of a complex waveform containing a fundamental of 10 V r.m.s. with a 30% third harmonic (i.e., 3 V r.m.s.) and a 15% fifth harmonic (i.e., 1.5 V r.m.s.)

From the graphical construction, it is seen that the resultant r.m.s. voltage is 12.13 V.

267

16.6 Power and power factor of a complex wave

It can be shown that the average value of the product of two sine waves of different frequencies is zero. It follows that when considering power only the products of voltages and currents of the *same frequency* need be taken into account. Thus, the total power conveyed by an e.m.f. and current with complex waves is given by the sum of the powers due to the fundamental and harmonic e.m.f.s and their respective currents. A wattmeter in the circuit will indicate the true active power, including the harmonic power.

In practice, the harmonic power is so small that it can usually be neglected and the measured power is assumed to be due to the fundamental only. However, this does indicate the need to keep the harmonic content of a wave as low as possible as harmonic currents, if present, can cause heat losses in cables, overhead lines, and equipment, resulting in a lowering of efficiency.

For many a.c. calculations, a phasor diagram is used and the power factor is quoted as the cosine of the phase angle ϕ between the voltage and current phasors, assuming a fundamental sine wave only. With a complex wave, there can be no such phasor diagram, as the angular velocities of the fundamental and the harmonics are all different. It is also possible for the phase angle to be different for the various harmonics. Thus, for a complex wave, cos ϕ has little meaning as far as the power factor is concerned, although in practice, if the harmonic content is low, there is little difference between the power factor of the complex wave and that of the fundamental.

For a complex wave the power factor can be obtained from wattmeter, ammeter, and voltmeter readings,

i.e.,
$$\text{Power factor} = \frac{\text{active power}}{\text{apparent power}} = \frac{P}{VI}$$

It may be noted that in any circuit where the voltage wave and current wave are different, as in the case of supplying a non-linear impedance circuit, the power factor must be less than unity even when there is no inductance or capacitance in the circuit. An example of this is the carbon arc with a series resistance, which may operate at a low power factor.

16.7 Resonance due to a complex wave

Resonance occurs in a series circuit when the inductive reactance equals the capacitive reactance. This gives a minimum impedance, the current being restricted only by the circuit resistance. If the resistance is low, the resultant current could be excessive. Circuits connected to the normal supply system rarely have components that will produce resonance at the fundamental frequency of 50 Hz. It has been seen already (Sec. 16.4) that inductive reactance is proportional to frequency, whereas capacitive reactance is inversely proportional to frequency so, although resonance does not occur at fundamental frequency, it could quite well occur at one of the harmonic frequencies, producing an excessively large harmonic current. Very high harmonic voltages may also occur across the inductance and the capacitance in the circuit. This is another very good reason for keeping the supply voltage waveform as near a sine wave as possible.

16.8 Harmonics in a three-phase system

Harmonics occur in a three-phase system just as in the single-phase system, although even harmonics are not often present. Odd harmonics may be present but it is the triplens, and particularly the third harmonic, that have particular properties in the three-phase system.

Consider the wave forms of Fig. 16.7. The fundamentals have phase

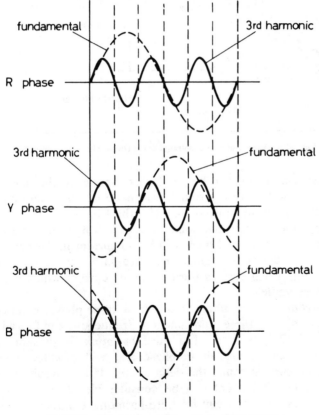

Fig. 16.7   Third harmonic in a three-phase system

269

differences of 120°, but there is no phase difference between the third harmonic waves of each phase. So the third harmonic waves are in phase and are identical in each phase of a balanced system.

Star Connection. In a balanced star-connected system, the voltages are considered as acting outwards from the star point, so the line voltage is the phasor difference of two phase voltages. With the fundamental there is a phase difference of 120°, giving a line voltage of 1.73 times the phase voltage. The third-harmonic voltages of two phases are in phase and of equal amplitude, therefore their phasor difference is zero. Thus, in a star-connected system containing identical third-harmonic voltages in each phase, no third harmonic appears in the line voltage if there is no fourth-wire connection. This is shown in Fig. 16.8.

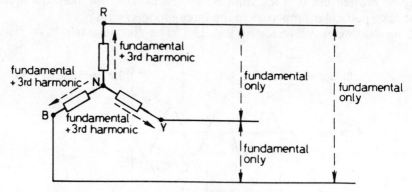

Fig. 16.8   Line and phase voltages for a three-wire star connection

Four-wire System. There can be no third harmonic in the line voltage as shown above, but if there is a fourth-wire neutral a third harmonic may be present in the line-to-neutral voltage. If a third harmonic is present in the phase voltage then a third harmonic current will flow in a star-connected load. If the load is balanced there will be no current in the neutral wire at fundamental frequency, but since the third-harmonic currents are all in phase, the neutral will carry a third-harmonic current which will be three times its phase value.

Delta Connection. The resultant e.m.f. in a three-phase, delta-connected circuit, due to the three fundamental frequency e.m.f.s with phase differences of 120°, is zero. If a third harmonic is present, the three third-harmonic e.m.f.s are all in phase and will produce a circulating third-harmonic current round the delta circuit. If the circuit impedance is low, this circulating current can be considerable. Thus, the delta connection becomes a short circuit for third-harmonic e.m.f.s (and all triplens) and the third harmonic cannot appear in the voltage between lines.

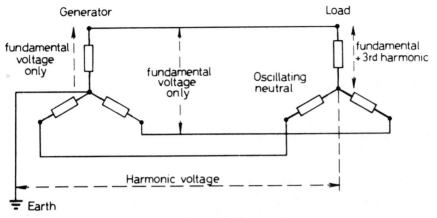

Fig. 16.9 Oscillating neutral

Oscillating Neutral (Fig. 16.9). Suppose a reactor star-connected load with an unearthed neutral is supplied by a line voltage of sinusoidal waveform. If magnetic saturation is caused, the magnetizing current will contain a third harmonic (Sec. 16.3). As there is no third harmonic in the line voltage, there will be a third-harmonic voltage set up in each phase between line and star point. Between line and star point of the generator there is fundamental voltage only, while between line and star point at the load there is fundamental voltage plus a third harmonic. Thus, there is a third-harmonic voltage existing between the star points of generator and load. If the generator star point is earthed, the insulated load star point will have a potential which oscillates about earth potential at third-harmonic frequency. This is known as an *oscillating neutral*.

Appendix

Test questions

Chapter 1   Consumer's supplies

1. What are the advantages of the Grid system of supply? State the standardized line–line voltages used for both transmission and distribution networks within the supply system.

2. Why is a three-phase, four-wire system of distribution preferred to a single-phase system? Explain why a single-phase, three-wire system is often used instead of a two-wire system when there is only a single-phase h.v. transmission line available. Illustrate your answers by showing how domestic and power supplies are connected to both the three-phase and single-phase systems.

3. Draw a diagram of a simple single-phase consumer's supply showing the sequence of equipment from the incoming supply to the consumer's distribution fusebox. What are the essential features of the equipment at this supply point?

4. What is meant by (a) a single supply, (b) an alternative supply, and (c) a firm supply to an industrial consumer? Draw a diagram of each type. What factors would determine the choice?

Chapter 2   Switchgear and protection

1. Compare the advantages and disadvantages of circuit breakers and h.b.c. fuses. State *one* use for which each is particularly suitable, giving reasons for your answer.

(C&G)

2. Explain why
   (a) the neutral point of a three-phase, high-voltage network is earthed;
   (b) the metal enclosures of electrical apparatus are earthed;
   (c) in the latter case the resistance of this 'earth' should be low:
   (d) a circuit breaker is sometimes inserted in the earth lead.

(C&G)

3. Give a summary of the four general groups into which the term 'switchgear' can be divided and explain where each type can be used in a circuit. With the aid of a circuit diagram explain how a contactor can be operated from a remote control position.

4. What is the function of a circuit breaker in an installation? When opening a circuit under fault conditions explain how the arc is extinguished in (a) an oil circuit breaker, (b) an air-blast circuit breaker, and (c) a gas-blast circuit breaker. Give the advantages and disadvantages of each of these three types of breaker regarding installation, operation, and maintenance.

5. Explain, using suitable circuit diagrams, how a person may receive an electric shock from the metal casing of an unearthed electrical appliance, and show how this can be prevented by earthing the appliance.

6. When is it necessary to install some form of earth-leakage circuit breaker? Draw the circuit diagram and explain the operation of one of the following types of earth-leakage circuit breakers; (a) voltage operated type, (b) a core-balance type.

Chapter 3   Economics—tariffs

1. Define the following terms:
    (a) maximum demand;
    (b) diversity factor;
    (c) power factor.
Explain why industrial tariffs usually include a charge per kVA of maximum demand.
   It is usual for power factor correction capacitors to be connected as near as possible to the equipment which is the cause of low lagging power factor. Explain the reasons for this. In some cases, such capacitors have been connected across the motor supply terminals, and the motor has 'burnt out' as a result. Give possible reasons for this, and state the essential check that must be made before capacitors are connected across motor terminals.

(EMEU)

2. Explain why
    (a) industrial tariffs usually include a fixed sum per kVA of maximum demand; and
    (b) capacitors for power factor correction purposes are usually installed as near as possible to motors and other appliances which have a low lagging power factor.
A tariff is based on £6 per kVA of maximum demand plus 0.5p per kW h.

273

If the maximum demand during a given period is 400 kV A at a lagging power factor of 0.7 when 250 000 kW h are used, what would be the saving in the power bill, for a similar period, when the power factor at the time of maximum demand is improved to 0.95 and 500 000 kW h are used? It may be assumed that the maximum demand in kW has remained the same.

(Saving in m.d. charge = £630) (EMEU)

3. Define power factor and explain why capacitors are often used when the power factor is to be improved. A single-phase load when connected to a 240 V, 50 Hz supply takes 30 kV A at a lagging power factor of 0.8. Determine the kV Ar rating of a capacitor which, connected in parallel with this load, will improve its overall power factor to 0.95 lagging.

Draw a diagram to scale in support of your calculations.

(10.1 kV Ar) (EMEU)

4. A factory has a load of 750 kW at 0.8 power factor lagging. The plant is to be extended by the addition of a 200 bhp (149.2 kW) synchronous motor of 85% efficiency and operating at a leading power factor such that the overall power factor will be 0.95 lagging. What would be the kV A rating of the motor?

At what power factor would the motor operate when supplying its full load of 200 bhp in addition to improving the power factor of the whole factory load?

(315 kV A, 0.56 leading) (C&G)

5. A factory has three 250 bhp (186.5 kW) induction motors operating at 0.8 power factor and 85% efficiency, and a 250 bhp synchronous motor of 85% efficiency. At what power factor must the synchronous motor operate in order that the overall power factor of the factory load is 0.95 lagging on full load? A graphical solution will be acceptable.

(0.727 leading) (C&G)

Chapter 4   Generator and motor principles

1. Explain how an e.m.f. is induced in a single-turn coil rotating in a magnetic field. Show, with diagrams, why (a) a commutator is required to provide a d.c. supply, and (b) slip-rings are required to provide an a.c. supply.

2. What are the essential differences between a lap and a wave winding and when is it most likely for one winding to be used rather than the other?

3. Develop the e.m.f. equation for a d.c. generator.

A six-pole wave wound d.c. generator has 650 armature conductors and

274

the flux per pole is 0.02 Wb. Calculate the e.m.f. generated if the generator is driven at 1500 rev/min.

(975 V)

4. If the machine of Question 3 delivers a current of 50 A and armature circuit resistance is 0.2 ohm what will be the terminal voltage? If the machine is run as a motor at 1200 rev/min and takes a current of 75 A what must be the supply voltage applied to the terminals? (In both cases neglect field current.)

(965 V, 990 V)

5. A four-pole lap wound shunt motor has an armature circuit resistance of 0.2 Ω and takes an armature current of 60 A. If there are 800 armature conductors and the flux per pole is 22 mWb what will be the gross torque developed? Find the speed at which the motor will run if the mechanical output (including losses) is 14.426 kW. What will be the electrical power supplied to the motor? Neglect the effect of the field circuit.

(168 N m, 820 rev/min, 15.146 kW)

Chapter 5   D.C. machines

1. Explain the function of the back e.m.f. in a d.c. motor.

A 5 kW, 215 V shunt motor has an efficiency of 82% at full load. The armature circuit has a resistance of 0.2 Ω and the field circuit resistance is 247 Ω. When running at full load at the rated voltage find:

(a) the current taken from the supply;
(b) the armature current;
(c) the back e.m.f. set up in the armature.

(28.37 A, 27.5 A, 244.5 V)

2. Sketch and explain the load characteristics of the series, shunt, and compound generators and motors and give examples where each type of machine would be used.

3. What is the effect of armature reaction in a d.c. generator and how can these effects be minimized?

4. What is meant by commutation in a d.c. machine and what steps can be taken to reduce any adverse effects?

5. Draw a diagram of connections for a face-plate starter suitable for a d.c. shunt motor and explain why and how over-current and under-voltage protection is provided. State

(a) why the motor is started with the maximum current in the field circuit;

(b) how a field regulator may be connected and explain why it controls the speed of the motor;

(c) a load application for which such a starter and motor may be suitable.

(EMEU)

6. Explain why a d.c. shunt motor is fitted with

(a) a starter,

(b) a field regulator.

A 220 V d.c. shunt motor has an armature resistance of 0.25 ohm. Calculate

(a) the resistance to be connected in series with the armature to limit the armature current to 80 A at starting;

(b) the value of the generated e.m.f. when the armature current has fallen to 55 A with this value of resistance still in circuit.

Brush voltage drop may be neglected.

(2.5 Ω, 68.75 V)   (EMEU)

7. Describe a laboratory test to determine the efficiency of either (a) a 250 V, 2.5 kW d.c. shunt motor, or (b) a 250 V, 2.5 kW d.c. shunt generator. Draw the circuit diagram for the test showing the type and range of instruments and any other equipment used. Sketch the type of efficiency characteristic you would expect to obtain for the machine chosen.

Chapter 6   Transformers

1. With the aid of suitable sketches describe the basic construction of a transformer. How does the construction of a three-phase transformer differ from that of a single-phase transformer? Sketch the phasor diagram of a single-phase transformer on no-load, including the no-load currents.

2. A 1000/200 V step-down single-phase transformer has a no-load current of 1 A at a power-factor of 0.2 lagging. What will be the primary current and power factor when it is supplying a secondary load of 40 A at a power factor of 0.8 leading?

(7.625 A at p.f. 0.865 leading)

3. A 100 kV A, 2200/250 V single-phase step-down transformer has a primary resistance of 0.45 Ω and leakage reactance of 1.2 Ω. The resistance and leakage reactance of the secondary winding are 0.01 Ω and 0.1 Ω, respectively. What are the values of equivalent resistance and reactance referred to the secondary? Find the precentage regulation when the transformer is delivering full-load current at (a) 0.85 p.f. lagging, and (b) 0.95 p.f. leading.

(0.0145 Ω, 0.1012 Ω, 9.55%, −3.43%)

4. Explain what losses occur in a transformer and how these losses vary with load. Describe, with circuit diagrams, how these losses can be determined from tests carried out on a transformer.

5. A 50 kV A, 6600/400 V, three-phase step-down transformer has a star-connected secondary winding. The no-load iron loss for the transformer is 750 W. The equivalent resistance per phase referred to the secondary is 0.05 Ω. What will be the efficiency of the transformer when it is delivering full-load current at a power factor of 0.96 lagging?
   (96.9%)

6. A three-phase star–delta step-down transformer having a turns ratio of 15:1 supplies a three-phase 440 V load of 425 kW at a power factor of 0.9 lagging. Assuming no losses, calculate the transformer primary and secondary line and phase values of both voltages and currents.
(Pri: $V = 11\,418$ V, $V_{ph} = 6600$ V, $I = I_{ph} = 23.9$ A)
(Sec: $V = V_{ph} = 440$ V, $I = 620.36$ A, $I_{ph} = 358.6$ A)

7. Outline with the aid of sketches the main features of
   (a) a voltage transformer;
   (b) a current transformer;
   (c) an auto-transformer.
   A current transformer is used in conjunction with an ammeter. Assuming the ammeter becomes defective and is to be sent away for repairs, explain clearly, with particular reference to safety, how you would arrange for its removal and for the supply to be restored, pending the repair of the ammeter.
   (EMEU)

Chapter 7 The three-phase a.c. generator

1. Describe, with the aid of diagrams, the construction of a low-speed synchronous generator. If the generator has 16 rotor poles and its speed of rotation is 450 rev/min, what will be the frequency of the generated e.m.f.?
   (60 Hz)

2. Explain how to carry out an open-circuit test on a star-connected three-phase synchronous generator. The following results were obtained from such a test. The voltage measurements were taken across two phases as the star point connection was not available.

Field current, A	2	4	6	8	10	12	14	16	18
Line voltage, V	98.6	197.2	287.2	361.6	413.5	449.8	477.5	501.7	519

Draw the open-circuit characteristic and from it determine the field current necessary to produce an open-circuit e.m.f. per phase of 200 V.
   (7.5 A)

3. With the aid of simple sketches give constructional details of the two main types of rotor used on large synchronous generators, and indicate the application for which each type is most suited.

A steam turbine drives a three-phase synchronous generator at 1510 rev/min at no-load and at 1485 rev/min at full load when operating at unity power factor. If the generator has four poles, calculate:

(a) the generated frequency at no-load;

(b) the generated frequency at full load;

(c) the generator speed when generating 50 Hz.

Explain briefly why a low lagging power factor load is uneconomical from a supply authority's point of view.

(50.33 Hz, 49.5 Hz, 1500 rev/min)   (EMEU)

4. A diesel engine has a speed characteristic giving 760 rev/min at no-load and 720 rev/min at full load. If this engine is coupled to an eight-pole, single-phase synchronous generator, calculate:

(a) the generated frequency at no-load;

(b) the generated frequency at full load;

(c) the engine speed when generating 50 Hz.

If the generator is supplying its rated kV A at a lagging power factor of 0.6, explain why the diesel engine is not operating at full load, and with the aid of a phasor diagram describe how the installation of a capacitor may improve matters.

(50.6 Hz, 48 Hz, 750 rev/min)   (EMEU)

5. Describe the open-circuit and the short-circuit tests for a synchronous generator and show how these tests can be used to find the synchronous impedance of the generator.

6. A 415 V, three-phase, star-connected synchronous generator has a full-load current of 80 A. On open-circuit test the terminal line–line voltage is 415 V for a certain value of excitation. A short-circuit test gives an estimated short-circuit current of 204 A for the same excitation. It is found that the resistance per phase is 0.15 ohm. Using the synchronous impedance method, find the regulation at full load when the power factor is (a) 0.9 lagging, and (b) 0.8 leading.

(18.9%, −9.16%)

Chapter 8   The three-phase synchronous motor

1. Explain why a synchronous motor is not self-starting. Describe, with circuit diagrams, one method of starting a synchronous motor and synchronizing it with the supply.

2. What are the main advantages and disadvantages of a synchronous motor and where is such a motor likely to be used?

3. State why the power factor of a synchronous motor working on a constant load depends on its excitation.

A three-phase, star-connected synchronous motor has an equivalent armature reactance of 5.25 Ω and negligible resistance. The exciting current is adjusted to such a value that the generated phase e.m.f. is 1750 V.

If the motor is operating from a 2200 V three-phase supply at a power factor of 0.9 leading, determine the power input to the machine.

(506 kW)   (C&G)

4. What are the conditions necessary before a three-phase synchronous machine can be connected to an existing supply? Draw the circuit diagram and describe one method of synchronizing a machine with the supply.

5. A 750 V, three-phase, star-connected synchronous motor has a full-load output of 150 kW and operates at an efficiency of 91%. The synchronous reactance per phase is 1.2 ohm. Its resistance may be neglected. When operating on full load at unity power factor, the excitation current is 8 A. At times the motor is operated at leading power factors for the purpose of power factor improvement for the factory installation. Assuming linear magnetization and the motor running at full load, find the value of excitation required to operate the motor at (a) 0.75 leading, and (b) 0.91 leading power factors. A graphical solution may be used.

(10.27 A, 9.17 A)

6. If the motor of Question 5 is running at unity power factor at full load, what will be the power factor at half full load if the excitation remains at 8 A, assuming the efficiency remains the same? To what will the excitation have to be changed to bring the motor back to unity power factor?

(0.97 leading, 7.68 A)

Chapter 9   The three-phase induction motor

1. Explain by a series of diagrams how three coils spaced at 120 degrees to each other and fed from a three-phase supply can set up a rotating magnetic field of constant magnitude.

A six-pole 415 V three-phase 50 Hz mesh-connected induction motor develops 10 hp (7.46 kW) with a 5% slip, efficiency of 80%, and power factor of 0.75. Find its speed, torque, and line current.

(950 rev/min, 75 N m, 17.3 A)   (C&G)

2. Describe the various methods of starting squirrel cage induction motors, explaining the limitations of starting this type of motor. How are these limitations overcome when using a wound-rotor induction motor?

3. A six-pole induction motor operates on a 50 Hz supply. What will be its synchronous speed? Why will the motor not run at this speed, and at what speed will it run if it has a slip of 4%?

   (1000 rev/min, 960 rev/min)

4. Sketch a typical torque–speed characteristic of an induction motor and from it deduce the starting and running characteristics of such a motor. How does its characteristic over the normal working range compare with that of a d.c. shunt motor?

5. In connection with induction motors explain the following terms:
   (a) synchronous speed;
   (b) slip speed;
   (c) starting torque;
   (d) stalling torque;
   (e) no-load torque.
Sketch a typical torque–speed characteristic for a three-phase squirrel cage induction motor, and proceed to explain why a wound-rotor type of machine may prove more suitable when dealing with loads requiring high torque during the starting cycle. State the condition for maximum torque in an induction motor.

(EMEU)

6. A 415 V three-phase, 50 Hz, four-pole induction motor has a full-load electrical input of 57 kW at a lagging power factor of 0.8 and drives the load at 1410 rev/min. The stator loss is 2 kW and the mechanical losses amount to 1.7 kW. Find (a) the rotor copper loss; (b) the output power; (c) the motor efficiency at full load; (d) the current taken from the supply.

   (3.3 kW, 50 kW, 87.7%, 99.2 A)

7. Explain how a load test can be carried out on a 415 V, 50 Hz, three-phase induction motor with a full load output of 10 kW. The motor operates at a power factor of 0.8 lagging. Draw the circuit diagram for such a test and indicate the types and ranges of the instruments used. Sketch the type of characteristics you would expect to obtain from such a test.

Chapter 10   Small a.c. motors

1. A single-phase winding produces an alternating field, not a rotating field. Explain how a rotating field is achieved in order to start a single-phase induction motor.

2. With the aid of circuit diagrams and characteristic curves discuss the relative merits of the split-phase, two-capacitor, and shaded-pole induction motors. Where could each type of motor be used?

3. Describe the construction of a shaded-pole induction motor and explain how a rotating field is produced. Is such a motor reversible? Comment on its efficiency and uses.

4. Show, by a sequence of diagrams, how a rotating magnetic field is produced by the stator of a single-phase, capacitor-run motor.

Give a diagram of connections and indicate how these must be changed to reverse the direction of rotation.

(C&G)

5. Explain how and why the single-phase series or universal motor differs from a d.c. series motor. Compare the operation of the universal motor on both a.c. and d.c. and sketch typical characteristic curves for both types of supply.

Chapter 11   Industrial drives

1. Discuss the relative merits of operating machines in a factory (a) by group drive using one motor, or (b) by using a separate motor to drive each machine.

2. What type of motor could be used for each of the following drives, assuming both a.c. and d.c. supplies can be made available?
   (a) A small motor in a control system giving a wide range of precise speed variations.
   (b) A large continuously running air-conditioning fan with the ability to be used to improve the power factor of the whole plant.
   (c) To drive a small machine at almost constant speed with no load at starting.
   (d) A small desk fan.
   (e) A two-speed drive for a hoist—a constant low speed for heavy loads and a constant higher speed for light loads.

3. Describe, with the aid of diagrams, the following types of motor enclosures and state the type of factory or workshop where they would be used. If possible examples should be given from a knowledge of local industries. (a) Protected type. (b) Drip-proof type. (c) Totally enclosed. (d) Flameproof.

4. What factors must be considered to determine the rating of an electric motor? Does the type of enclosure affect the rating? What is the difference between *continuous maximum rating* and *short-time rating*?

5. What is meant by *duty cycle rating*?

Find the theoretical continuous rating of a motor which has the follow-

ing 15 minute duty cycle. (Assume a cooling time of one-third of the standstill time.)
18 kW for three minutes;
12 kW for five minutes;
stopped for one minute;
30 kW for four minutes;
stopped for two minutes.
   (19.55 kW, say a 20 kW motor)

Chapter 12   Three-phase rectifiers

1. Draw the circuit diagrams of a three-phase half-wave rectifier and a three-phase full-wave rectifier. Describe the principle of operation of both rectifiers and compare their output waveforms.

2. With the aid of a circuit diagram show how a three-wire d.c. supply can be obtained from a three-phase circuit and describe the operation of such a circuit.

3. Why is it necessary to add a smoothing circuit to the output of many rectifiers? With the aid of a circuit diagram explain the operation of a Π-filter.

4. With the aid of wave form diagrams show and explain the effect of placing (a) a capacitor across, and (b) an inductor in series with, the output of a rectifier. Describe the operation of a choke-input filter.

Chapter 13   Control systems

1. What is meant by *open-loop* and *closed-loop* control systems? Illustrate your answer with suitable labelled block diagrams.

2. Explain the function of the following elements in a control system: (a) monitoring element; (b) comparing element; (c) controlled device; (d) measuring element; (e) controlling element.

3. What do you understand by *feedback* in a control system? Discuss the relative merits of positive and negative feedback.

4. Develop the equation for closed-loop gain for an amplifier. An amplifier with a negative feedback of 0.02 of the output has a forward gain of 500. What will be the overall gain? Calculate the overall gain if the forward gain is reduced to 400.
   (45.4, 44.4)

5. What is meant by the *transfer function* of an element in a control system

and how can the overall transfer function of a control system be determined? Explain the relationship between the transfer function and the stability of a system.

6. Describe the principle of a synchro unit and with the aid of diagrams show how these units can be used to rotate a piece of equipment such as an aerial into a desired position.

7. Draw a block diagram of a closed-loop temperature control system, explaining the function of each element in the system.

Chapter 14   Measuring instruments and testing

1. Explain where errors may occur in indicating instruments and what steps can be taken to minimize or eliminate these errors. What sort of accuracy would you expect from an instrument with a classification of 2.5 and where would such an instrument be used?

2. What type of measuring instrument would be used in the following circuits? Briefly give reasons for the choice.
  (a) To measure incoming current in one phase of a three-phase switch-board.
  (b) To measure the test voltage when testing e.h.v. equipment using voltages up to 20 kV.
  (c) To measure small currents in radio equipment.
  (d) To measure the output current from a rectifier providing a smoothed supply to a d.c. motor.
  (e) A portable instrument to measure power in either a.c. or d.c. circuits.

3. Explain how a d.c. voltmeter with a full-scale reading of 60 V can be calibrated using a digital voltmeter for reference. Draw the circuit diagram. In such a test the following results were obtained; tabulate the results and from them draw a graph of the percentage error for this instrument.

Voltmeter being tested V	0	10	20	30	40	50	60
Digital voltmeter reading V	0	10.6	21.2	30.7	39.4	49.4	60.6

4. Describe how a cathode ray oscilloscope can be used to form Lissajous figures and explain what information can be obtained from these figures.

5. Describe, with diagrams, the principle of operation of the 'MEGGER' and explain how it is used for both insulation and continuity tests.

6. Each core of a two-core cable has a resistance of 0.7 Ω/km and the total length of the cable is 2 km. Show how a fault to earth which developes in one core can be found by using the Murray loop test. At balance the arm of

the bridge connected to the good core reads 12.5 Ω and the arm connected to the faulty core reads 5 Ω. What is the distance of the fault from the test end of the cable?

(1.143 km)

7. Explain the basic principle of the potentiometer. What is its main advantage over a voltmeter for the measurement of voltage in a circuit? What is the limit to the range of measurement of the simple potentiometer? Show how this limit can be extended by the use of a 'volt box'.

8. Describe the principle of a digital voltmeter and comment upon its use, its advantages, and its disadvantages.

Chapter 15 The measurement of power

1. (a) Sketch the construction and explain the action of an electrodynamic wattmeter. Comment on the following:

   (i) limitations on voltage, current, and frequency ranges;
   (ii) reasons for not using iron cores.

   (b) Describe with the aid of a circuit diagram how the voltage and current ranges of a wattmeter may be extended when the instrument is used to measure power in a single-phase circuit. Comment on any precautions that should be taken.

   List the factors which must be taken into account in converting the wattmeter reading into the power being measured.

(C&G)

2. (a) (i) Show with the aid of a circuit diagram how two wattmeters may be connected to measure the power in a three-phase circuit. Assume that the line voltage is 660 V and the load current is about 200 A.

   (ii) Sketch the phasor diagram for balanced load conditions, and using this diagram explain when it is necessary to add and when it is necessary to subtract the wattmeter readings.

   (b) Can this method of measurement be used for both balanced and unbalanced loads? Give reasons for the answer.

(C&G)

3. Draw the circuit diagrams and explain how power can be measured in (a) a three-phase, three-wire system, and (b) a three-phase, four-wire system using only *one* wattmeter. Will these methods be suitable if the system carries an unbalanced load?

4. With the aid of circuit diagrams show the number of wattmeters required to measure the power taken by an unbalanced load in (a) a three-wire a.c. system, and (b) a four-wire a.c. system. In each case how is the total three-phase power given?

Chapter 16   Complex waves

1. Explain how harmonics are formed in the current taken by each of the following when a sinusoidal p.d. is applied to:
   (a) a coil with an iron core;
   (b) a fluorescent lamp;
   (c) a transformer supplying a half-wave rectifier.

   (C&G)

2. Explain
   (a) why the wave form of the current taken by a circuit containing an iron-cored coil may contain harmonics and give the conditions under which they occur;
   (b) why the third harmonic is absent from the waveform of the voltage supplied by a three-phase mesh-connected transformer.

   (C&G)

3. A complex wave is made up of three sinusoidal waves:
   (a) peak value 100 V and frequency 50 Hz;
   (b) peak value 50 V and frequency 150 Hz;
   (c) peak value 20 V and frequency 250 Hz.
   The peak value of the wave (b) occurs $\frac{1}{300}$ s after the peak of wave (a) and the peak of wave (c) occurs $\frac{1}{1000}$ s after the peak of wave (a).
   (i) Draw, to scale on the same axes, the three waves.
   (ii) Derive the complex wave from these waves.
   (iii) State the steps necessary to find, graphically, the r.m.s. value of the complex wave.

4. A series circuit consists of a resistor of 1 ohm, an inductor of 0.1013 H, and a capacitor of 4 μF connected to an a.c. supply with a fundamental e.m.f. of 240 V at 50 Hz. The voltage wave also contains a 20% third harmonic and a 5% fifth harmonic. Calculate the currents at the fundamental and harmonic frequencies and the fifth-harmonic p.d. across the capacitor.
   (0.314 A, 0.283 A, 12 A, 1909.8 V)

5. Find the r.m.s value of a complex wave consisting of a fundamental a.c. wave of 120 V, a 20% third harmonic, and a 10% fifth harmonic with a d.c. e.m.f. of 50 V superimposed on the a.c. supply.
   (132.7 V)

Index

Printed in Great Britain
by W. & J. Mackay Limited, Chatham